6D 24

SCHOLASTIC
READ XL™ >>

Acknowledgments and credits appear on pages 374–376, which constitutes an extension of this copyright page.
Copyright © 2001 by Scholastic Inc. All rights reserved. Published by Scholastic Inc. Printed in the U.S.A.

ISBN 0-439-19863-1

5 6 7 8 9 10   09   09 08 07 06 05 04 03 02 01

CONTENTS

CONTENTS

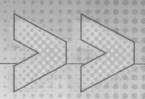

S.O.R. LOSERS

by Avi

Most students at South Orange River (S.O.R.) School are big on sports. But not this soccer team. They break all school records—for losses.

THE TENSION BUILDS

I should have guessed what was going to happen next when this kid from the school newspaper interviewed me. It went this way.

Newspaper: How does it feel to lose every game?

Me: I never played on a team that won, so I can't compare. But it's . . . interesting.

Newspaper: How many teams have you been on?

Me: Just this one.

Newspaper: Do you want to win?

Me: Wouldn't mind knowing what it feels like. For the novelty.

Newspaper: Have you figured out why you lose all the time?

Me: They score more goals.

Newspaper: Have you seen any improvement?

Me: I've been too busy.

Newspaper: Busy with what?

Me: Trying to stop their goals. Ha-ha.

Newspaper: From the scores, it doesn't seem like you've been too successful with that.

Me: You can imagine what the scores would have been if I wasn't there. Actually, I'm the tallest.

Newspaper: What's that have to do with it?

Me: Ask Mr. Lester.

Newspaper: No S.O.R. team has ever lost all its games in one season. How do you feel about that record?

Me: I read somewhere that records are made to be broken.

Newspaper: But how will you feel?

Me: Same as I do now.

Newspaper: How's that?

Me: Fine.

Newspaper: Give us a prediction. Will you win or lose your last game?

Me: As captain, I can promise only one thing.

Newspaper: What's that?

Me: I don't want to be there to see what happens.

Naturally, they printed all that. Next thing I knew some kids decided to hold a pep rally.

"What for?" asked Radosh.

"To fill us full of pep, I suppose."

"What's pep?"

Hays looked it up. "Dash," he read.

Saltz shook his head.

"What's dash?" asked Porter.

"Sounds like a deodorant soap," said Eliscue.

And then Ms. Appleton called me aside. "Ed," she said, sort of whispering (I guess she was embarrassed to be seen talking to any of us), "people are asking 'Do they *want* to lose?'"

"Who's asking?"

"It came up at the last teachers' meeting. Mr. Tillman thinks you might be encouraging a **defeatist** attitude in the school. And Mr. Lester . . ."

"What about him?"

"He doesn't know."

It figured. "Ms. Appleton," I said, "why do people care so much if we win or lose?"

"It's your . . . attitude," she said. "It's so unusual. We're not used to … well … not winning sometimes. Or . . . or not caring if you lose."

"Think there's something the matter with us?" I wanted to know.

"No," she said, but when you say "no" the way she did, slowly, there's lots of time to sneak in a good hint of "yes." "I don't think you *mean* to lose."

"That's not what I asked."

"It's important to win," she said.

"Why? We're good at other things. Why can't we stick with that?"

But all she said was, "Try harder."

I went back to my seat. "I'm getting nervous," I mumbled.

"About time," said Saltz.

"Maybe we should **defect.**"

"Where to?"

"There must be some country that doesn't have sports."

Then, of course, when my family sat down for dinner that night it went on.

"In two days you'll have your last game, won't you," my ma said. It was false cheerful, as if I had a terminal illness and she wanted to pretend it was only a head cold.

"Yeah," I said.

"You're going to win," my father announced.

"How do you know?" I snapped.

"I sense it."

"Didn't know you could tell the future."

"Don't be so smart," he returned. "I'm trying to be **supportive.**"

"I'm sick of support!" I yelled and left the room. Twenty minutes later I got a call. Saltz.

"Guess what?" he said.

"I give up."

"Two things. My father offered me a bribe."

"To lose the game?"

"No, to win it. A new bike."

"Wow. What did you say?"

"I told him I was too honest to win a game."

"What was the second thing?"

"I found out that at lunch tomorrow they are doing that pep rally, and worse. They're going to call up the whole team."

I sighed. "Why are they doing all this?" I asked.

"Nobody loves a loser," said Saltz.

"Why?" I asked him, just as I had asked everybody else.

"Beats me. Like everybody else does." He hung up.

I went into my room and flung myself on my bed and stared up at the ceiling. A short time later my father came into the room. "Come on, kid," he said. "I was just trying to be a pal."

"Why can't people let us lose in peace?"

"People think you feel bad."

"We feel *fine!*"

"Come on. We won't talk about it any more. Eat your dinner." I went.

FULL OF PEP

Next day, when I walked into the school eating area for lunch there was the usual madhouse. But there was also a big banner across the front part of the room:

Make the Losers Winners
Keep Up the Good Name of S.O.R.

I wanted to start a food fight right then and there.

I'm not going through the whole bit. But halfway through the lunch period, the president of the School Council, of all people, went to a microphone and called for attention. Then she made a speech.

"We just want to say to the Special Seventh-Grade Soccer Team that we're all behind you."

"It's in front of us where we need people," whispered Saltz. "Blocking."

The president went on. "Would you come up and take a bow." One by one she called our names. Each time one of us went up, looking like **cringing** but grinning worms, there was some general craziness, hooting, foot stomping, and an occasional milk carton shooting through the air.

The president said, "I'd like the team captain, Ed Sitrow, to say a few words."

What could I do? Trapped, I cleared my throat. Four times. "Ah, well . . . we . . . ah . . . sure . . . hope to get there . . . and . . . you know . . . I suppose . . . play and . . . you know!"

The whole room stood up to cheer. They even began the school chant.

"Give me an S! Give me an O. . . ."

After that we went back to our seats. I was madder than ever. And as I sat there, maybe 250 kids filed by, thumping me hard on the

Words, Words, Words

defeatist: expecting to lose or accepting loss very easily
defect: to escape to another country, especially one that's hostile to your own
supportive: helpful
cringing: shrinking back in fear or panic

back, shoulder, neck, and head, yelling "Good luck! Good luck!" They couldn't fool me. I knew what they were doing: beating me.

"Saltz," I said when they were gone and I was merely numb, "I'm calling an emergency meeting of the team."

SECRET MEETING

Like thieves, we met behind the school, out of sight. I looked around. I could see everybody was feeling rotten.

"I'm sick and tired of people telling me we have to win," said Root.

"I think my folks are getting ready to **disown** me," said Hays. "My brother and sister too."

"Why can't they just let us lose?" asked Macht.

"Yeah," said Barish, "because we're not going to win."

"We might," Lifsom offered. "Parkville is supposed to be the pits too."

"Yeah," said Radosh, "but we're beneath the pits."

"Right," agreed Porter.

For a moment it looked like everyone was going to start to cry.

"I'd just like to do my math," said Macht. "I like that."

There it was. Something clicked. "Hays," I said, "you're good at music, right?"

"Yeah, well, sure—rock 'n' roll."

"Okay. And Macht, what's the lowest score you've pulled in math so far?"

"A-plus."

"Last year?"

"Same."

"Lifsom," I went on, getting excited, "how's your painting coming?"

"I just finished something real neat and . . ."

"That's it," I cut in, because that kid can go on forever about his painting. "Every one of us is good at something. Right? Maybe more than one thing. The point is, *other* things."

"Sure," said Barish.

"Except," put in Saltz, "sports."

We were quiet for a moment. Then I saw what had been coming to me: "That's *their* problem. I mean, we are good, good at *lots* of things. Why can't we just plain stink in some places? That's got to be normal."

"Let's hear it for normal," chanted Dorman.

"Doesn't bother me to lose at sports," I said. "At least, it didn't bother me until I let other people make me bothered."

"What about the school record?" asked Porter. "You know, no team ever losing for a whole season. Want to be famous for that?"

"Listen," I said, "did we want to be on this team?"

"No!" they all shouted.

"I can see some of it," I said. "You know, doing something different. But I don't like sports. I'm not good at it. I don't enjoy it. So I say, so what? I mean if Saltz here writes a

Why can't they just let us lose?

stinko poem—and he does all the time—do they yell at him? When was the last time Mr. Tillman came around and said, 'Saltz, I *believe* in your being a poet!'"

"Never," said Saltz.

"Yeah," said Radosh. "How come sports is so important?"

"You know," said Dorman, "maybe a loser makes people think of things *they* lost. Like Mr. Tillman not getting into pro football. Us losing makes him remember that."

"Us winning, he forgets," cut in Eliscue.

"Right," I agreed. "He needs us to win for *him*, not for us. Maybe it's the same for others."

"Yeah, but how are you going to convince them of that?" said Barish.

"By not caring if we lose," I said.

"Only one thing," put in Saltz. "They say this Parkville team is pretty bad too. What happens if we, you know, by mistake, win?"

That set us back for a moment.

"I think," suggested Hays after a moment, "that if we just go on out there, relax, and do our best, and not worry so much, we'll lose."

There was general agreement on that point.

"Do you know what I heard?" said Eliscue.

"What?"

"I didn't want to say it before, but since the game's a home game, they're talking about letting the whole school out to cheer us on to a win."

"You're kidding."

He shook his head.

There was a long, deep silence.

"Probably think," said Saltz, "that we'd be ashamed to lose in front of everybody."

I took a quick count. "You afraid to lose?" I asked Saltz.

"No way."

"Hays?"

"No."

"Porter?"

"Nope."

And so on. I felt encouraged. It was a complete vote of no confidence.

ASK Yourself

■ What kinds of things can the soccer players do well?
Reread to find out what three of them are good at doing.

"Well," I said, "they just might see us lose again. With Parkville so bad I'm not saying it's automatic. But I'm not going to care if we do."

"Right," said Radosh. "It's not like we're committing **treason** or something. People have a right to be losers."

We considered that for a moment. It was then I had my most brilliant idea. "Who has money?"

"What for?"

"I'm your tall captain, right? Trust me. And bring your soccer T-shirts to me in the morning, early."

I collected about four bucks and we split up. I held Saltz back.

"What's the money all about?" he wanted to know. "And the T-shirts."

"Come on," I told him. "Maybe we can show them we really mean it."

BACK WORDS

When I woke the next morning, I have to admit, I was excited. It wasn't going to be an ordinary day. I looked outside and saw the sun was shining. I thought, "Good."

For the first time I *wanted* a game to happen.

I got to breakfast a little early, actually feeling happy. "Today's the day," Dad announced.

"Right."

"Today you'll really win," chipped in my ma.

"Could be."

My father leaned across the table and gave me a tap. "Winning the last game is what matters. Go out with your head high, Ed. "

"And my backside up if I lose?" I wanted to know.

"Ed," said my ma, "don't be so hard on yourself. Your father and I are coming to watch."

"Suit yourselves," I said, and beat it to the bus.

As soon as I got to class Saltz and I collected the T-shirts. "What are you going to do with them?" the others kept asking.

"You picked me as captain, didn't you?"

"Mr. Lester did."

"Well, this time, trust *me.*"

Words, WORDS, Words	confessed: admitted
	farewell: good-bye

When we got all the shirts, Saltz and I sneaked into the home ec room and did what needed to be done. Putting them into a bag so no one would see, we went back to class.

"Just about over," I said.

"I'm almost sorry," **confessed** Saltz.

"Me too," I said. "And I can't figure out why."

"Maybe it's—the team that loses together, really stays together."

"Right. Not one fathead on the whole team. Do you think we should have gotten a **farewell** present for Mr. Lester?"

"Like what?"

"A begging cup."

It was hard getting through the day. And it's impossible to know how many people wished me luck. From all I got, it was clear they considered me the unluckiest guy in the whole world. I kept wishing I could have banked it for something important.

But the day got done.

It was down in the locker room, when we got ready, that I passed out the T-shirts.

Barish held his up. It was the regular shirt with "S.O.R." on the back. But under it Saltz and I had ironed on press letters. Now they all read: *S.O.R. LOSERS.*

Barish's reaction was just to stare. That was my only nervous moment. Then he cracked up,

ASK **Yourself**

▪ What makes the soccer players feel better about losing?

Explain their attitude toward sports in your own words.

laughing like crazy. And the rest, once they saw, joined in. When Mr. Lester came down he brought Mr. Tillman. We all stood up and turned our backs to them.

"Oh, my goodness," moaned Mr. Lester.

"That's sick," said Mr. Tillman. "Sick!" His happy beads shook furiously.

"It's honest," I said.

"It's defeatist," he yelled.

"Mr. Tillman," I asked, "is that true, about your trying out for pro football?"

He started to say something, then stopped, his mouth open. "Yeah. I tried to make it with the pros, but couldn't."

"So you lost too, right?"

"Yeah," chimed in Radosh, "everyone loses sometime."

"Listen here, you guys," said Mr. Tillman, "it's no fun being rejected."

"Can't it be okay to lose sometimes? You did. Lots do. You're still alive. And we don't dislike you because of that."

"Right. We got other reasons," I heard a voice say. I think it was Saltz.

Mr. Tillman started to say something, but turned and fled.

Mr. Lester tried to give us a few final pointers, like don't touch the ball with our hands, only use feet, things that we didn't always remember to do.

"Well," he said finally, "I enjoyed this."

"You did?" said Porter, surprised.

"Well, not much," he admitted. "I never coached anything before. To tell the truth, I don't know anything about soccer."

"Now you tell us," said Eliscue. But he was kidding. We sort of guessed that before.

Just as we started out onto the field, Saltz whispered to me, "What if we win?"

"With our luck, we will," I said.

And on we went. ●

Is There Too Much PRESSURE to Win?

These days, more kids than ever are playing sports like soccer, basketball, and hockey. Sounds like fun, right? Well, yes and no. While many kids enjoy playing these sports, others feel there is too much pressure to win. Many experts agree. They claim that parents and coaches often put winning ahead of having fun. But not everyone agrees. For some kids, winning *is* what's fun. They don't mind getting pressured to win. In fact, they already put that pressure on themselves.

What do you think? Read this debate and decide for yourself.

YES
Playing sports should be fun. What's important is that players try hard and enjoy themselves, not that they win. Too much pressure to win from parents and coaches can keep kids from enjoying themselves. As the saying goes, It's not whether you win or lose, it's how you play the game.

Plus, the pressure to win can put some kids off sports. Then they might not get the exercise they need. Kids' lives today are already very complicated and stressful. There is a lot of pressure to do well in school. Playing sports should be fun and games, not another stressful activity.

If you said yes:
▪ How can games be made exciting if there is no pressure to compete and win?

NO
The point of playing a sport is to win. That's the goal that players work for during practice. A record of wins and losses tells players how they are doing. A trophy or a championship is something players strive for.

Plus, coping with the pressure to win teaches players some valuable life skills. People face pressure all the time at their jobs. It's important to learn how to deal with it. And striving for a goal, such as winning a game, builds good discipline. It's not the pressure to win that takes the fun out of a game—it's losing.

If you said no:
▪ What can be done to ensure that everyone has fun playing sports—win or lose?

What's your point of view?

Talk About It

Now that you've read *S.O.R. Losers* and "Is There Too Much Pressure to Win?" what do you have to say about these questions?

▶ Why is winning so important to some people?

▶ What is your definition of a winner?

Comprehension Check

Write your answers to the questions below. Use information from the novel and debate to support your answers.

1. Why does the school hold a pep rally for the team?

2. Why are others bothered by the soccer team's attitude toward winning?

3. Why doesn't the team care about winning?

4. Do you think the S.O.R. Losers are really losers? Explain.

5. Do you think there is too much pressure to win at sports? Explain your opinion.

Vocabulary Check

Answer each question below with a complete sentence. Before you answer, think about the meaning of the vocabulary word in bold.

1. How can a **defeatist** attitude be a bad thing?

2. How would you describe a **supportive** friend?

3. What might cause a dog to be **cringing?**

4. If someone **confessed** to lying, what would you say?

5. What are two other ways you could say **farewell?**

Write About It

Choose one of the writing prompts below.

▶ Write a short article about the S.O.R. Losers, as if you were a reporter for the school paper. Make up an exciting headline to go with it.

▶ One of the S.O.R. Losers liked to write poetry. Write a poem about how it feels to win or lose.

▶ Someone once said, "Winning isn't everything. It's the only thing." Write a short essay explaining why you agree or disagree with that statement.

About the AUTHOR

Avi has more in common with the S.O.R. Losers than you might think. He knows what it feels like to be bad at something. Avi has a writing disability that causes him to reverse letters or misspell words. When he was in school, many teachers didn't know about this kind of problem. They thought Avi wasn't paying attention or that he just didn't know how to write.

But like the S.O.R. Losers, Avi refused to feel bad about himself. In fact, he decided to become a writer anyway. Avi has gone on to publish more than 40 books. Today he enjoys visiting schools and talking to kids who have reading or writing problems. He likes to show them one of his manuscripts full of spelling mistakes. He wants kids to see that making mistakes doesn't mean they can't succeed.

Evaluating Sports Statistics

You can find out about a player's strengths and weaknesses by checking out his or her statistics. Take a look at Mark McGwire's statistics for the 1986–1999 baseball seasons. Do you understand what they mean?

Mark McGwire's Stats, 1986–1999

Here's some help with the abbreviations: G = games played; AB = at bats, or number of times McGwire batted; R = runs scored; H = number of hits.

More help: HR = home runs; RBI = runs batted in; SB = stolen bases; AVG = batting average.

These columns tell what year each set of statistics is for, and what team McGwire played for that year. "OAK" stands for Oakland and "ST.L" stands for St. Louis.

MARK McGWIRE

STATS 1986–1999

YEAR	TEAM	G	AB	R	H	HR	RBI	SB	AVG
1986	OAK	18	53	10	10	3	9	0	.189
1987	OAK	151	557	97	161	49	118	1	.289
1988	OAK	155	550	87	143	32	99	0	.260
1989	OAK	143	490	74	113	33	95	1	.231
1990	OAK	156	523	87	123	39	108	2	.235
1991	OAK	154	483	62	97	22	75	2	.201
1992	OAK	139	467	87	125	42	104	0	.268
1993	OAK	27	84	16	28	9	24	0	.333
1994	OAK	47	135	26	34	9	25	0	.252
1995	OAK	104	317	75	87	39	90	1	.274
1996	OAK	130	423	104	132	52	113	0	.312
1997	ST.L	156	540	86	148	58	123	3	.274
1998	ST.L	155	509	130	152	70	147	1	.299
1999	ST.L	153	521	118	145	65	147	0	.278
TOTALS		1688	5652	1059	1498	522	1277	11	.265

"A player's 'batting average' equals his number of hits divided by his number of turns at bat. McGwire's batting average for 1991 was .201 (97 hits ÷ 483 at bats). That means he got a hit about 20% of the times he went to bat."

By the Numbers

Just how good is "Big Mac"? Take another look at his stats and the tips that go with them. Then answer the questions below. Write your answers on your own paper.

1. What is the first year listed on the chart? How many home runs did Mark McGwire hit that year?

2. As of 1999, in what year did Mark McGwire have his highest batting average? In what year did he have his lowest batting average?

3. As of 1999, how many home runs had Mark McGwire hit in his major-league career? How many **more** would he need to break Hank Aaron's record of 755 home runs?
   a. 522; 200 more
   b. 722; 33 more
   c. 522; 234 more

4. Mark McGwire has had problems with injuries. In which two years in the 1990s was he probably hurt? How can you guess? (Hint: Look at the number of games he played in each year.)

Best and Worst
Look at the years in which McGwire played more than 150 games. Which year do you think was his best all-around? Which one was his worst? Write a sentence explaining your answers.

Write All About It
Imagine that Mark McGwire just broke Hank Aaron's home-run record. Write the headline that would appear on the front page of the newspaper. Then write the first paragraph of an article about McGwire's new record.

"Want to get statistics for other players? Visit www.majorleaguebaseball.com. Most other professional sports leagues have Web sites, too."

Real-World Words

abbreviation: short form of a word
all-around: in all categories
runs batted in: runs scored when a batter's hit sends a base runner to home plate

Eat Your

Looking for a tasty treat?

Roasted grasshoppers
are good and crunchy.

Bugs

Bug food may be the answer.

by Miguel Vilar and Laura Allen

Looking for a tasty new treat? Bug food may be the answer.

Imagine this: You're going out to lunch with some friends. You're starving, and your stomach is growling. Then you open a menu. You see *caterpillar soup*. The special of the day is *grasshopper tacos*.

And for dessert—*chocolate-covered crickets*. Suddenly you don't feel so hungry anymore!

To you, this meal may sound too disgusting to eat. But scientists think that more Americans will dine on insects in the future. Why? One reason is that many Americans want

to eat healthier food. And, believe it or not, insects are good for you.

Americans also like to try new, interesting meals. (How does cricket stew sound?) In addition, the number of humans on the planet is growing fast. There may not be enough food to go around. Insects may be the healthiest way to fill up all the hungry bellies in the years ahead.

Still think eating insects is in really bad taste? Read on.

Who Eats Bugs?

Most Americans don't consider bugs to be part of their diet. But the fact is that many of us eat bugs every day. It's impossible to keep insects out of food headed for the grocery store. The U.S. government knows that bugs can't harm humans. That's why it allows up to 34 fruit fly eggs in every cup of raisins and up to three crushed fly maggots in a can of tomato juice.

Red agave (ah-GAH-vay) worms go great with Mexican tortillas.

But some of us don't eat bugs by accident. According to Larry Peterman, a growing number of people actually like them. Peterman owns Hot Lix, a company that makes insect snacks. He says the demand is rising for foods like crispy-fried grasshoppers and chocolate-covered ants. His company makes lollipops with crickets or mealworms inside. It also makes Larvets: toasted mealworm snacks that come in BBQ, cheddar cheese, and Mexican-spice flavors.

Still, most people in America think the idea of eating bugs is gross. The truth is, most people will only eat what they are used to eating. But stop and think of some of the foods you *do* eat. Cheese is really just spoiled, moldy milk. And hot dogs are ground-up animal parts like stomachs, livers, and tongues wrapped in a tube-like **casing.** To someone in another country, your cheese-covered chili dog may sound as disgusting as a plate of worm spaghetti!

In fact, 80 percent of people around the world eat bugs. Families in Venezuela roast tarantulas over fires. In South Africa, people go buggy over fried termites. In Japan, diners may spend as much as $40 on one plate of fly larvae! People in Bali hunt dragonflies. They take off the wings and boil the bodies in coconut milk and garlic. In Nigeria, people gather piles of termites. They dry them in the sun until they are crisp. Then they blend the dried termites into flour to bake bread.

So many people eat insects because they are easy to find and simple to cook. They also eat insects because insects are good for you!

Bugs Can Make You Big and Strong

The human body is perfectly built for bug-eating. Our body systems can **digest** insects just like any other kind of food. And insects are full of **nutrients.**

Crickets and grasshoppers are loaded with carbohydrates. This nutrient gives your body energy. Termites, beetles, and earthworms are very high in protein. The human body uses protein to build muscles and bones. And caterpillars are rich

WORDS, WORDS, WORDS

casing: an outer cover
digest: to take in and break down inside your body
nutrients: things in food that your body needs to be healthy
survive: to stay alive through or after some dangerous event

in fat. Fat provides energy for the body to use later.

Insects are also packed with vitamins and minerals. Just pick up a cricket when you want some calcium. Calcium helps bones grow strong. Termites and caterpillars can help you get your daily dose of iron. Iron is a building block of your red blood cells.

You may be surprised that eating bugs is good for you. But it's actually old news. People have been dining on bugs for many thousands of years.

Food of the Past

"As long as humans have lived, people have eaten insects," says Faith Thayer. Thayer is a scientist at the University of Massachusetts. Scientists know that more than five million types of insects and worms exist. Humans eat about 1,400 kinds.

People learned which bugs were safe to eat by watching animals. If an animal didn't eat

In Cambodia you can buy locusts by the bagful. Diners cut off the wings and legs before they munch them.

A̶S̶K̶ YOURSELF

■ Why are bugs healthy to eat? Think about what the article says about the different nutrients in bugs.

a bug, then humans steered clear of it. Humans probably also just tried different bugs to see which were safe.

In time, people discovered that insects such as red ants and some butterflies could make them sick. In fact, the most colorful bugs tend to taste the worst. These insects developed bright colors to help them **survive.**

Eventually, some people decided not to eat bugs at all. About 4,000 years ago, humans started to farm their food. Farmers tend to think of bugs as pests, not snacks. "Soon, these creepy critters seemed dirty and ugly to some people," says Thayer. Those are two things people *don't* want their food to be.

Food of the Future

Scientists are betting on bugs to be the food of the new millennium. In 1999, the world's population reached 6 billion people. To feed everyone, we farm areas of land until the rich topsoil is used up. We fish the ocean so much that we may run out of fish. But right now, there are about 200 million insects for every person alive on the planet. Bugs may be our best hope to feed everyone.

Also, raising insects is easier than raising cows or

ASK YOURSELF

- How do you feel about the idea of eating bugs?

Think about how willing you are to try new things.

chickens. It takes up less space, too. Thousands of termites can live in a mound as high as a doorway. Some families in Kenya own their own termite mounds. They can easily grab termites from it, fresh for dinner!

Bugs to Go—the New Fast Food

Insects also need less food to grow than other animals do. Check out these numbers: It takes 100 pounds of "cricket food" to raise 45 pounds of crickets. But it takes 1,125 pounds of cow feed to raise 45 pounds of beef! Plus, a cow isn't ready to eat until it's two years old. But in six short weeks, crickets are ready to munch. Now that's fast food! And cricket mothers can lay 1,500 eggs at a time. Talk about supersizing!

Eating insects would make the environment safer, too. We kill billions of insects a year with strong poisons, called pesticides. But the poisons wash away in the rain. They end up in rivers and kill fish and other living things. If we farmed insects instead of killing them, we could help protect the Earth.

So How Do They Taste?

With most bugs, your first bite will be nice and crunchy. Most of an insect's body is made of a thin outer shell. The shell is a little like a fingernail. Human bodies can't digest this shell. That's why insect diners carefully spit out the shells and tuck them on the side of their plate. Still, bits of bug shell can get stuck in your teeth like popcorn kernels!

Underneath their shells, insects don't have much muscle, which is the part of an animal we call meat. So you shouldn't expect to slice up a juicy grasshopper steak. If you've ever eaten a clam, you have some idea what bug insides are like. (Think squishy.) You're actually eating the bug's organs. Those are body parts that help it breathe and digest food.

But what about the million-dollar question—how's the taste? Each bug has its own special flavor. One caterpillar has been compared to a mushroom omelet. And a type of Mexican stinkbug makes anything but a stinky meal! When added to salsa or tacos, they taste something like cinnamon.

Try Them for Yourself

Think you're ready to eat a bug? Check with your local zoo or science museum for insect events. They may have a special "insect snack day" when you can taste them yourself.

Or, if you're brave enough, try making the homemade treat from the recipe below. You can buy crickets or mealworms at your local pet store. But remember: Bugs should always be cooked before they are eaten. (No raw bugs!) Your friends may be shocked. But just tell them to eat up—in the name of science! ●

CHART

Bugs and Burgers. How do they stack up?

This chart compares the nutrition found in raw insects with that in cooked animal food. Protein and fat are listed as the amount in grams. Carbohydrates, calcium, and iron amounts are measured in milligrams (1/1000 grams).

FOOD	Protein	Fat	Carbo-hydrates	Calcium	Iron
CRICKETS	12.9	5.5	5.1	75.8	9.5
GRASSHOPPERS	20.6	6.1	3.9	35.2	5
WATER BEETLES	13.9	3.5	2.9	47.8	5.7
TERMITES	14.2	0	0	0.1	35.5
WEEVILS	6.7	0	0	0.2	13.1
LEAN BEEF (BROILED)	24.0	18.3	0	9	2.1
COD FISH (BROILED)	22.9	0.9	0	0.03	1.0

RECIPE

Grasshopper Tacos

½ lb grasshoppers

2 cloves of garlic, minced

1 lemon

   salt

2 ripe avocados, mashed

6 tortillas

- Preheat the oven to 350°. Roast grasshoppers in a shallow oven pan for 10 minutes.

- Toss with garlic, lemon juice, and salt to taste.

- Spread mashed avocado on a tortilla.

- Sprinkle on grasshoppers to taste.

From *Man Eating Bugs: The Art and Science of Eating Insects* by Peter Menzel and Faith D'Aluisio.

Cockroach *Cafeteria*

BY LYNDA JONES AND LAURA ALLEN

EATING BUGS MAY BE GOOD FOR YOU. BUT WOULD YOU SHARE YOUR LUNCH WITH THEM IN THE SCHOOL CAFETERIA? ONE NEW YORK STATE SCHOOL SAID, "NO WAY!"

Imagine finding a large cockroach in the middle of your grilled cheese sandwich. You'd probably drop your lunch and race for the door!

So what did one school do when they found cockroaches

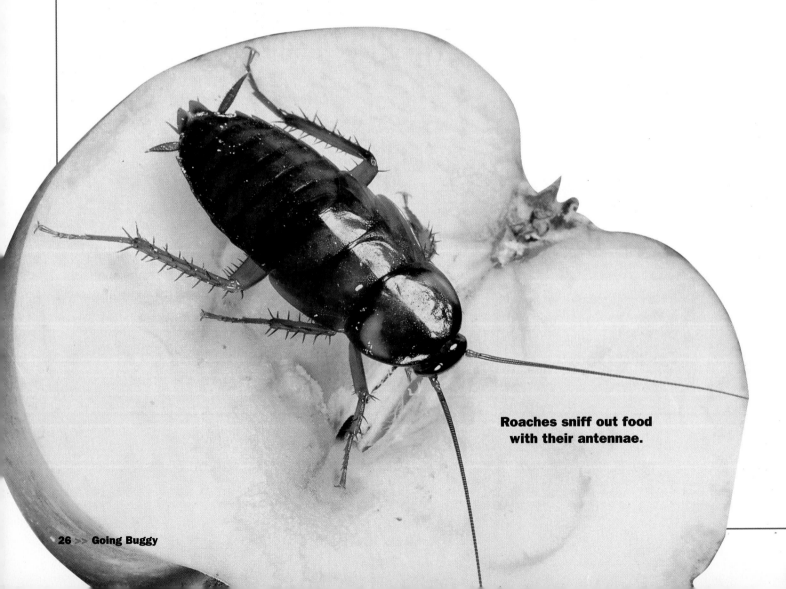

Roaches sniff out food with their antennae.

crawling in every crack of their cafeteria? The school called Bernard Wendell, an **exterminator.**

TRICKY TRAITS

Getting rid of roaches isn't easy. Roaches have been around about 350 million years. During that time, they have developed many traits that help them survive.

First of all, cockroaches usually come out at night. It's safer that way—you're not around. And they tend to run away when you flick on the lights.

A roach's speed helps it escape dangers. It can cruise along at 3 miles per hour. That may not sound like much. But if cockroaches were as big as cars, they could race at speeds of 150 miles per hour!

The critters also can easily slide into tiny spaces to escape. The shell of one common roach is coated in a slippery oil. An adult male can squeeze through tiny cracks in walls no thicker than the edge of a quarter!

Roaches also can "see" behind them. They've got two hairs on their rear ends. So if something is sneaking behind the cockroach, the hairs feel the air move. The cockroach races the other way.

Cockroaches spend most of their time hidden behind the walls. Mostly they're just hanging out. The other thing that roaches do is make more roaches. A single roach pair can have several thousand babies in less than a year. Imagine a family that big!

All of this information might make Wendell's bug battle seem hopeless. But as the saying goes: Knowledge is power.

ROACH RAID

Step one for Wendell was to get rid of the roach's main food **source.** The workers cleaned behind the stove to take away the grease. Then Wendell chose a strong chemical that wouldn't harm humans or the environment, and he was careful about where he put it. He slipped bait containing the chemical

into the electric outlets. He also put bait in holes in the metal feet of the stove. Wendell knew roaches were likely to hide out there.

BUGS TAKE THE BAIT

Next, Wendell needed to see if his plan was working. He set sticky traps in spots around the kitchen. If he found dead roaches in the traps, he would know the plan was working. If he found live roaches stuck in the traps, it would mean the bugs *weren't* eating the bait.

A few days later, Wendell returned to the school to check on his work. "There were roaches both dead and alive in the sticky traps," he says, "so I knew the bait was starting to work."

Wendell set more bait and traps for the next few weeks. He stopped only when there weren't any more roaches in the traps. The whole project took about a month. But it was worth the effort. The school's roach problem is now "no problem"! ●

WORDS, WORDS, WORDS

exterminator: a person who gets rid of insect pests
source: the place, person, or thing from which something comes

Talk About It

Now that you've read "Eat Your Bugs" and "Cockroach Cafeteria," what do you have to say about these questions?

▶ Do you think the idea of eating bugs is disgusting? Why?

▶ Why do you think some people love to try new foods and others hate to?

Comprehension Check

Write your answers to the questions below. Use information from the two articles to support your answers.

1. Why do some people eat bugs without knowing it?

2. Why don't some people want to eat bugs?

3. What do you think is the best argument for eating bugs?

4. What did the exterminator do to get rid of the cockroaches?

5. If you found a bug in your food in the school cafeteria, do you think it would be safe to eat it? Why or why not?

Vocabulary Check

Complete each sentence starter below. Before you answer, think about the meaning of the vocabulary word in bold.

1. The sandwich was hard to **digest** because . . .

2. A food that has a lot of **nutrients** is . . .

3. The **casing** was made of . . .

4. No one knew the **source** of . . .

5. To **survive,** people need . . .

Write About It

Choose one of the writing prompts below.

▶ Create an original recipe for a dish whose main ingredient is bugs. Use the recipe given in the article as a model for your own.

▶ Write a review of a new restaurant called BUGS "R" US. What dishes do they serve? How did they taste?

▶ Think about whether or not more people should eat bugs. Then write a paragraph stating your point of view. Give three reasons why you feel the way you do.

Fact FILE

Don't Eat Me!

People may eat bugs, and many animals eat bugs. But that doesn't mean the bugs want to be eaten. Some bugs do amazing things to avoid being eaten.

▶ If the bombadier beetle thinks it's about to be eaten, it releases two chemicals. When these chemicals mix, they make an explosion that frightens their enemies.

▶ A group of moths known as Aegerids have furry legs. If they hold their legs against their bellies, they look like bees. Animals leave these bugs alone. They don't want to get stung!

▶ The fulgoroid bug has hidden eyelike patterns on its hind wings. When bugged by a bird, this insect flashes its "eyes." The bird will flee, thinking the eyes belong to a larger animal.

Real-World Reading >>2

Ordering From a Menu

You've chosen your favorite restaurant for lunch. The big question is, what should you order? Look at the menu! It lists all the available foods and drinks, along with the prices.

Check out this menu. Compare the prices. Are you ready to order?

Fantastic Foods Menu

M E N U

Sandwiches

Grilled Chicken Sandwich............................2.49

♥ Turkey Burger...2.49

Roast Turkey Sub.......................................2.89

Wraps

✹ Cajun Chicken Wrap...............................2.75

Turkey and Cheese Wrap 2.95

♥ Veggie Wrap 2.25

Salads

♥ Nothin' But Veggies 1.95

Chicken Salad Supreme.............................2.95

Roast Turkey Salad 2.95

♥ = Extra Healthy!

Side Dishes

Mashed Potatoes/French Fries

Large: 1.75 .... Small: 1.25

Macaroni and Cheese

Large: 1.75 .... Small: 1.25

✹ Chips and Salsa

Large: 1.75 .... Small: 1.25

Soups and Chili

Broccoli Cheese Soup .....bowl: 1.95......cup: 1.50

♥ Tomato Rice Soup.......bowl: 1.95......cup: 1.50

✹ Chili with Cheese ....bowl: 1.95......cup: 1.50

Beverages

Sodas/Teas	Large: 1.50	Medium: 1.25	Small: .99
Milk/Juices	Large: 1.75	Medium: 1.50	Small: 1.25
Coffee:	Large: 1.25	Small: .75	

✹ = Extra Spicy!

> A menu lists the names of the foods served. It also tells how much each item costs.

Special Meal Deals!

1 **Chicken Deluxe!**
Grilled Chicken Sandwich
Large French Fries
Medium Beverage

$4.50

2 **Vegetarian Delight!**
Veggie Wrap or Nothin'
But Veggies Salad
Broccoli Cheese Soup (cup)
Medium Beverage

$4.25

3 **Turkey Delight!**
Turkey Burger
Large Mashed Potatoes
Medium Beverage

$4.50

4 **Salad Sensation!**
Chicken Salad Supreme
or Roast Turkey Salad
Tomato Rice Soup (cup)
Medium Beverage

$5.00

> Some restaurants offer a special price for complete meals. Usually, the specials cost a bit less than ordering all the items separately.

" See the symbols on the menu? They give information about some of the food. For example, on this menu ✹ points out extra-spicy dishes. "

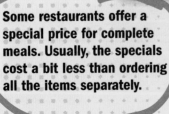

Ready to Order?

What looks good? Reread the menu and the tips that go with it. Then use the menu to answer the questions below. Write your answers on your own paper.

1. What are the different sizes of soups and chili you can order?
   a. large and small
   b. bowl and cup
   c. large, medium, and small

2. According to this menu, which foods are extra healthy?
   a. Tomato Rice Soup, Chips and Salsa, Veggie Wrap
   b. Veggie Wrap, Chili with Cheese, Vegetarian Delight
   c. Turkey Burger, Veggie Wrap, Nothin' But Veggies, Tomato Rice Soup

3. You're in the mood for a Turkey Burger, some mashed potatoes, and a soda. Which Meal Deal should you order?
   a. Meal Deal #1
   b. Meal Deal #2
   c. Meal Deal #3

4. You'd like the Chicken Salad Supreme, a cup of Tomato Rice Soup, and a medium beverage. Is it cheaper to order these items separately or to order Meal Deal #4?
   a. It's cheaper to order these items separately.
   b. It's cheaper to order Meal Deal #4.
   c. It's the same price either way.

5. You have $5 to spend on lunch. What would you order?

Real-World Words
beverages: drinks
symbols: pictures that stand for words or phrases

Place an Order
Your mom has given you $18 and asked you to buy dinner for yourself, your sister, and a friend. You are trying to avoid bread, potatoes, and chips. Your sister doesn't like spicy food. Your friend only wants to eat healthy foods. Write down what you would order for each person.

Write About It
Pretend that you are a restaurant critic for a local newspaper. Choose a restaurant you've tried, or make one up. Write about the food, the prices, and how the restaurant looks.

" Many large restaurant chains have Web sites. Check them out! You might be able to find out how healthy their food is."

DREAMING OF YOU ★ ★

THE LIFE AND MUSIC OF SELENA

Selena was a great singer and she had an amazing career. People say that she could have been the greatest singer ever. They say that she could have been bigger than Janet Jackson, Gloria Estefan, and Madonna combined.

It's possible. Selena had Spanish-speaking fans and English-speaking fans. She also had incredible talent. And she worked very hard.

But tragically, Selena died when she was only 23. So we'll never know what could have happened.

THIS IS SELENA'S STORY.

Selena Quintanilla was born in Lake Jackson, Texas, on April 16, 1971.

Her family was Mexican-American. She had an older brother named Abraham (nicknamed A.B.) and an older sister called Suzette. Selena's parents' names were Marcella and Abraham. They were all very close.

As Selena grew up, she was a **typical** kid. She had many interests. She liked to play football and to roller-skate and bike with her friends. She also had another hobby she loved. She made shiny costumes for her dolls. She kept making costumes all her life. She never stopped—even when she was a superstar.

Selena also liked school. She was a good student. One teacher said, "Selena had a very bubbly personality. She was eager to please and eager to learn. She was the type of little kid that you would like to have in a class." Even as a kid, Selena had fans!

Family Life

It's probably not surprising that Selena became a singer. Her whole family loved music. When her dad was a teenager, he joined a band. It was called Los Dinos. Although Los Dinos worked really hard, they never made it big.

Eventually, Selena's dad left the band. But he didn't give up music. Years later, he began to teach A.B. and Suzette music. A.B. started learning the bass guitar. Suzette played the drums.

"What about me?" Selena would say. She felt left out. So what did she do about it? "I got this music book of my dad's. It had old songs in it. I started singing in front of my family," Selena said.

Yes, Selena was a tiny girl. But she could really belt out those songs. "My dad noticed that I picked it up right away. My timing was right there." So her father began to include Selena in the family music lessons.

In 1980, when Selena was nine years old, her dad opened a Mexican restaurant. It was called Pappagallos. Her dad wanted to have live music in the restaurant, so the family built a small stage. Sometimes Selena, A.B., and Suzette would perform with other local acts. Everyone who heard Selena sing liked her. She could *really* sing.

Singing and playing music wasn't easy. It took lots of hard work. The kids came home right after school each day and practiced their songs in the garage. Mr. Quintanilla was tough on them. He made sure they kept at it.

Selena's dad wanted the kids to learn songs in Spanish, but Selena could barely speak the language. So he often sat down with her and gave her lessons.

In 1981, tough times fell upon Selena's family. When Selena was 10, Mr. Quintanilla's restaurant went out of business.

WORDS, WORDS, WORDS

typical: just like any other
designed: came up with an idea for something
unique: one of a kind; unlike any other

Selena's father worked harder than anyone to help make her a star.

By the age of 16, Selena was already on her way.

It had only been open for one year. The family didn't have enough money to pay the bills. They had to leave their home and stay with relatives.

Then the family bought an old bus and started traveling around, playing music. They called their band Selena and Company and played at little clubs, birthday parties, and weddings. Selena **designed** the clothes for everyone in the band. Soon, the family added a guitar player and a keyboard player. Then they changed the band's name to *Selena y Los Dinos*. That means Selena and Los Dinos.

Selena's family didn't have much money. But they stayed close and helped each other. They also believed in Selena. She was such a good singer! "I always knew that Selena was going to make it. She had that extra thing that makes an artist," her father says.

ASK YOURSELF

- As a reader, what do you know about Selena so far?
Think about the details that the writer has given you.

Her Own Style

Selena and the Dinos played Tejano music. The word *Tejano* means Texan, and the Mexican Americans who live along the Texas/Mexico border speak a language called Tejano. It is a **unique** blend of Spanish and English.

Tejano music is a mix of styles and has a sound all its own. Part of it comes from Mexican folk music. Part of it comes from German polka. It has Cuban rhythms. It also has country music sounds. Tejano music is popular in Texas because the rhythm is good for

⭐ Selena made it all sound easy. But every
one of her hits took hours of work.

dancing, and many Spanish-language radio stations play it.

Although Selena started out playing only Tejano music, she had always liked Top 40. So she added pop and rock touches to her songs, making her Tejano style special. Soon people started to notice her singing. They loved her catchy music and lyrics.

Selena made her first recording when she was 12. Her first album was **released** in 1984 and was called *Mis Primeras Grabaciones (My First Recordings)*. During this time, Selena was also attending West Oso Junior High in Molina, Texas. But as most young performers find out—it's hard to perform and go to school. Her dad wanted her to work on her music. So he took her out of school. The principal and teachers weren't happy, but her dad felt it was the right thing to do.

Still, an education was important to Selena. So she kept studying. She took classes by mail and earned her GED when she was 17. That meant that she had the skills of a high school graduate. Selena always told her fans, "Stay in school. Get the best education you can."

Selena turned 15 in 1986. She recorded a song called "Dame un Beso," which was written by her brother A.B. The title means "Give Me a Kiss." It became Selena and Los Dinos' first hit, and both Spanish and **bilingual** radio stations played it.

That year, Selena appeared on a magazine cover for the first time. The magazine was called the *Tejano Entertainer.* Soon, radio stations started interviewing her, too. Then Selena released her first big album. It was called *Alpha.* People loved Selena's voice. Her songs were appealing and fun. It was starting to look like Selena might become a big star.

Star of Texas

"And the winner is . . . Selena!" In 1987 those words were heard again and again.

Selena was only 15. But she was the star of the Tejano Music Awards. She was **nominated** for about a dozen awards and won both "Female Vocalist of the Year" and the "People's Choice Award." Her song "Give Me a Kiss" was also nominated for two awards. One was "Single of the Year." The other was "Song of the Year." And her band was nominated for "Most Promising Band."

That year, Selena appeared in soft drink ads in Texas. There was even a soda bottle with her picture on it! It seemed like everyone in Texas knew Selena.

ASK YOURSELF

- What have been the major events in Selena's life so far? Retell the events in your own words.

Making it Big

In 1989, Selena got a big break and landed a major recording deal. The following year, she released a new album called *Selena and Los Dinos* on the Capitol/EMI Latin label.

That year, Selena was again the star of the Tejano Music Awards, winning both "Female Entertainer of the Year" and "Female Vocalist of the Year." She won these awards every year for the rest of her life. And Selena's popularity continued to grow.

In 1991, she recorded "Buenos Amigos" ("Good Friends"). It was her first hit to get air-time outside of Texas. Now she had Spanish-speaking fans all over America.

WORDS, WORDS, WORDS

released: made available to the public for the first time
bilingual: able to speak two languages
nominated: recommended—usually for an award

The following year, she **captured** a new audience with her album *Entre A Mi Mundo (Enter My World)*. Two songs on it became very popular in Mexico. The songs were "La Carcacha" ("The Old Car") and "Como la Flor" ("Like a Flower").

In September 1993, Selena sang in front of 70,000 people at a concert in Nuevo Leon, Mexico. She was the first Tejano artist to make it big in that country. People called her the "Latina Madonna."

Romance

In 1988, Selena met Chris Pérez through a friend. He was a guitarist, and in 1992 he joined Selena's band. After a while, she started to like him.

In one interview, Selena said, "We were friends first. I never thought I wanted to marry a musician."

Chris and Selena spent time together on the road. Soon Selena's dad saw that they liked each other and told Selena to stay away from Chris.

"I was a very **possessive** father," her dad explained. "I thought Selena was too young. Her career was beginning to blossom. I knew she had a great future ahead of her. I didn't want anything to distract her."

So Selena's dad fired Chris from the band. Everyone was surprised. And Selena was very upset. But after four months passed, Selena's dad rehired Chris.

Selena and Chris were married in 1992 at City Hall in Nueces County, Texas. She was 21. He was 22.

Selena's family came to accept the marriage. Selena and Chris moved into a house in La Molina, Texas. Her parents lived next door. A.B. and his wife and kids lived two houses down.

Selena was very happy. Her family and friends supported her and she was at the top of the charts.

A Fan Club

Selena grew more and more popular, and by 1991 she had her own fan club. Here's how it happened. That year, she met a woman named Yolanda Saldivar. Yolanda was much older than Selena. But they became close friends. Yolanda wanted to start a fan club for Selena. Selena's dad agreed and Yolanda became the club's president. The club cost $20 to join and members received club newsletters and T-shirts. Yolanda also set up parties and events. In less than four years, 5,000 fans signed up for the fan club.

Yolanda seemed to be a great friend.

Crossing Over

In 1993, Selena was 22 years old. She had already **accomplished** a lot. She was taking college courses by mail. She was working hard. Her records were popular.

WORDS, WORDS, WORDS

captured: won; took possession of
possessive: jealous and protective
accomplished: did something important

At the 1994 Tejano Music Awards, Selena was named best female entertainer and best female vocalist.

Selena was also a good person. She helped others and she didn't smoke, drink, or do drugs.

In November she got another big break. Selena and Los Dinos signed a new deal. They would make their first English-language record. It would be Selena's "crossover" album. English-speaking audiences would join Selena's fans.

The contract was with SBK, part of the EMI label. Selena was the first Tejano singer to sign a big deal with SBK. The head of EMI's record group was thrilled to sign Selena. "Selena is the closest artist I've got to Madonna," he said. "She's definitely a pop star."

Next year, Selena also got her first part in a movie. The movie was called *Don Juan DeMarco* and starred Johnny Depp. One of Selena's songs was on the movie's soundtrack.

There was another first that year. She won a Grammy for the "Best Mexican-American Performance."

In 1994, another dream came true. Selena opened her first clothing store in her hometown, Corpus Christi, Texas. It was called "Selena Etc." Selena designed all the jewelry and clothes in the store. Eight months later, she opened another store in San Antonio, Texas. She hired her fan club president, Yolanda Saldivar, to manage the stores.

ASK YOURSELF

- What are some of Selena's accomplishments?

Look for details that can help you answer this question.

☆ Selena's story is an inspiration. As she once sang: "Life is so beautiful. Live each day without measuring it."

But Selena still had one big project. She wanted to learn to speak Spanish. So she went to Monterey, Mexico, and studied Spanish there. Before long, she spoke it very well.

She said, "If I ever have children, I want them to know Spanish. It only makes you a better person—or an even smarter one—to know two languages."

A Tragic End

In 1995, Selena performed in Houston's Astrodome. Over 60,000 people came!

She was also hard at work on her next album. It would be called *Dreaming of You* and would include songs in English and in Spanish. Selena was a superstar. But she had one big problem. Yolanda Saldivar wasn't doing her job well.

Suzette and A.B. warned Selena. They said Yolanda might not be a true friend. In fact, Yolanda might be a thief. They thought she was stealing from the fan club and the stores.

At first, Selena wouldn't listen. She was sure A.B. and Suzette were wrong. Why would Yolanda trick her? Selena decided to talk with Yolanda. On March 31, 1995, they met at a local hotel. Selena told Yolanda that the family had accused her of stealing. They also wanted Yolanda to stay away from Selena and didn't want her to be president of the fan club. Yolanda was **furious.** And when Selena turned to leave, Yolanda pulled out a gun and shot her. Tragically, Selena was killed.

Yolanda would eventually regret what she had done. But it was too late. Selena was dead.

After Selena

Selena was dead. When people heard, they were shocked. Selena's family couldn't believe it. Their lives stopped.

Thousands of fans came to Selena's funeral. They traveled from far away to pay their respects to the Quintanilla family and to say goodbye to Selena.

Today, Selena's memory lives on. She still inspires many young people. The Quintanilla family set up a **foundation** in her honor to help kids to stay in school. In 1997, it donated $33,000 to schools in Texas. "This is something Selena would have wanted," her dad said.

A movie has even been made about Selena's life. "We made this film to keep her spirit and her dream alive," the director said.

Jennifer Lopez played Selena in the movie. "I don't think I'll ever have a role like this again," she said. "I got to play such a beautiful person."

Many people loved Selena. She was their role model. She was an important person in the music world and she helped her community.

A student at the University of Houston said, "She was such a great person. She meant so much to the Latino people. We'll never put her behind us." ●

WORDS, WORDS, WORDS

furious: very angry
foundation: an organization that gives money to worthy causes

Selena ON THE WEB

By Glaston Ford

Can't get enough of Selena? Start surfing.

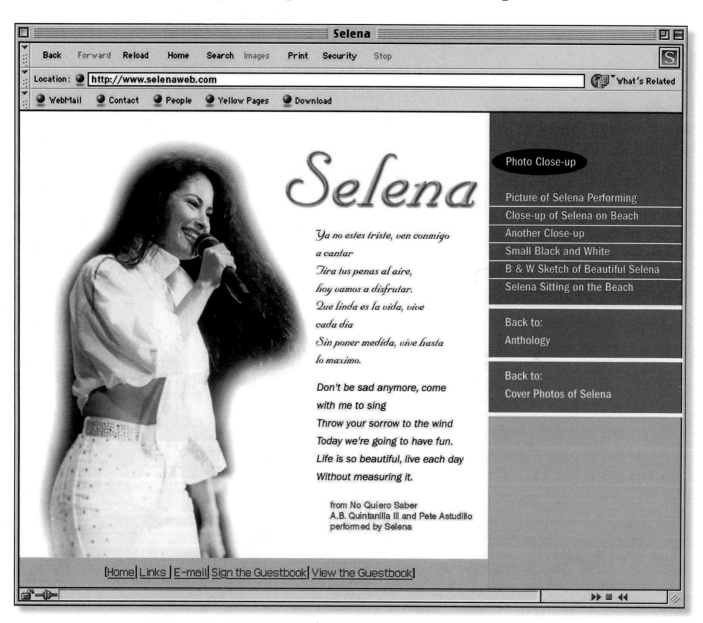

Selena

```
Selena

Back    Forward    Reload    Home    Search    Images    Print    Security    Stop

Location: http://www.selenaweb.com                          What's Related

WebMail    Contact    People    Yellow Pages    Download
```

Ya no estes triste, ven conmigo
a cantar
Tira tus penas al aire,
hoy vamos a disfrutar.
Que linda es la vida, vive
cada dia
Sin poner medida, vive hasta
lo maximo.

Don't be sad anymore, come
with me to sing
Throw your sorrow to the wind
Today we're going to have fun.
Life is so beautiful, live each day
Without measuring it.

from No Quiero Saber
A.B. Quintanilla III and Pete Astudillo
performed by Selena

Photo Close-up

Picture of Selena Performing
Close-up of Selena on Beach
Another Close-up
Small Black and White
B & W Sketch of Beautiful Selena
Selena Sitting on the Beach

Back to:
Anthology

Back to:
Cover Photos of Selena

[Home| Links | E-mail| Sign the Guestbook| View the Guestbook]

Caller-Times Interactive: NEWS

Where can you go to get more information about Selena? Try the Internet. Memories of Selena Quintanilla-Perez fill the World Wide Web. Her pictures, her music, lyrics to her songs, and outpourings of devotion from her fans decorate dozens of Web pages.

"Dear Selena, I love your music!" wrote one girl from Ridley Park, Pennsylvania, who signed an Internet fan book. "You were the most kind and generous person."

There are also sites for her movie, her foundation, her boutique, and even her doll.

One of the oldest sites was created by a fan shortly after the singer's death. "This is not an official site for Selena information," reads the Web page. "It is just a Web page I started as a tribute to her." The site includes the author's description of his trip to Corpus Christi, complete with pictures of the Quintanilla residence. This Selena admirer also put together a huge collection of photographs from *Texas Monthly, People* magazine, the *National Enquirer,* and the Selena calendar.

It's clear from the World Wide Web that Selena's appeal is not limited to South Texas. Some students at a high school in Maryland also set up a tribute page to Selena. Their site includes words to more than a dozen of her songs, among them "Como La Flor" and "Dreaming of You."

This site—the Caller-Times Interactive—has more than 40 articles on Selena. The articles cover her life, her music, and her movie.

"Since we first went up in August of 1995, the Selena part of the site has always been popular," said one Caller-Times editor.

"It's one of the few news sites about Selena on the Internet that's actually updated on a regular basis," said the Web-site editor. "Because of that, it attracts regular users from throughout the United States and the world."

It's very clear! If you want more information about Selena—you can find it. It's just a click away! ●

You can check out some of the most popular Selena Web sites on the Internet.

Selena City
http://members.tripod.com/~theselenamaster/selenacity.html
This Web site is huge. It contains song lyrics with translations, CD information, facts about Selena, links to other sites, and much more!

Caller-Times Interactive
http://www.caller.com/selena/selena.htm
This is a local Corpus Christi, TX, Web newspaper. Corpus Christi is where Selena lived. The site is updated regularly with news stories related to her.

The Selena Foundation
http://www.selena.org
This is the only site that is approved by Selena's father, Abraham Quintanilla. Here you can buy official products. And you can find out about what the Selena Foundation is all about, too.

Talk About It

Now that you've read "Dreaming of You" and "Selena on the Web," what do you have to say about these questions?

★ Do you think Selena *really* made a difference in the world? Why or why not?

★ Why do you think Selena still has so many fans?

Comprehension Check

Write your answers to the questions below. Use information from the biography and the Web-site article to support your answers.

1. What kind of music is Selena most famous for?

2. How did Mr. Quintanilla feel about education? Explain your answer.

3. What quality do you most admire about Selena? Tell why.

4. What are three things you can find on the Selena Web sites listed at the end of the article?

5. Do you think Selena would have liked her Web sites? What do you think she would have said about them?

Vocabulary Check

Complete each sentence starter below. Before you answer, think about the meaning of the vocabulary word in bold.

1. One thing that makes me **unique** is . . .
2. This isn't a **typical** day, in fact, it is . . .
3. I get **furious** every time . . .
4. I **designed** a great . . .
5. On the list of things I've already **accomplished** is . . .

Write About It

Choose one of the three writing prompts below.

⭐ Selena and her family traveled in a bus. Imagine that you traveled with her for a while. Write two postcards from the bus. Tell what your experience with Selena is like.

⭐ Would you like to be famous like Selena? Write a paragraph telling what you would like and/or dislike about being famous.

⭐ Who is your favorite music star? Describe the star and the music he or she makes. Tell what you like about the music.

Fact FILE

Selena's Final Album

In 1995, Selena recorded *Dreaming of You*. Sadly, before the album was released, Selena died. Still, the album sold 175,000 copies its first day. It was the second-fastest-selling album ever made by a female performer. And it was the first mostly Spanish-language record ever to start off as number one on the *Billboard 200*. (*Billboard* is the name of a magazine that tracks song and record sales.)

Below are some of the lyrics from the song *Dreaming of You*. Like many songs on that album, the words are in both English and Spanish. Selena wanted her music to appeal to everyone. And judging from the album sales, she succeeded.

Corazón
I can't stop dreaming of you
No puedo dejar de pensar en ti
I can't stop dreaming
Cómo te necesito
I can't stop dreaming of you
Mi amor, cómo te extraño

—*from* Dreaming of You

Scheduling Your Time

Is your day always jammed with stuff to do? Do you have homework, chores, family stuff, and activities after school? How can you ever get it all done?

It helps if you make a schedule. Look at the one below. Are you ready to organize your time?

This schedule is only for school days. If you like, you can make a schedule for the weekends, too.

See where it says "field hockey practice"? That shows that Wanda will start practice at 3 P.M. The arrow shows that practice is over at 5 P.M.

Wanda's Weekly Schedule

Time	Monday	Tuesday	Wednesday	Thursday	Friday
8:00A.M.–3:00P.M.	School				
3:00P.M.	field hockey practice	field hockey practice	field hockey practice	work on history report at the library	help mom at home
4:00P.M.					meet friends at the mall
5:00P.M.	watch Josh	watch Josh	watch Josh	watch Josh	have dinner with friends at mall
6:00P.M.	dinner	work	dinner	dinner	work
7:00P.M.	math homework		math homework	work on history report	
8:00P.M.	study for English test		plan history report		
9:00P.M.	TV		listen to music	watch TV	movie with friends
10:00P.M.	read in bed				

"A big project like a school report takes a lot of time. You probably won't want to do it all in one day. Break up the report into small chunks. Do a little bit at a time until the report is complete."

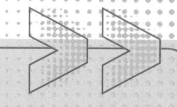

It's About Time

A schedule will help you map out your time. Read Wanda's schedule and the tips again. Use them to answer the questions. Write your answers on your own paper.

1. When is Wanda in school?
   a. Monday–Friday, from 8 A.M. to 3 P.M.
   b. Tuesday, Wednesday, Thursday, and Friday, from 8 A.M. to 3 P.M.
   c. Monday, from 8 A.M. to 3 P.M.

2. When is Wanda watching her brother Josh this week? How long each day will she watch him?

3. What is Wanda doing Monday, Tuesday, and Wednesday from 3 P.M. to 5 P.M.?

4. Which big project is Wanda going to start this week? When is she planning to work on it?

5. What does Wanda do almost every night before she goes to bed? What will she be doing Friday during that time?

Make a List
Make a list of all the things you have to do next week. Start with school, homework, chores, and after-school activities. Then list all the things you'd like to do, such as read a book, listen to music, and go out with friends.

Plan a Schedule
Use your list from above. Organize your activities into a schedule like Wanda's. First, write in the things you *have* to do. Then use the remaining time to schedule the things you do for fun.

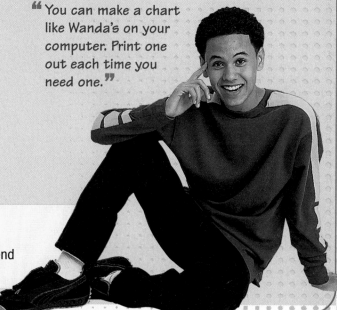

" You can make a chart like Wanda's on your computer. Print one out each time you need one. "

Real-World Words

activity: something that you do
organize: to put things in order
schedule: a plan for how you will spend your time

The Hostage

Adapted from the classic novel by Theodore Taylor

It's up to Jamie to decide whether or not the whale goes free.

CAST OF CHARACTERS

Jamie Tidd, a boy, 15*
Perry Tidd, his father*
Lacy Tidd, his mother*
Angie Pinheiro, 16
Zachary Cooke, a sea-park owner
Georgie Tebbetts, a whale trainer
Doc Greenlee, a marine biologist
Narrator 1*
Narrator 2*

*Starred characters are major roles.

SCENE 1

Narrator 1: Jamie Tidd and his father, Perry, are out on their fishing boat. They live in a tiny fishing community in British Columbia, Canada.

Narrator 2: The sky is dark and boiling. The wind begins to howl. A dangerous storm is **approaching.**

Jamie: Time to call it a day, Dad?

Perry: We barely caught $40 worth of fish, Jamie. Just 15 more minutes, then we'll head back. We'll beat the storm. Don't worry.

Narrator 1: But Perry is wrong. A moment later, a cold, driving rain breaks from the sky. Ten-foot waves crash against the boat.

Narrator 2: The boat's engine stalls. Perry tries to restart it. But the engine seems dead. The waves rise 20 feet in the air and toss the boat around.

Narrator 1: Jamie feels very **panicked.** The storm **rages,** and his father tries desperately to restart the motor. Hundreds of fishermen have gone to a watery grave in this sea.

Narrator 2: Just then, Perry gets the engine going. They head toward shore. Jamie breathes a sigh of relief.

Perry: Boy, you'll never get closer to death than that.

SCENE 2

Narrator 1: As the boat docks onshore, Jamie's mom, Lacy, runs to them with blankets.

Lacy: Thank goodness you're all right! I saw that storm and realized you weren't back. I couldn't get you on the radio!

Perry: Things got rough out there. We lost the engine, then the radio.

Lacy: I wish you would quit fishing.

Perry: I will, Lacy. As soon as I hit the lottery. Then we can move to a nice house in Prince Rupert.

Jamie: And I can go to the high school there instead of taking courses through the mail.

Perry: And we can take our dream vacation in Hawaii.

Jamie: Don't forget my dirt bike!

Narrator 2: The Tidd family goes inside to get warm. They have talked of Hawaii and dirt bikes and moving for years. They know it is all a dream.

SCENE 3

Narrator 1: Storms rage up and down the coast that month. It is hard to get food and supplies. Finally, when the storms die down, the fishermen return to sea to earn their living.

Narrator 2: One night after Jamie and Perry have returned from fishing, Jamie goes to get the mail that has been delivered. He brings home a huge bag of mail wrapped in plastic.

Lacy: Look at all this mail.

Jamie: Is there a letter for me?

Narrator 1: Lacy smiles at her son and shakes her head no. She knows he is waiting for a letter from Angie Pinheiro. Angie is 16 and the only person in their town who is near Jamie's age. She has been away at school in Prince Rupert. Jamie misses her.

Narrator 2: The family settles down to read mail. Suddenly, Perry lets out a low whistle.

Words, WORDS, Words

approaching: moving nearer
panicked: terrified or fearful about something
rages: continues violently
environmentalists: people who protect the earth and its living things

Perry: Well, look at this. Some guy in California will pay $100,000 for a killer whale.

Jamie: A hundred thousand for an old blackfish? I can't believe it!

Perry: He wants it for some sea park. He wants to teach it tricks, I guess. Can you imagine all that money?

Jamie: Get us one, Dad!

Lacy: Yeah, Perry. Get us one. Hawaii, here we come.

Narrator 1: Perry laughs and returns to reading the paper.

Jamie: Hey, Dad? Has anyone ever caught a blackfish?

Perry: Twenty years ago, two guys caught one and got $8,000 for it. But this sea park guy wants the granddaddy of all blackfish. He wants a 25-foot killer whale.

Lacy: Aren't there rules about capturing a killer whale?

Perry: Far as I know, there aren't. And of course, those Greenpeace folks put up a stink when anyone captures a whale.

Narrator 2: Jamie knew who his father was talking about. The Greenpeace people were **environmentalists.** They fought against people who killed baby seals for their fur.

Jamie: Do you think those Greenpeace people would bother us if we got a whale?

Perry: It doesn't really matter, Jamie. I wouldn't even know how to catch one. It's too big to catch in a net. If you tow it in, it would likely drown. Whoever this Zachary Cooke is, he's going to have to wait a long time for a 25-foot blackfish.

ASK Yourself

- What have you learned about Jamie's family?

Think about the things that Jamie's family dreams of having.

SCENE 4

Narrator 1: The next day, Jamie and his father are out fishing.

Jamie: Dad, did you always want to be a fisherman?

Perry: I was born into it, Jamie—just like you.

Jamie: But do you like it?

Perry: It's what I do, Jamie. It's all I know how to do. There are some awful days. But there are good days too.

Narrator 2: Jamie doesn't want to be a fisherman. But he doesn't know how to tell his father.

Narrator 1: Just then, a humpback whale spouts 100 yards away.

Perry: Hey, look! We're coming up on an old humptyback.

Jamie: Looks like there's something else up there.

Narrator 2: Perry takes some binoculars and studies the sea.

Perry: Blackfish!

Jamie: You're kidding? A killer whale?

Perry: Looks like three of them. A huge one and two smaller ones. We might be in for a real show.

Narrator 2: Perry and Jamie watch as the killer whales circle the humpback.

Narrator 1: Suddenly, the killer whales attack the humpback. It is a bloody, sickening sight.

Perry: No one's going to believe this. I've got to take some pictures.

Narrator 2: Perry grabs his camera and starts snapping photos.

SCENE 5

Narrator 2: That night, Angie comes home. The two old friends take a walk and talk. Jamie tells Angie about the blackfish attacking the humpback.

Angie: That sounds so gross.

Jamie: It was hard to watch.

Angie: But those blackfish sure are beautiful, aren't they?

Jamie: Not after what I saw.

Angie: Just to watch them swim is a major treat.

Narrator 1: Later, Jamie goes home and hears laughter.

Jamie: What's so funny?

Lacy: We're talking about how we're going to spend the money.

Jamie: What money?

Lacy: The hundred thousand.

Perry: That blackfish we saw today has to be at least 25 feet.

Jamie: More like 35 feet. But how are we going to catch it, Dad? That thing is a monster.

Perry: Yeah, I know. But a man can dream, Jamie.

SCENE 6

Narrator 2: A few days later, Jamie and his father are out on the boat. They are having a good day, catching lots of fish.

Narrator 1: All of a sudden, Perry grabs the binoculars.

Jamie: What is it?

Perry: That crazy blackfish is heading right into the cove!

Jamie: Is it that big one that killed the humpback?

Perry: Sure is. Let's go.

Narrator 2: Perry starts the engine and steers to the cove.

Jamie: We're not going to try and catch him, are we?

Perry: If he's dumb enough to head to that cove, Jamie, maybe . . .

Jamie: Maybe what?

Perry: Just keep your fingers crossed. It could mean Hawaii, your dirt bike, school in Prince Rupert, and a new boat for me!

Narrator 1: Jamie is scared as the boat nears the whale.

Perry: He's in there! I don't believe it. This just might work! Get the nets ready.

Narrator 2: Perry drives the boat up to one end of the narrow cove entrance. He drops an anchor. Then he and Jamie block the entrance to the cove with three layers of netting. They drop an anchor at the other end of the entrance and trap the killer whale in the cove.

Narrator 1: After exploring the cove, the whale turns around and heads toward the net. Jamie **winces.** But the whale stops just short of the net.

Jamie: I don't understand. That whale can go through that net like it's nothing. He could also jump over it. Why won't he?

Perry: Whales use **sonar.** The net is confusing him. He knows something is there. But he doesn't know what. The net might as well be a cement wall.

SCENE 7

Narrator 2: Perry radios Lacy.

Perry: Want to go to Hawaii?

Lacy: Why are you asking me?

Perry: We just got the ticket. Jamie and I trapped that big blackfish at the cove.

Words, WORDS, Words

winces: shrinks back, as if in pain or expecting it
sonar: a means of determining how far away something is by sending out sound waves
communicate: to give or share information, ideas, and feelings

"Anything that big and beautiful ought to be free to do what it wants."

Lacy: I can't believe it, Perry. I'll be right there!

Narrator 1: Perry uses the boat telephone to dial the number in the magazine ad.

Cooke: Hello?

Perry: My name is Perry Tidd. I'm a fisherman in British Columbia. Mr. Cooke, I've got your whale.

Cooke: You do? Well, that's great. You're sure he's 25 feet?

Perry: You betcha.

Narrator 2: Perry gives Cooke directions to the small cove.

Cooke: We'll leave in the morning. You hang on to that whale, Mr. Tidd.

SCENE 8

Narrator 1: Word about the whale spreads. People walk to the cove to check it out. As Jamie stands guard, he sees Angie approaching.

Angie: Why don't you let that whale loose?

Jamie: You're kidding. Right?

Angie: Anything that big and beautiful ought to be free to do what it wants. Let him go!

Jamie: Come on, Angie. You know what this whale is worth?

Angie: Yeah, I've heard. But if my papa had trapped that whale, I'd tell him the same thing.

Narrator 2: Angie notices two other blackfish outside the net. They are talking to the trapped whale. They **communicate** with clicks and high-pitched sounds.

Angie: I bet those two are females.

Jamie: How do you know that?

Angie: I can tell. That means you're standing in the way of love! You have a whale hostage. Let it go, Jamie.

Narrator 1: Angie walks toward the water. The whale surfaces and puts its huge head on the rock, right near Angie! She leans toward the whale.

Jamie: What are you doing? Get away. That thing is a killer!

Narrator 2: Angie leans closer to the whale and pets its head.

Narrator 1: Jamie tugs at Angie.

Jamie: Are you crazy?

Angie: What's crazy is you keeping this beautiful animal trapped. Let's cut the net. Your father will never know.

Jamie: No way, Angie. We're keeping the whale. My family's future depends on it. Besides, my dad would know a knife cut in a net if he saw it.

ASK Yourself

- What do you think Jamie and his father will decide to do with the whale?

Consider what you might do in their place.

SCENE 9

Narrator 2: The next day, Cooke arrives at the cove with Georgie Tebbetts and Doc Greenlee.

Perry: Welcome, I'm . . .

Cooke: Let's cut the small talk. This is Georgie Tebbetts. He used to work at Sea Kingdom. I stole him away to work for me. He's going to make sure this whale of yours is smart enough to teach to do tricks.

Georgie: Pleased to meet you.

Cooke: And this is Doc Greenlee. He's going to make sure this whale is healthy.

Doc: That whale is a monster, maybe the biggest I've seen. Looks to be about 20 years old.

Perry: So, you think this whale meets the **requirements**?

Doc: Too soon to tell. We'll need a few days to do tests.

Cooke: Well, work quickly, gentlemen. Time is money, and I'm sure Mr. Tidd would like that check as fast as he can get it.

Perry: You certainly got that right, Mr. Cooke.

Cooke: Meanwhile, I'll send these photos you took to the right people. We want to get **exposure** for this whale. I'm calling him Tyrannus.

SCENE 10

Narrator 1: The men do tests with Jamie looking on.

Narrator 2: Jamie is interested in the way the two smaller whales continue to come by and talk to the larger whale.

Jamie: What are they doing?

Georgie: They're talking to each other. Whales have their own language, you know.

Doc: And those two are female whales, probably his mates. I think they're both pregnant with his children.

Jamie: Doc, do you think whales like being in sea parks?

Doc: It's hard to tell. They get fed well and get great care.

Georgie: Some whales even love performing for people. They're playful creatures, and they seem happy when they're doing tricks. But no matter how good it is, it's still not the sea; it's not their natural environment.

Narrator 1: The word *natural* sticks in Jamie's brain. Is it *natural* to trap a whale in a cove? Is it *natural* to sell a whale to a sea park and make it do tricks? He thinks about what Angie said.

Jamie: I really wish we could understand their language. Then he could tell us what he wants.

SCENE 11

Narrator 2: After days of testing, Georgie and Doc convince Cooke the whale is worth the money. They go to a warehouse to build a special pen to carry the whale to California.

Narrator 1: Jamie stays at the cove to keep an eye on the whale. It gets late and he falls asleep. He is awakened by a scream.

Narrator 2: Jamie looks in the direction of the scream. He sees Angie, in the water with the whale. He knows why she is there. She has gone in to cut the net and free the whale.

Jamie: Oh, no!

Narrator 1: The whale has grabbed Angie with its teeth. Angie is **flailing** around and screaming at the top of her lungs. The whale drags her under.

Jamie: Angie! Angie!

Narrator 2: Jamie grabs a large salmon from a bucket filled with fish for the whale. He dives into the water and sees Angie, pinned to the bottom by the whale.

Narrator 1: Jamie swims up to the whale quickly and waves the fish in its face. The whale lets go of Angie and grabs the fish. Jamie gets a hold of Angie and swims to the surface.

Narrator 2: Once Angie is safely out of the water, Jamie runs for help.

SCENE 12

Narrator 1: It is two days later. Angie is out of the hospital and doing better. Jamie and his parents are heading to the cove.

Jamie: I think we should let him go, Dad.

Perry: We can't Jamie. We need the money. For Hawaii. For our new life.

Jamie: Angie was right. This whale deserves to be free. Plus, we owe him. He could have killed both Angie and me.

Perry: We're not turning him loose. If you hadn't been around, he would have killed Angie for sure.

Jamie: I wish Angie had cut the stupid net!

ASK Yourself

- What kind of person is Jamie? Think about what he says and does.

SCENE 13

Narrator 2: When they reach the cove, Doc Greenlee is there.

Perry: How are things, Doc?

Doc: Not good, Perry. Ever since those whale pictures hit the airwaves, people are going nuts.

Lacy: What do you mean?

Doc: News stations are airing negative stories. Environmental groups are threatening to **boycott** the sea park and anyone connected with it. Cooke is

Words, WORDS, Words

requirements: things that are needed; terms of a deal
exposure: media attention
flailing: moving or swinging wildly
boycott: to protest by refusing to buy or support something

scared of the bad **publicity.** He's calling off the deal.

Perry: It's all over?

Doc: I'm afraid so.

Perry: What about us?

Doc: Cooke doesn't want any trouble. He'll **reimburse** you for all your expenses. He'll pay you for the pictures he used. I'm sorry.

Perry: It's not your fault, Doc.

Narrator 1: Doc leaves.

Lacy: I never did trust that guy from the sea park.

Perry: Never mind him. We'll survive.

Lacy: Yes, we will.

Narrator 2: They all hug each other.

Perry: Okay, we're letting that whale go, Jamie. But not because of Cooke, or the environmental groups, or the TV stations.

Jamie: Why, then?

Perry: Because you were right, Jamie. That blackfish traded you and Angie for his freedom. That's the kind of thing I respect, fish or man. You can tell everybody I said that.

Jamie: I will, Papa.

Perry: Now, let's go get our fishing net. We'll need it another day. ●

publicity: information that is given out to the public through the media
reimburse: to pay someone back

SHOULD ALL ANIMALS BE ALLOWED TO LIVE FREE?

In the movie *Free Willie*, a boy helps a killer whale escape from a sea park. In movie theaters everywhere, audiences cheered to see the whale go free. In real life, not everyone agrees. Some people say that places like aquariums and wildlife parks are nothing more than dressed-up jails. But others say that captive animals are protected, cared for, and fed healthy diets. They argue that aquariums and wildlife parks also give people the chance to learn about animals. And that helps us appreciate them more.

WHAT DO YOU THINK? READ THIS DEBATE AND DECIDE FOR YOURSELF.

Yes Animals don't belong in aquariums or wildlife parks. They belong in the wild. Like people, they feel afraid and upset when they are taken from their homes and separated from their families. Once caught, some animals show signs of boredom and unhappiness. Some refuse to eat.

Nothing that scientists may learn makes up for these animals' suffering. What right do humans have to make animals suffer?

If you said yes:
- How will people get the chance to see wild animals and learn about them?

No Aquariums and wildlife parks help educate people about animals. They remind people that we need to protect endangered animals and preserve the places where they live in the wild.

Also, in aquariums and wildlife parks scientists can study animals up close. They could never do that in the wild. Learning about an animal's habits and diet could help save some animals from becoming extinct.

If you said no:
- How can we make sure that animals are not abused in these places?

What's your point of view?

Talk About It

Now that you've read *The Hostage* and "Should All Animals Be Allowed to Live Free?" what do you have to say about these questions?

▶ Suppose that Jamie and his family had sold the whale. Do you think they would have felt good about the money? Why or why not?

▶ Should a person be able to sell an animal he or she has caught? Should living things be for sale? Why or why not?

Comprehension Check

Write your answers to the questions below. Use information from the play and the debate to support your answers.

1. How do Jamie and his father catch the whale?

2. Why does Angie dive into the water with the whale?

3. Why does Cooke cancel the deal?

4. If you were in Jamie's place, what would you have done about the whale?

5. Which side of the debate do you think Jamie would have agreed with? Explain your answer.

Vocabulary Check

Complete each sentence starter below. Before you answer, think about the meaning of the vocabulary word in bold.

1. You might say a storm **rages** if . . .

2. Being an **environmentalist** is the kind of career that I . . .

3. Our school received lots of good **publicity** when . . .

4. One reason you might decide to **boycott** something is . . .

5. You might feel **panicked** if . . .

Write About It

Choose one of the writing prompts below.

▶ If whales could talk, what would they say? Write a short conversation between the trapped whale and the two whales outside the net.

▶ Write a letter from Jamie to Angie, explaining why his family wanted to sell the whale.

▶ Write a letter to the editor about the captured whale. Do you think Jamie and his family have a right to sell it? Or do you think they should set it free? Give two reasons for your opinion.

About the AUTHOR

Theodore Taylor is the author of more than 30 books. One of these books, *The Cay*, has won many awards. Taylor gets a lot of his ideas from his own life experience. He grew up on the coast in Norfolk, Virginia. During his life, he has worked as a sports reporter, crime writer, merchant sailor, manager, and movie press agent. He got his start as a writer at age 13, writing about school sports events. Taylor, who describes himself as "a terrible student," knew nothing about writing. He learned, in part, by studying the work of other good writers.

Reading a Pie Chart

Where do you get your spending money? That's the kind of question often asked in surveys.

The pie chart below shows how a group of teenagers responded to a survey about where their spending money comes from. Take a look at the chart. Does it make sense to you?

How Do Kids Get Their Money?

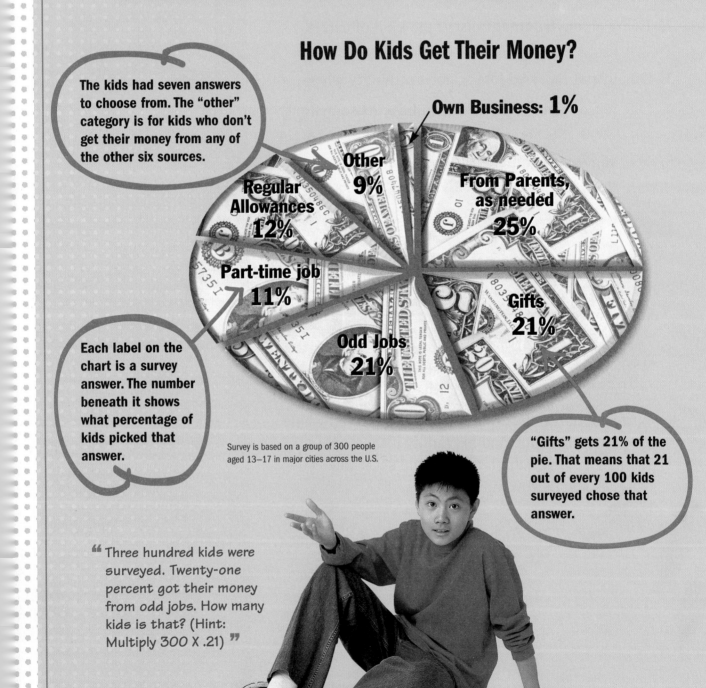

The kids had seven answers to choose from. The "other" category is for kids who don't get their money from any of the other six sources.

Own Business: 1%

Other 9%

Regular Allowances 12%

From Parents, as needed 25%

Part-time job 11%

Gifts 21%

Odd Jobs 21%

Each label on the chart is a survey answer. The number beneath it shows what percentage of kids picked that answer.

Survey is based on a group of 300 people aged 13–17 in major cities across the U.S.

"Gifts" gets 21% of the pie. That means that 21 out of every 100 kids surveyed chose that answer.

" Three hundred kids were surveyed. Twenty-one percent got their money from odd jobs. How many kids is that? (Hint: Multiply 300 X .21) "

Grab a Slice

Reread the pie chart and the tips that go with it. Then use them to answer the questions below. Write your answers on your own paper.

1. According to the chart, how do the largest number of teens get their money? How do the smallest number of teens get their money?

2. What percentage of kids get their money from gifts? What percentage of kids get their money from regular allowances?

3. According to the chart, which of the following statements is **not** true?
   a. More kids get money from gifts than from part-time jobs.
   b. More kids get money from their own businesses than from regular allowances.
   c. As many kids get money from gifts as from doing odd jobs.

4. What is the total percentage of kids who get most of their money from odd jobs and part-time jobs?
   a. 25%   b. 10%   c. 32%

5. Three hundred kids were surveyed. Only 1 percent of the kids own their own businesses. How many kids is that? (Hint: Multiply 300 x .01).
   a. 1   b. 3   c. 13

Take a Survey

Ask 10 kids in your class where they get most of their money. Give them the same choices that are listed on the chart in this lesson. Keep track of how many kids pick each answer.

Chart It Out

Make a pie chart that shows your results from "Take a Survey." (Hint: Your survey is based on 10 kids. If two kids get their money from gifts, then gifts will be 20% of your pie, and so on.)

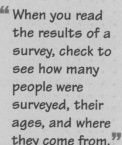

" When you read the results of a survey, check to see how many people were surveyed, their ages, and where they come from. "

Real-World Words

percentage: a number out of 100 (14% is 14 out of 100.)
source: the place, person, or thing from which something comes
survey: a report or study on people's opinions or habits

GOT QUESTIONS? GET Answers!

BY MELVIN AND GILDA BERGER

What's the best way to get information? By asking questions! The next three selections will give you lots of questions—and answers—on weather, the human body, and space.

Can It Rain Cats and Dogs?

Questions and Answers About Weather

Q Can it rain cats and dogs?

A No—but it can rain frogs and fishes! In the United States, frogs fell on Tennessee in October 1946 and on Arkansas in January 1973. Fish fell on Glamorgan, Wales, in 1859, on Frankston, Australia, in 1935, and on Louisiana in 1947—each time during the month of October. Every time, rainstorms swept up the animals, which then came down with the rain.

People like to say, "It's raining cats and dogs" when it is raining very hard. The saying comes from an old belief that cats bring rain and dogs bring wind. But don't believe it. While it can rain frogs and fishes, it can't rain cats and dogs!

Q Why does the weather keep changing?

A Because the sun heats the earth unevenly. Places around the equator—called the tropics—get lots of heat. The air in the tropics is always warm. Places near the North Pole and South Pole—called the polar regions—get very little heat. The air in the polar regions is always cold.

In general, air moves from where it's cold—the polar regions—to where it's warm—the tropics. The moving air creates the winds that make the weather change.

Q What is the hottest place on Earth?

A The town of Al'Aziziyah, Libya. On September 13, 1922, the temperature in the shade reached a scorching 136 degrees Fahrenheit (58°C)!

The record in the United States is held by Death Valley, California. The temperature there

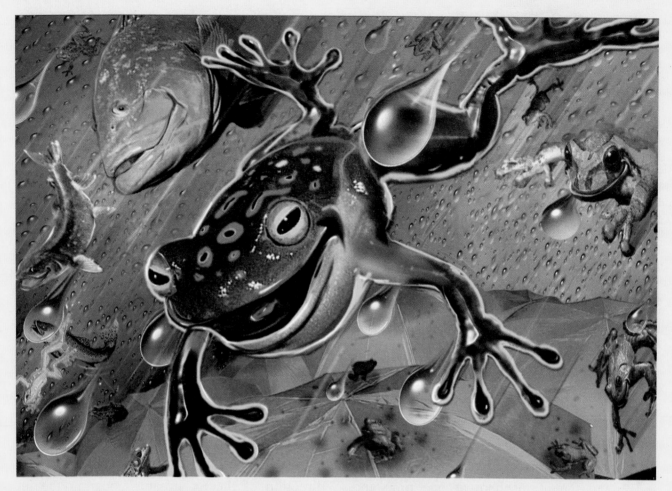

Can it rain cats and dogs? No—but it can rain frogs and fishes.

has reached 134 degrees Fahrenheit (57°C). Every summer a race is held in Death Valley. But the ground is so hot that it sometimes melts the soles of the runners' sneakers.

Q What is the coldest place on Earth?

A A place called Vostak in Antarctica. On July 21, 1983, the temperature hit a bonechilling −128.6 degrees Fahrenheit (−89.2°C).

The lowest temperature in the United States, −80 degrees Fahrenheit (−62°C), was recorded in Prospect Creek, Alaska. Boil a pot of water in Prospect Creek and fling it into the air. You'll see the water turn instantly into ice.

Q Are mountaintops colder than valleys?

A Yes. The higher you go, the colder you get. The temperature drops about 11 degrees Fahrenheit (6°C) for every 3,300 feet (1,000 m) you climb. That's why people on a mountaintop can be shivering while people in the valley are trying to cool off!

Can you smell rain? Sometimes.

Q Is weather the same as climate?

A No. Weather is the condition of the air and the atmosphere at one time and place. A summer hot spell and a sudden winter storm are examples of weather.

Climate is the usual weather in an area. Little rainfall on a desert and high temperatures around the equator describe climate.

Q How can you slow down global warming?

A Cut back on activities that require burning of fuels. Walk or bike short distances instead of depending on car rides. Turn off lights when not in use to save electricity. And in the winter, dress warmly indoors so you can keep your house at a lower temperature and burn less fuel for heating.

Q Where are the windiest places in the world?

A Commonwealth Bay, Antarctica, has winds that reach 200 miles (320 km) an hour. These winds blow for more than 100 days a year. Winds just one-third as fast would blow you off your feet!

The all-time record for wind speed over land was set on the top of Mount Washington, New Hampshire, on April 12, 1934. On that date the winds raced along at 231 miles (381.3 km) an hour. That's faster than the top speed of any car on the road today!

Q What is the jet stream?

A It is a fast-moving river of air high in the atmosphere that takes a wavy path from west to east. These powerful winds can reach speeds of more than 200 miles (320 km) an hour. Large weather systems tend to follow the direction of the jet stream. Locating the jet stream helps weather scientists, called meteorologists, predict changes in the weather.

Q What is at the center of every raindrop?

A A tiny bit of dust. The water **condenses** around a speck of dust, which is at the center of the raindrop.

Q Why do clouds have different shapes and colors?

A Because clouds form in various ways. White and fluffy cumulus clouds form when warm, moist air rises quickly from the ground and is cooled fast.

Cirrus clouds form so high in the sky that they contain only ice crystals. They are light and wispy, and look like feathers or curls of hair.

When air rises very slowly over a large area, low layers of clouds form. They look like heavy, gray blankets stretched over vast areas of the sky.

Q Is fog the same as clouds?

A The same—and different. Both fog and clouds **consist** of tiny droplets of water. But clouds form high in the sky. Fog forms at ground level.

You get fog on calm, cool nights when the ground is cold. The water vapor in the air condenses into droplets of water. Fog forms as the air near the ground fills with these droplets. The drops are so tiny, it takes about seven trillion to make one tablespoon of water!

Q Can you smell rain?

A Sometimes. Plants always give off a certain oil. When rain is coming, there is a drop in air pressure, and the air picks up a trace of the oil's **odor.** One sniff and you may be able to tell that rain is on the way.

Also, your sense of smell is the sharpest when the air is moist. Breathe deeply on the next damp day. You may even pick up the weak scent of soggy soil.

Q When do you see a rainbow?

A When the sun comes out after a morning or late-afternoon shower. Sunlight looks white, but it is really made up of many different colors. The sun's rays strike the drops of rain in the sky. This breaks the white light into the colors of the rainbow—red, orange, yellow, green, blue, indigo, and violet.

Q Is snow always white?

A No. Red snow fell in Switzerland in 1755. The color came from red sand that blew over from the Sahara Desert. In 1926, black snow fell in France. **Alas,** no one knows why.

Q Can you have thunder without lightning?

A Never. Thunder and lightning always come together. But you'd never know it. You always see the lightning before you hear the thunder. That's because light travels super fast, at 186,000 miles (300,000 km) a second! Sound is much slower, at only about $\frac{1}{5}$ mile (0.3 km) a second. So first you see the lightning, then you hear the thunder.

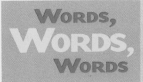

WORDS, WORDS, WORDS

condenses: turns from a gas, or vapor, to a liquid, usually as a result of cooling
consist: to be made up of
odor: a smell or scent
alas: sadly

WHY DON'T HAIRCUTS HURT?

Questions and Answers About the Human Body

Q Why don't haircuts hurt?

A Because hair is mostly keratin, a substance found in dead skin cells. And cutting dead cells doesn't hurt.

Only one part of your hair is alive. It is the part you can't see. The live part grows in hair follicles under your scalp. As live hair pushes up above the scalp, it dies. That's why haircuts don't hurt. The scissors are only cutting threads of dead cells.

The longest hair on record belonged to Mata Jagdamba of India. Her hair measured 13 feet, $10\frac{1}{2}$ inches (417 cm). What a lot of dead cells!

Q What are cells?

A Cells make up every part of your body. There are skin cells, muscle cells, bone cells, blood cells, and many other kinds of cells.

Each cell has a different shape. And each type has a special job to do. For example, the live cells in hair are rectangles. They produce the keratin that makes your hair strong.

Q What gives hair its color?

A All hair gets its color from melanin. Pure melanin makes hair brown or black. About 80 percent of the people in the United States have brown or black hair. If melanin contains iron or sulfur, the hair is blonde or red.

Q What are freckles?

A Clumps of melanin in your skin. The small brownish spots show up mostly on the face and hands. Spending lots of time in the sun may increase the number of freckles and darken them.

Sometimes older people develop "freckles" on the backs of their hands. The dark spots show up because aging skin often produces extra amounts of melanin in certain places.

Q What makes your lips red?

A Blood. The skin of your lips is very thin. This lets blood flowing in the tiny **vessels** under the skin show through.

Q Do you keep the same skin for life?

A Far from it: 50,000 tiny bits of dead skin cells fall off every *minute!* They make up about 75 percent of the dust floating around in your house. By the time you reach age 70, you'll have shed 40 pounds (18 kg) of dead skin.

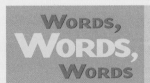

WORDS, WORDS, WORDS

vessels: tubes in the body that fluids pass through
epidermis: the top layer of your skin

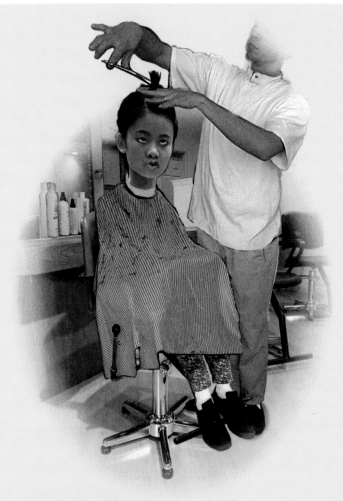

Why don't haircuts hurt?

Every hour your **epidermis** is making about one and a half million new cells to replace the lost skin cells. Just think of that. Every two weeks you get completely new skin!

Q Do you get more bones as you grow older?

A No. In fact, babies have more bones than grown-ups do! At birth, you have about 300 bones. As you get older, some small bones join together to make big ones. By the time you graduate from high school, you will be down to 206 bones.

Q Do bones wear out?

A Yes. The tiny cells of your bones are constantly dying and being replaced by new bone cells. In seven years, your body grows enough bone to make an entirely new skeleton!

Q Are you the same height all day long?

A No. You're taller in the morning. During the day you get shorter. The pull of gravity squeezes the bones in your spine together. You can lose as much as 1 inch (2.5 cm) of height!

Ask YOURSELF

■ What does melanin do?
Reread the answers that tell you about hair color and freckles.

At night, when you're asleep in bed, the bones in your spine move slightly apart. In the morning, you're back at your full height.

Q Which muscles get used the most?

A The little muscles of the eye. They tighten and loosen about 100,000 times a day! You would have to walk about 50 miles (80 km) a day to give your legs that much exercise.

Q Is it easier to smile or frown?

A To smile. It takes about 17 muscles to create a smile. But it takes 43 muscles to make a frown. So smile—it's much easier—and friendlier.

Can You Hear a Shout in Space?

Questions and Answers About Space

Q Can you hear a shout in space?

A Not unless you have a radio in your space suit. There is hardly any air in space. Without air, or any other way to carry the sound waves, there is no sound.

Q Where does space begin?

A Beyond Earth's atmosphere—about 60 miles (96 km) above the surface of the earth. The atmosphere is like a blanket of air. It covers the whole earth and provides the oxygen we need to stay alive. The higher you go, the thinner the air gets. When you reach 60 miles (96 km) there are only a few **traces** of air left. This is about where the atmosphere ends—and space begins.

Q Where does space end?

A It doesn't. Space is endless. It goes on way beyond the solar system and past the most distant stars.

Q Can airplanes fly into space?

A No. Airplanes need air to fly. Air moving around the wings makes a lifting force that keeps the plane up in the air. Oxygen in the air lets the fuel burn in the plane's engines. Without air, a plane would fall and crash to Earth. That's no way to get into space, you'll agree!

Q How can you get into space?

A By rocket. Only a rocket can provide enough power and go fast enough to overcome Earth's gravity and enter space.

A rocket doesn't need wings to fly. It uses its own **thrust** to climb. A rocket also carries its own supply of oxygen. This means it can burn fuel far out in space where there is hardly any air.

Q What makes a rocket go?

A The burning fuel. It creates hot gases under great pressure. The gases have nowhere to go—except out through a small opening at the bottom of the rocket. The gases rush out very fast and with great force. The rushing hot gas shoots the rocket up into the air. A rocket can move much faster than the speed of sound!

Q Who invented the first rockets?

A The Chinese, about 800 years ago. Their rockets were powered by gunpowder. People set the gunpowder on fire. The gunpowder burned quickly or exploded and sent out a burst of hot gas. The burning gas shot the rocket into the air.

At first, the Chinese used rockets for fireworks. Later, they attached arrows to the rockets and used them in war.

Can you hear a shout in space? Not unless you have a radio in your space suit.

Q Does space look blue like the sky?

A No. Space is black. Without air to **scatter** the sun's light, there is no color.

Q Does it feel good to be weightless?

A Not at first. Your sense of balance is upset and you may feel light-headed and giddy. Turn your head quickly, and you'll feel like you are spinning or tumbling around.

Also, your blood shifts towards your head, your face puffs out, and your nose gets stuffy. Astronauts say that in space you have the same full feeling in your head that you get from hanging upside down from gym bars.

Of course, most people get used to being weightless in a day or so. Or else, how could anyone work in space?

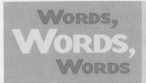

WORDS, WORDS, WORDS

traces: small amounts
thrust: the forward-moving force produced by a rocket engine
scatter: to spread

Q What is it like to work when you're weightless?

A Every job takes about twice as long as on Earth. To turn a screw, for example, you have to use arm or foot grips to keep yourself steady. If not, you'll twist around instead of the screw. Using a hammer is just as tricky. A very hard strike can throw you backward. Small wonder astronauts are pooped by the end of the day.

Q Do you get taller or shorter in space?

A Up to 2 inches (5 cm) taller. Without the pull of gravity, your spine stretches out. At the same time, your waist shrinks because many of your organs float upward to your upper chest.

Q Do astronauts exercise in space?

A Yes, they do. Astronauts must work out because being weightless weakens their bones and muscles. The exercise takes a lot of time and energy, but is necessary. Riding a bicycle in place, for example, forces the muscles to push and pull, just as they do against gravity on Earth. By cycling for 90 minutes, which is one orbit, an astronaut can pedal around the world!

Ask YOURSELF

- What problems would you have to solve to live in space?

Think about the things that Earth has and space doesn't.

Q How do you eat, sleep, and use the bathroom in space?

A You eat food from plastic or foil packages. If it weren't kept in a package, the food would float away. Thirsty? Just squeeze juice or water from a foil drink bag into your mouth. If a liquid were in an open glass, it would crawl up the sides and drops would float around the cabin.

You sleep in a sleeping bag that is attached to a wall. If you don't zip yourself in, you'll end up drifting around the cabin.

You go to the bathroom as you do at home—except that you must use the handles to hold yourself down on the seat. Air, not water, sucks the waste away.

Q Can you take a shower in space?

A Not on the shuttle; there's no room! But on a space station there is a shower with a special nozzle that squirts water on your body. Then a vacuum-cleaner-like attachment sucks off the soapy water. Just be sure to have enough water to rinse off the soap!

Most astronauts keep clean with sponge baths. They put water and soap on a washcloth and wash that way. They use special soap that does not need rinsing. Drying off with a clean towel is all it takes.

Q How do you comb your hair in space?

A With care. Long hair gets snagged and tangled when you're weightless. So most astronauts wear their hair short—and just give it a quick brush in the morning.

Q Will kids ever travel to space?

A Maybe! Every year spaceflight is becoming cheaper, safer, and more frequent. In time, a trip into space may be like an airplane flight in the early days of aviation.

Q Where will the first visitors stay in space?

A Most likely in space hotels. A large Japanese company, Shimizu, already has plans for a hotel in space.

The first "space hotel" will be built inside a giant wheel. The wheel will slowly spin around, creating a feeling of gravity. People will be able to walk around just as they do on Earth. The hotel will have 64 rooms. Guests will go on space walks, take sightseeing trips to the moon, and even play weightless sports!

Q Will people ever live in space cities?

A Very likely. Scientists plan to build huge colonies in space, on the moon, or on Mars. The moon may be a stopping-off point for travelers on their way to far distant planets. Thousands of people will live in these communities for long periods of time.

Q Will people work in space?

A Yes. Certain special medicines, metals, and microchips may be made best in weightless space factories. The first "Made in Space" products already exist. They are tiny

Will people ever live in space cities? Very likely.

balls made from liquid plastic. Scientists use the spheres, each as big as a pinpoint, to measure the superfine holes in certain filters. When made on Earth, each ball is not exactly round. The ones made in space are all perfect.

Q Will we ever get energy from space?

A Yes. Scientists plan to send a gigantic panel of solar cells into orbit. The cells would capture the sun's light and change it into electricity. This energy would then be beamed down to Earth.

The problem is weight. A solar power station would be very heavy. The panels would weigh about 600 times as much as *Skylab,* the heaviest object ever launched into space. Space shuttles might need about 5,000 flights just to carry up all the parts! ●

Talk About It

Now that you've read "Got Questions? Get Answers!" what do you have to say about these questions?

▶ What answers in the reading surprised you the most? Why?

▶ Were there other questions that you'd like to ask? What are they?

Comprehension Check

Write your answers to the questions below. Use information from the nonfiction collection to support your answers.

1. How was it able to rain frogs and fishes?

2. Why is it harder to "smell rain" in a city?

3. Why does it hurt when you pull your hair, if hair is nothing but dead cells?

4. Why are you taller in space or when you sleep?

5. If space has hardly any air, can it have weather? Explain.

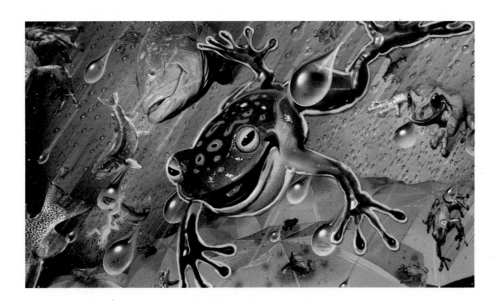

Vocabulary Check

Complete each sentence with the correct vocabulary word.

condenses   consist   traces   odor   scatter

1. If you _____ the seeds all over the yard, it will be full of flowers this summer.

2. The refrigerator had an _____ like rotten eggs.

3. Our tests usually _____ of true-or-false questions.

4. On the living room floor were _____ of the popcorn we ate during the movie.

5. If you blow on a cool window pane, you can see how the moisture in your breath _____.

Write About It

Choose one of the writing prompts below.

▶ Think about a subject you know well. Make a list of three questions and answers on that topic.

▶ Think of a science question. Then tell how you could go about answering it. List the kinds of books you could read, the people you could talk to, or an experiment you could do.

▶ Who could answer questions about the human body, space, and the weather? Think about the jobs these experts might have. Which job seems the most interesting to you? Explain why.

More to READ

Still have questions? Still looking for answers? Check out these books. You won't be sorry!

Do Stars Have Points?
by Melvin and Gilda Berger

Explore space from the comfort of your own home! Learn about stars. When it comes to the universe, this book has it all.

Do Tornadoes Really Twist?
by Melvin and Gilda Berger

This book gives you the facts on tornadoes and hurricanes. Find out how fast hurricanes travel, where tornadoes usually touch down, and how to stay safe in severe weather.

How Do Flies Walk Upside Down?
by Melvin and Gilda Berger

If you've ever wondered if mosquitoes fall in love, whether flies have tongues, or how strong the legs of a grasshopper are, then this is the book for you.

Taking a Phone Message

You get home and see an urgent message to call your friend. But wait! When did your friend call? Where should you call her back? If you can't answer these questions, someone didn't write a very complete phone message.

Look at the phone messages below. Which message includes the most helpful information?

Message 1

Mrs. Harris:
The plumber called.

Message 2

Mrs. Harris:
The plumber called.
555-8381 Tuesday.

Message 3

A good message states exactly who the message is for and who the message is from.

Mrs. Harris: 3:30 P.M.
Peabody Plumbing called on 6/9. They are confirming your appointment for 6/18. Please call back to confirm.
555-8381   Mana

Politely ask the person why they are calling, and if they need to be called back.

When taking a message, write down the date, the time, and, of course, the phone number to call back.

" When taking a phone message, write neatly. And be sure to leave the message in a place where people can see it. "

Phone Service

It's time to test your message-taking skills. Reread the phone messages and the tips that go with them. Use them to answer the following questions. Write your answers on your own paper.

1. Message 1 is missing important information. What should be added to make the message more complete? (Choose three.)
   a. the plumber's phone number
   b. the time and date the message was taken
   c. what you were doing when the phone rang
   d. the reason for the call

2. Why is Message 2 more helpful than Message 1?
   a. Message 2 includes Mrs. Harris's name, and Message 1 doesn't.
   b. You can't read Message 1, and you can read Message 2.
   c. Message 2 includes the plumber's phone number, and Message 1 doesn't.

3. Imagine you had not read Message 3. What does the word *Tuesday* refer to in Message 2?
   a. The message was taken on Tuesday.
   b. Tuesday is the plumber's birthday.
   c. You can't tell.

4. Why did the plumber call Mrs. Harris?
   a. to set up a plumbing appointment for June 9
   b. to confirm a plumbing appointment for June 18
   c. to cancel a plumbing appointment for June 18

Make a Form
A message pad can make taking a message easy. Design a message form to keep by the phone. Include helpful headings and lines for recording the message.

Take a Message
Choose a partner. Ask your partner to pretend to call you and leave an important message. Take the message on the form you created. Did you get the facts? Now, switch roles with your partner.

" Sometimes people leave long messages. Write down the important details while you're on the phone. When you hang up, you can complete the message. You might also want to copy it over. "

Real-World Words

confirm: to say that something will definitely happen
recording: writing down information so that it can be read later
urgent: needing quick or immediate action

short story

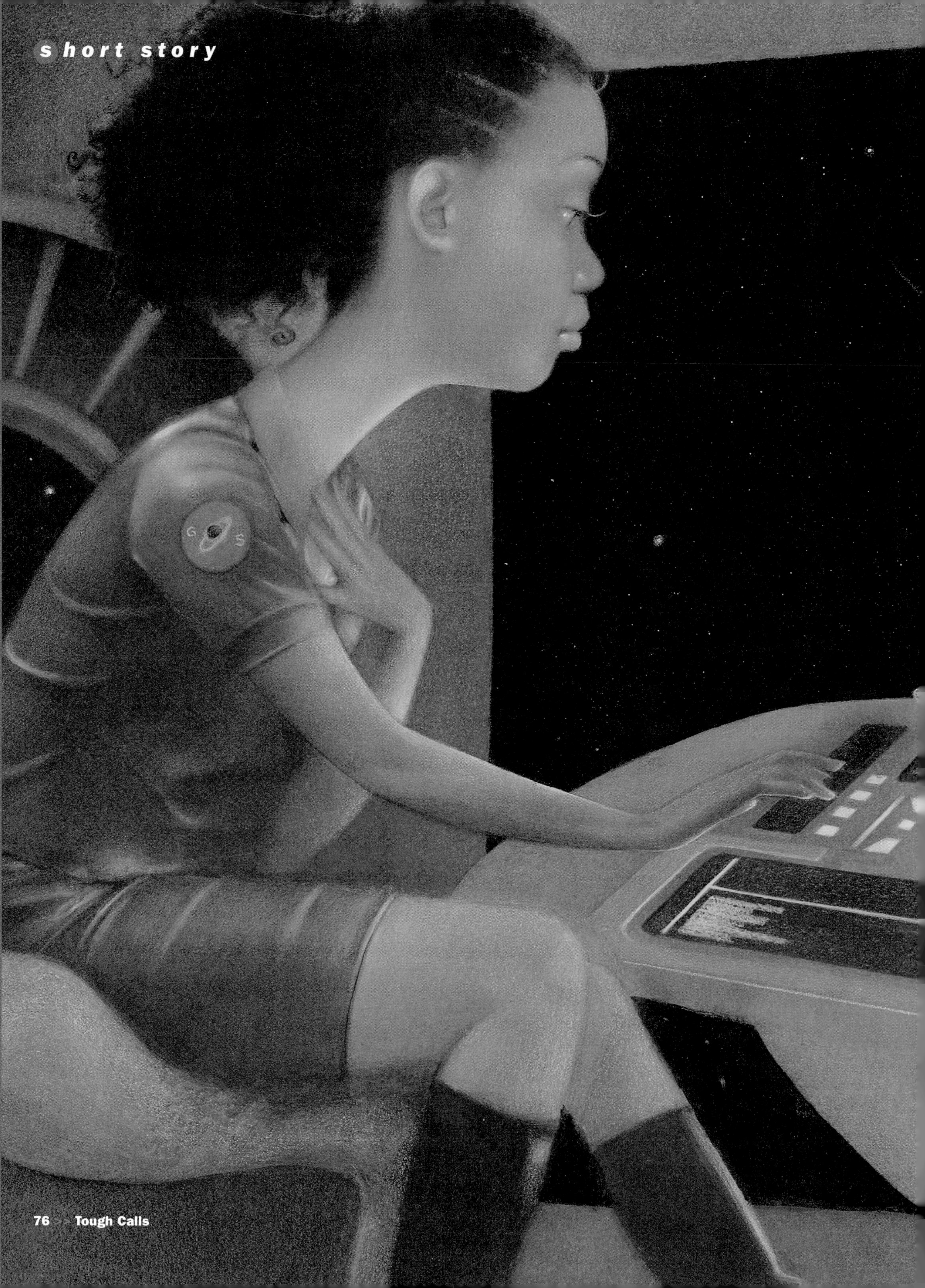

CODE RED

Paul E. Stawski

Push the button. **Don't push** the button.
Either way, people could die. That's the choice that Becky faces.
What would you do?

The first thought that struck Becky when she awoke was how quiet everything seemed on board the spacecraft. She didn't hear any of the others. The only sound was the constant low hum of the ship as it found its way among the stars.

Startled, she jumped and called, "Anybody here?"

Quickly, Becky connected the ship's voice controls and asked about the rest of the crew. The ship's computer-voice, Comptrol, answered in perfect, understandable English.

"They're in space sleep," it said.

"All of them?" she asked. "Then why did you wake me?"

"Code Red," Comptrol replied.

Becky's eyes widened. She knew what Code Red meant and the extreme danger they were in. Alien ships were nearby.

"When will they get here?" she asked, her voice **trembling** slightly.

"One hour," said Comptrol, "and counting."

Becky tried to sound unafraid. "Then you've got to wake the others," she said.

There was no answer.

"I'm only twelve years old!" she screamed.

"Age," said Comptrol, "has nothing to do with it. Under Code Red conditions, I am required to awaken one crew member. I chose you."

ASK YOURSELF

▪ What problem is Becky facing? Reread the beginning of the story to see what "Code Red" means.

"But I've never been in a Code Red before!" Becky cried.

"You've done very well in practice," said Comptrol.

Becky put her head down and sighed. Yes, she thought, I did do well in practice. But that was only a video game! This is real life. And this time their lives **depended** on it. Besides, Jim had been better in practice than she was, and he was a grown-up. He'd know what to do. Why didn't the ship's computer wake him?

"Code Red, Code Red," said Comptrol again, interrupting her thoughts.

Becky lifted her head and looked around the ship through blurry, tear-filled eyes. *Code Red,* she thought to herself, as she saw the rest of the crew unmoving in their space sleep. And it's all up to me.

Becky sat at the video game—practicing, pressing buttons, working hard at destroying the game's enemy spaceships. She had won three out of the last five games. But that meant she had lost twice—two times the ship and Becky's crew mates wouldn't have made it in real life.

"How much time left?" she asked.

"Nineteen minutes," said Comptrol.

She cleared the screen and started the game again. This was silly! Even if she won every game, how could she be sure she'd win when it really counted—in real life?

Nobody won every time. Not even Jim. Sure, you could decide to let the computer run the game, but then all you could do was watch. None of the crew ever let the computer do that,

Words, Words. Words

trembling: shaking
depended: counted on

ASK YOURSELF

- What do you think Becky will do?

Think about what you might do in the same situation.

except . . . except her, she thought.

Becky's mind **whirled.** Things just didn't make sense. When she let the computer play, it often did just as poorly as anyone else. So how could letting it take over now help?

"Code Red," said Comptrol. "Three minutes and counting down."

Becky ran her fingers through her hair in one quick, nervous motion. Then **hesitantly** she took over the controls and flipped the switch from GAME to ON/EMERGENCY.

"Code Red," said Comptrol again. "Two minutes and counting."

Rapidly Becky pressed buttons that gave commands. PREPARE DEFENSE WEAPONS. ALL SYSTEMS ALERT. Her fingers danced over the controls until she came upon the button that said FIRE.

She hesitated and thought for a moment about the alien ships. Who was in them? Were they beings who wanted to destroy her ship, or would they let her pass if she didn't fire at them first? What if—just what if—the aliens were as frightened as she was? Did she have a right to destroy them for that?

"Code Red," said Comptrol. "One minute and counting: 60, 59, 58 . . ."

Becky searched the computer panel for the

One minute and counting: 60, 59, 58 . . .

HOLD FIRE button. "I'm sorry," she said to the sleeping crew as she pressed the button. "I hope I'm not letting you down." Now, she knew, it was out of her hands.

She watched the screen as it filled with the glowing dots of alien ships. What now? she wondered.

"Code Red," said Comptrol. "Zero."

She waited **anxiously** as the dot that **indicated** her own spaceship moved slowly ahead. And as her ship passed the last alien ship, Becky broke into a long sigh of relief.

Not one ship had fired. They were safe.

"I did it!" she yelled through her tears. "*We* did it! Thanks, Comptrol, for choosing me!"

"Code Red over," said Comptrol.

Becky smiled and wiped the tears from her eyes. "You knew what I'd do all along, didn't you?" she asked with a sigh.

Comptrol didn't answer. It didn't have to. Becky knew the truth. As she climbed into bed and slipped into space sleep, there was nothing more she needed to know. ●

Words, Words, Words

whirled: spun around
hesitantly: in an uncertain way
anxiously: in a worried way
indicated: showed

I n "Code Red," Becky has to make a tough call. Her decision will affect the lives of many people. In real life, some decisions can be difficult—even when they're not a matter of life and death. Below are some examples of sticky situations. What would you do if these decisions were yours to make? Record your answers on a separate piece of paper.

1. You are at the mall. You see a girl you know from school. You start to say hi but then realize that this girl is shoplifting. What would you do?

A. Tell the security guard. Shoplifting is against the law.
B. Tell the girl that she'd better stop before she gets caught.
C. Nothing. It's none of your business.
D. Tell all your friends what the girl did. No one wants to be friends with a thief.
E. Another solution would be . . .

2. Your friend tells you that he's been asked to join this cool club. You know that this "club" is more like a gang. What would you do?

A. Nothing. Not all gangs are bad.
B. Call your friend and try to convince him not to join.
C. Tell a counselor at school or another adult you trust.
D. Ask your friend if you could join, too.
E. Another solution would be . . .

Swipe!

3. You are in the ticket line for a Saturday afternoon movie. Your friend's boyfriend gets in line a few people behind you. Then you notice that he's with a girl you don't know. What should you do?

A. Go up to the boy and demand to know what's going on.
B. Nothing. It's none of your business.
C. Say nothing to the boy, but call your friend as soon as you get home.
D. Leave an unsigned note in your friend's locker at school the next day, explaining what you saw.
E. Another solution would be . . .

4. One of your friends is a big joker. The problem is that lately the jokes have been on you. It's really starting to hurt your feelings. What should you do?

A. Talk to your friend and tell him how you feel.
B. Just deal with it. He's a great friend and everyone knows he's just kidding around.
C. Drop him. A real friend wouldn't tell jokes about another friend.
D. Start making jokes at his expense right back. See how he likes it when the tables are turned.
E. Another solution would be . . .

5. You're having lunch in the cafeteria. You overhear a bunch of kids at the next table. They're talking loudly about how they are going to beat up another kid after school that day. What should you do?

A. Warn the kid who is going to get beaten up. That way, he can do something to protect himself.
B. Tell a teacher or the guidance counselor at school.
C. Call the police.
D. Tell the kids you know what they are planning to do. Tell them if they don't change their plans, they'll be sorry.
E. Another solution would be . . .

Discuss your answers with your class. Why did your classmates make the choices they did? Why did you?

Talk About It

Now that you've read "Code Red" and "What Would You Do?"
what do you have to say about these questions?

▶ When might a young person really have to make a life-or-death
decision?

▶ What would it be like to live aboard a spaceship? Would you
choose to, if you could? Why or why not?

Comprehension Check

Write your answers to the questions below. Use information from
the story and the decision-making quiz to support your answers.

1. What was the rest of the crew doing while Becky was making
her decision?

2. Why didn't Becky fire at the other spaceships?

3. Do you think that such a young crew member should have made
such an important decision? Why or why not?

4. Which decision on the quiz was the most difficult for you? Why?

5. What kinds of things do most people consider when they make
a difficult decision?

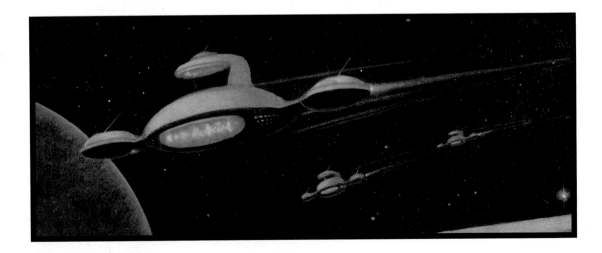

Vocabulary Check

Complete each sentence starter below. Before you answer, think about the meaning of the vocabulary word in bold.

1. I was **trembling** when . . .

2. I wouldn't mind if someone **depended** on me to . . .

3. I raised my hand **hesitantly** because . . .

4. My brother **indicated** that he was tired by . . .

5. I looked at my watch **anxiously** because . . .

Write About It

Choose one of the writing prompts below.

▶ Write a message from Becky to someone on the alien ships. What could she say to find out if they were friendly or not?

▶ Write a journal entry Becky might have written after the Code Red alert. Explain why she made the decision not to fire at the ships.

▶ Rewrite the end of "Code Red." What might have happened if Becky had decided to fire? What might have happened if the alien spaceships were unfriendly?

More to READ

If you liked this story about outer space, you might also enjoy:

Nosepickers From Outer Space
by Gordon Korman

Devin can hardly believe his bad luck. His exchange buddy Stan is such a nerdy nosepicker. All the other exchange students seem so cool. But Stan is from another planet—really another planet. Devin soon learns that Stan isn't picking his nose at all—he's actually operating a nose computer. In fact, Stan is in a race against time to save Earth!

Fat Men From Space
by Daniel Manus Pinkwater

After a trip to the dentist, William's life begins to change. The filling in his cavity is picking up radio signals. His tooth works great for playing practical jokes. But it's no joke when he starts to pick up messages about an invasion from outer space. Soon thousands of spacemen cover every square mile of Earth. They're eating all the junk food they can find. But what can William do? He's being held prisoner aboard an enemy spaceburger.

Comparing Products

You've saved enough money for a CD player. But you're not really sure which model to buy. You might want to check a consumer magazine that compares products.

Check out the chart below. It includes information about five CD players. Can you figure it out?

The key tells what the letters and the symbols on the chart stand for.

This column shows how well the CD player did overall. The longer the bar, the better the CD player.

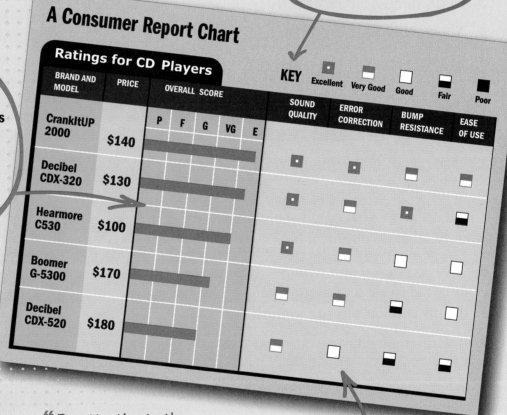

A Consumer Report Chart

Ratings for CD Players

KEY Excellent Very Good Good Fair Poor

BRAND AND MODEL	PRICE	OVERALL SCORE					SOUND QUALITY	ERROR CORRECTION	BUMP RESISTANCE	EASE OF USE
		P	F	G	VG	E				
CrankItUP 2000	$140									
Decibel CDX-320	$130									
Hearmore C530	$100									
Boomer G-5300	$170									
Decibel CDX-520	$180									

" Pay attention to the different categories in which products were tested. Some things may be more important to you than others. "

The "error correction" column tells how well a CD player handles scratched or dirty disks. The "bump resistance" tells how well the CD player handles movement.

Be a Smart Shopper

It's time to spend your hard-earned cash. But first, be sure you're spending it on the right item. Reread the chart and the tips. Then use them to answer the questions below. Write your answers on your own paper.

1. What is the highest rating a CD player could get in a single category? What is the lowest rating it could get?

2. Which CD player is the most expensive? Did the most expensive model get the best overall score?

3. Which CD player is the easiest to use? Which two players are the hardest to use?

4. Which CD player was rated "poor" in at least one category?
   a. Decibel CDX-520
   b. Decibel CDX-320
   c. Hearmore C530
   d. none of the above

5. You want to buy one of the CD players on this chart. The only things you really care about are sound quality and bump resistance. Which player should you buy?
   a. CrankItUP-2000
   b. Decibel CDX-320
   c. Boomer G-5300
   d. Decibel CDX-520

Recommend It

You work in an electronics store. Recommend a CD player for each of these customers. Susan wants an excellent overall score. Brandon wants great sound quality at a low price. Sam cares most about the bump-resistance rating.

Rate Them

Put the CD players in order according to their bump resistance. Start with the highest rating and finish with the lowest rating. Now do the same for ease of use.

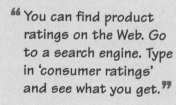

" You can find product ratings on the Web. Go to a search engine. Type in 'consumer ratings' and see what you get. "

Real-World Words

category: a class, group, or area
quality: a characteristic of something; a feature
rate: to judge the quality or worth of

MIA HAMM

SOCCER SUPERSTAR

Real-Life
HERO

Many celebrities use their money and fame to help others. Some even have a favorite cause. But one cause isn't enough for the most famous soccer player in the world.

The Mia Hamm Foundation has two goals. One is to fight bone marrow disease, which took the life of Mia's brother in 1996. The other is to support programs for girls in sports. As Mia says, "The Foundation is for two causes very close to my heart. These issues have had a big effect on me. And I am committed to raising funds and public awareness."

Chances are, she'll succeed. After all, when it comes to goals, no one scores quite like Mia Hamm! She is considered to be the best player in the history of women's soccer. Everywhere she goes, fans go nuts. She's also in demand as a spokesperson for many companies. Even with all her success, Mia is known as one of the most humble and thoughtful superstars in the world of sports.

"Mia is a neat person because all this fame hasn't really affected her. She's almost embarrassed by it," says Tony DiCicco. DiCicco coached Mia and the U.S. team to the 1999 Women's World Cup title. "Mia likes to give credit to her teammates. And it's very real. There is nothing phony about her."

Growing Up With Soccer

Mia is one of six children. Her mother was a ballet dancer. That explains Mia's graceful moves. Her father was a pilot in the U.S. Air Force. That explains her quick reflexes and self-discipline. She moved around a lot as kid. Each time her father's job moved to a new Air Force base, the family would pack up and go with him. As a result, Mia never really put down roots. She was shy. But she found that playing sports helped her to make new friends.

"I'd move to a new town and join a team," Mia says. "Right away I'd have a group of people who had the same interests as me."

Mia tried other activities when she was growing up. She took dance lessons but quit after only a few weeks. She played other sports, as well. But when she discovered soccer at the age of seven, she found her calling.

By the time she was a freshman in high school, the soccer world knew all about Mia. At 15 she became the youngest player ever to make the U.S. National Team. College coaches across the country wanted Mia to play for them. She chose the University of North Carolina. By the time she graduated in 1994, she had rewritten the NCAA record books. Mia was named All-American and National Player of the Year three times. She led the North Carolina Tar Heels to four straight NCAA championships. And she broke the NCAA records for goals, assists, and points.

Mia Hamm goes for the goal during a 1999 World Cup game.

Grace Under Pressure

Even though Mia gets very nervous before big games, she plays well in the spotlight. In 1995 she was named Most Valuable Player of the Women's World Cup. She was also voted U.S. Soccer's Female Athlete of the Year five years in a row—

from 1994 through 1998. She led the U.S. to another World Cup title in 1999.

Success has led to many **opportunities** for Mia. She earns a good living not only through her soccer, but also through **endorsements.** Some of the attention makes her uncomfortable. A few years ago, when she was named one of the "Fifty Most Beautiful People" by *People* magazine, Mia was shocked. She doesn't focus on her looks.

Mia receives a lot of attention, but she doesn't keep it all to herself. She prefers to use her fame to help others. In her book *Go for the Goal*, Mia didn't write about her own life. Instead, she wrote a guide for young soccer players. The book even includes essays by several of Mia's teammates. Although she doesn't like doing interviews or talking in front of big crowds, Mia does enjoy meeting with her young fans, especially girls.

"I'm no different from these kids," she explains. "That, to me, is an important message. I have a lot of the same worries they do.

opportunities: chances to do something
endorsements: acts of supporting or approving a product on the radio or television
affection: a great liking for someone or something
encouraged: given a reason to feel confident
soared: rose or increased very quickly

'Do my friends like me? Am I carrying out my responsibilities at home? Am I a good sister?' These things are so much more important than whether we won the game or not."

ASK Yourself

- How might being a famous soccer star be difficult for Mia Hamm?

Recall what Mia Hamm says and add any reasons of your own.

Helping Others

Her **affection** for her fans is one of the main reasons Mia created her foundation. "Although I'm **encouraged** by the growth of opportunities for girls, I want there to be more progress," she says. Through sports like soccer, Mia hopes girls will develop a strong sense of self and feel like winners in life.

The other reason Mia started her foundation, of course, is out of love for her brother. Garrett Hamm was an adopted child. Three years older than Mia, he joined the family when Mia was five. They quickly became best friends.

"We got along so well, right from the beginning," Mia says. "We were both athletic, and we loved to play sports together. He always let me hang out with his friends, even though he was older. And he always picked me to be on his team."

When Mia was away at college, Garrett became ill. He had a bone marrow disease. The disease eventually killed him.

"Garrett taught me so much," Mia says. "And not just about sports. He approached his illness with such great strength. He was amazing through the whole process. Even the last week of his life, he was cracking jokes, trying to make everyone else feel better."

As Garrett's medical costs **soared,** friends and relatives pitched in to raise money. Mia even asked the soccer community for support. The effort taught Mia the importance of helping others. And it encouraged her to start the Mia Hamm Foundation.

"Garrett's illness and death gave me the courage to stand up and ask for help," Mia says. "And to understand I can do things for people!" ●

RESUMÉ

Name: Mia Hamm

Born: March 17, 1972, Selma, Alabama

Goals:

- to be the best soccer player and person she can possibly be
- to raise money for charities through the Mia Hamm Foundation

Education:

- college degree in political science, University of North Carolina, 1994

Major Achievements:

- leading goal scorer in the history of women's soccer
- three-time NCAA Player of the Year
- youngest player ever to make the U.S. National Soccer Team
- broke NCAA scoring record
- two-time member of Women's World Cup championship team

Victory a Milestone for Female Athletes

by Allen Salkin for the *New York Post*

**Mia Hamm would never forget this World Cup game.
Nor would the record-breaking number of fans watching it.**

The U.S. women's soccer team and international soccer chief Sepp Blatter celebrate with the trophy. The U.S. defeated China in a 5-4 overtime shootout during the Women's World Cup Final in Pasadena, California.

"They just fought and fought and fought. America should be very proud."

PASADENA, California, July 10, 1999—The sporting event of the summer came to a red, white, and blue climax yesterday. The U.S. women's soccer team beat China in a tense and thrilling game to win the world championship.

The match was tied 0-0 after 90 minutes. Then the game went into sudden-death overtime as President Clinton and 90,000 fans looked on. One goal in either of the two extra periods would have won it.

But neither team could score. Finally, the game went to penalty kicks. Each team would have five chances to take a shot against the opposing goalie. The team that scored more shootout goals would win.

The Chinese scored. So did the Americans.

American goaltender Brandi Chastain made the fifth American kick. It was all over, and the huge crowd exploded.

A Crowd Responds

Girls in American-flag face paint, their pigtails fastened with tiny soccer balls, danced in the stands.

Waves of confetti filled the sky above Mia Hamm, Tiffeny Milbert, Julie Foudy, Shannon MacMillan, Michelle Akers, Sara Whalen, Coach Tony DiCicco, and the other 12 heroes as they lowered their heads one by one to accept their gold medals.

Arm in arm, they jumped up and down in unison. The roar of the crowd energized their exhausted legs.

The event captured the interest of a nation in which women did not even have the right to vote until 1920.

"I think the whole country was caught up in this. Not only fans of soccer, but young girls too," Clinton said.

"In some ways, it's the biggest sporting event of the last decade. It's new and exciting for the United States."

New American Heroes

The crowd on a perfect Southern California day was bursting to cheer for its heroes. Even during the third-place game between Brazil and Norway, fans were wildly chanting "USA! USA!"

"They're just such great role models," said Tim LaMacchia, a Miami resident, sitting with two of his young daughters before the match. "As *my* girls go through life, I hope they think back on this time and hopefully act like *these* girls."

After the game, Coach DiCicco spoke of his team's grit and their place in the history of sports. "This is a team of courage," he said. "They just fought and fought and fought."

"America should be very proud of these young ladies." ●

TALK ABOUT IT

Now that you've read "Mia Hamm" and "Victory a Milestone for Female Athletes," what do you have to say about these questions?

▶ Who is your favorite athlete? Why?

▶ Why do you think people look up to sports superstars?

COMPREHENSION CHECK

Write your answers to the questions below. Use information from the profile and the newspaper article to support your answers.

1. What two causes does Mia Hamm feel strongly about?

2. Why does Mia Hamm want to use her fame to help others?

3. How do you think Mia Hamm inspires her fans?

4. Why was the world championship game against China so exciting?

5. Do you think Mia Hamm played an important part in the U.S. team's World Cup win? Why or why not?

VOCABULARY CHECK

Answer each question below with a complete sentence. Before you answer, think about the meaning of the vocabulary word in bold.

1. If the price of jeans **soared**, what would you do?

2. Why do many ads contain celebrity **endorsements**?

3. If someone **encouraged** you to sing, what would you say?

4. If you feel **affection** for a pet, how might you treat it?

5. What kinds of **opportunities** do you hope to have?

WRITE ABOUT IT

Choose one of the writing prompts below.

▶ Write a fan letter to Mia Hamm. In your letter, tell Mia what you admire about her and why.

▶ Imagine you are a sports reporter. Write an article telling about America's victory over China in the 1999 World Cup. Don't forget to mention the crowd's response.

▶ Mia Hamm wants to help young people be winners in life. What advice would you give to young people about being a winner? Create a brief guide that includes at least three tips.

Fact FILE

Don't know much about the game of soccer? Here are some soccer terms to help you "talk the talk" like a pro:

assist: a pass that leads to a goal

bend the ball: to put a spin on the ball so that it dips and swerves around a defender or goalkeeper

cherry-pick: to hang around the goal waiting for the ball to come to you for an easy shot

dummy: a fake as if you're going to trap or kick the ball, but instead you let it roll by (ideally) to a teammate

50/50 ball: a loose ball that can be won by either team

golden goal: the first goal in sudden-death overtime, giving the scoring team the victory

hospital ball: a pass hit weakly or with poor accuracy

marking: soccer-speak for guarding an opponent

red card: the referee's signal that a player is ejected from the game

serve: to deliver an accurate pass to a teammate in scoring position

weak side: the side of the field where the ball is not

Joining a CD Club

You're reading an ad for a CD club. "Buy 12 CDs for $1!" it says. That sounds like a great deal! But is there a catch? Probably. Before you sign up for a club, be sure you know all the details.

Check out this membership form for a CD club. Read the fine print. Do you really want to join?

APPLICATION FOR MEMBERSHIP

12 CDs for $1!

Coolest Hits!

Great Classics, Too!

Thousands to Choose From!

Biggest Recording Artists!

Please accept my application for membership in the Cool CD Collectors Club. Upon returning this application, I will receive the 12 CDs I have listed. For these CDs, I will pay $1, plus the cost of shipping and handling. If I am not satisfied, I can return the 12 CDs within 15 days at the expense of the club, with no further obligation. The returned CDs must not be opened. If I do not return the 12 CDs, I agree to the following terms of the membership. I agree to buy 6 more CDs, at regular club prices over the next two years. Once I have purchased the 6 CDs at regular club prices, I may cancel my membership, or continue to purchase other CDs. Billing of future CDs will include the price of the CD, plus the cost of shipping and handling.

Name:
Address:
Country:
Phone Number:
Email Address:
Age:

Type of Music You Like:

Method of Payment:
☐ Check   ☐ Money Order   ☐ Credit Card
Please send me the following 12 CDs. (Write one selection on each line.)

I understand the terms stated, and I agree to comply with the terms upon receiving and accepting my package of 12 CDs.

Signature

This fine print explains the terms, or rules, of the club membership. It tells you what you'll be responsible for if you join.

How will you pay for the CDs once they send you a bill? Check with an adult to decide the best method of payment.

"Don't ever send cash through the mail. If you don't have a check or credit card, you can pay with a money order. You can get one at a post office or bank for a fee."

Sign Me Up

Is this CD club right for you? Reread the form and the tips that go with it. Then answer the following questions. Write your answers on your own paper.

1. How much do the first 12 CDs you order cost?
   a. $12 plus the cost of shipping and handling
   b. $1 plus the cost of shipping and handling
   c. $15.95

2. After you pay for and receive your first 12 CDs, what must you do next?
   a. buy 14 CDs over the next two years
   b. buy 2 CDs over the next two years
   c. buy 6 CDs over the next two years

3. You've received your 12 CDs. Now you have decided to purchase one CD at the regular price. What **two** charges will be included on your bill?
   a. the price of the CD
   b. a special listening charge
   c. a shipping and handling charge

4. If you have opened a CD, can you return it?
   a. yes
   b. no
   c. The fine print doesn't say.

Top Three
Imagine that you could order 3 CDs for $1. What 3 CDs would you order? Make a list.

Pros and Cons
Would you join this CD club? Fold a sheet of paper in half. Label one side "Reasons to Join" and the other side "Reasons Not to Join." Then list your reasons.

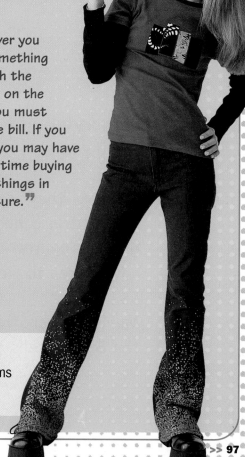

"Whenever you buy something through the mail or on the Web, you must pay the bill. If you don't, you may have a hard time buying other things in the future."

Real-World Words

obligation: an agreement to do something
shipping and handling: the packing and mailing of items
terms: the rules of an agreement or contract

KING ARTHUR

**A GRAPHIC CLASSIC BY
TERRY M. WEST**

**BASED ON THE STORY
"THE SWORD IN THE STONE"**

Storytellers have been talking about King Arthur for more than 1,000 years.

Arthur, they say, was the greatest ruler England ever had. He lived in a huge castle called Camelot. There, he met with his brave Knights of the Round Table. They planned dangerous adventures to rid their land of evil knights and horrible monsters.

Merlin was another important character at Camelot. "The Sword in the Stone" tells the story of the first time Merlin helped Arthur.

A LONG TIME AGO, KING UTHER WAS THE LEADER OF ENGLAND. HE WAS A GOOD RULER, BUT THE DAY CAME WHEN HE DIED. THERE WERE RUMORS THAT HE HAD A SON. BUT NO SON COULD BE FOUND. THERE WAS NO PRINCE TO TAKE UTHER'S PLACE.

SOON UTHER'S KNIGHTS STARTED FIGHTING OVER WHO WOULD BE KING. ENGLAND BECAME A DANGEROUS PLACE....

Meet in the town square tomorrow. Then you will see how to choose your king!

FINALLY, A WIZARD NAMED MERLIN CAME TO VISIT THE KNIGHTS. THEY WERE TERRIFIED. MERLIN HAD MAGIC POWERS THAT THEY COULD NOT FIGHT WITH THEIR SWORDS. THEY LISTENED AS HE SPOKE.

ASK YOURSELF

- What is the time and place of this story?

Look for clues in the pictures and in the introduction to this story.

THE NEXT MORNING, THE KNIGHTS MET IN THE SQUARE. THEY SAW A LARGE STONE WITH A SWORD STICKING OUT OF IT. THEY READ WHAT WAS WRITTEN ON THE STONE.

ALL OF THE KNIGHTS TRIED, BUT NO ONE COULD FREE THE SWORD.

FOR 13 YEARS, THE SWORD STAYED IN THE STONE. MANY PEOPLE TRIED TO PULL IT FREE. BUT NO ONE COULD.

Father, he'll just be in the way!

Arthur will be a knight soon. This will be a good lesson for him.

Thank you, Father. I promise I won't get in the way.

THEY RODE TOWARD THE CASTLE. ECTOR WAS WORRIED THAT THEY WOULD NOT BE ABLE TO FIND A PLACE TO STAY.

There will be many people at the contests tomorrow. I hope we'll be able to find an inn.

I could ride ahead and find us a room.

All right. See if you can find a place for us. Then meet us in the town square.

Whoever wins the contests tomorrow will get a chance to pull the sword from the stone.

Then the throne will be mine!

I have been practicing for months. I will win tomorrow!

WHEN ECTOR AND KAY ARRIVED, THEY FOUND ARTHUR WAITING IN THE TOWN SQUARE.

I have found us a place to stay.

JUST OFF THE SQUARE, THERE WAS A SMALL INN.

We should go to sleep early. We have a busy day ahead of us tomorrow.

THE NEXT MORNING, ECTOR TOOK KAY AND ARTHUR TO THE CASTLE. THE CONTESTS WERE ABOUT TO BEGIN.

WHEN ARTHUR RETURNED TO THE INN, HE DISCOVERED THAT IT WAS LOCKED.

EVERYBODY WAS AT THE CONTESTS. THE TOWN SQUARE WAS EMPTY. THERE WAS NOBODY AROUND TO OPEN THE DOOR.

ARTHUR WAS PANICKED UNTIL ...

That's just what I need!

ASK YOURSELF

■ Why does Arthur pull the sword from the stone?

Consider what Arthur's brother needs.

ARTHUR HAD NO IDEA WHO HAD LEFT THE SWORD IN THE STONE, BUT HE DIDN'T THINK THE OWNER WOULD MIND IF HE BORROWED IT. HE WAS SURPRISED AT HOW EASILY THE SWORD HAD SLID FROM THE STONE.

ARTHUR RETURNED AS QUICKLY AS HE COULD. HE HOPED THERE WAS STILL TIME TO GET THE SWORD TO KAY.

I'm back!

It's about time!

It's not your sword. The inn was locked. I found this sword in the square.

What?! But I wanted my ...

... sword....

ASK YOURSELF

■ How do people know that Arthur is the true king of England?

Think about what Arthur has just done.

Talk About It

Now that you've read *King Arthur*, what do you have to say about these questions?

▶ Does Arthur deserve to be king? What qualifications do you think a ruler should have?

▶ Why do you think the story of King Arthur has lasted for over 1,000 years?

Comprehension Check

Write your answers to the questions below. Use information from the graphic classic to support your answers.

1. Why do all the knights agree to follow Merlin's rules for choosing the new king?

2. How can you tell that Arthur didn't read the words on the stone?

3. Why doesn't Arthur's father believe Kay when he says he pulled the sword from the stone?

4. Why do you think Arthur's true identity was kept secret for so many years?

5. Do you think that a teenager could rule a kingdom?

Write About It

Choose one of the writing prompts below.

▶ Create a journal entry that Arthur might have written the day he discovered he was king. Explain how Arthur feels.

▶ Write a letter that King Uther might have written to his son the day he gave him away. Explain why King Uther is doing this.

▶ King Arthur becomes famous for gathering the Knights of the Round Table. Write a notice that Arthur might have posted throughout the kingdom. Describe the type of person who would make a good knight.

Fact FILE

How to Become a Knight

If you lived in the time of King Arthur, how would you become a knight? Here are the rules.

1. If you're a girl, forget it. Only boys get to be knights.

2. You can't be a knight unless your father was one, too. Your father's boss has to give the okay for you to be a page. A page is basically an errand boy. You begin your training as a page at age seven.

3. As a page, you learn the rules of knight service and how to use weapons.

4. When you are 15 or 16, you become a squire. You learn how to fight on horseback.

5. After five years of being a squire, you are ready to become a knight!

Reading a Table of Contents

The latest issue of your favorite magazine is here. The cover says it's got stories on part-time jobs, celebrity pets, and how to handle a bad-hair day. But when you open the magazine, all you see inside are a bunch of ads.

It's time to check out the table of contents. It will tell you where to find the stories you're looking for. Check out the sample table of contents below.

Magazine Cover and Table of Contents

Magazines often mention stories on their covers. Some tables of contents include symbols that help readers locate the stories listed on the cover.

" A table of contents is often divided into categories to make it easier to use. Looking for an article about celebrities? Check under 'Entertainment.' "

Every article is listed in the table of contents, along with the page it begins on. Some tables of contents also give brief descriptions of the articles.

Read On

Are you ready to read? Review the table of contents and the tips that go with it. Then use them to answer these questions. Write your answers on your own paper.

1. You're dying to read all five of the stories mentioned on the cover of *Teen Beat*. Where will you find them? List the title and page number of each article.

2. What is this month's cover story about? On what page does this story begin?

3. Suppose you wanted to find an article about new clothes. What section of *Teen Beat*'s table of contents would you look under?

4. Here are three article ideas. Which of them would **not** go in the "Life" section?
   a. the adventures of a teen rescue-worker
   b. a review of a new movie
   c. a quiz about kids' spending habits

5. Take another look at this issue of *Teen Beat*. Where might you find answers to the following questions? List a page number for each question.
   a. What are the duties of an employee at a fast-food restaurant?
   b. What kind of tricks can your favorite TV star's dog do?
   c. Do malls have the right to ban kids under 16?

Plan It

You're the editor of *Teen Beat*. Start planning your next issue. Think of one article to go in each of these sections: "Entertainment," "Style," and "Life." Write down the title and a short description of each article.

Publisher for a Day

You're starting your own magazine. What will you call it? What sections will appear in your table of contents? Write down your ideas.

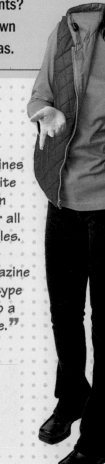

" Many magazines have a Web site where you can read some or all of their articles. To find your favorite magazine on the Web, type its name into a search engine. "

Real-World Words

celebrities: famous people, especially in the field of entertainment
features: important articles in newspapers or magazines

novel

Miles

by Jerry Spinelli

What makes Jason run? Could it be the girl who leaves him in the dust?

I didn't make the baseball team.

The coach said he already had a ninth-grader for shortstop, and an eighth-grade second-stringer, and I wasn't quite good enough to beat them out. I said I'd be willing to play another position. He said he had veteran ninth-graders at all the positions. I told him I wanted to be a major leaguer someday. I told him I hit almost .330 in Little League last year. He looked impressed. He said that's the kind of spirit he likes to see. He said it's not that I don't have the talent, it's just that I need another year to grow. To mature. In the meantime, he said, he wants me to stay in shape. He said he'd like to see me go out for track. It'd be good for me, he said, and nobody gets cut from track.

I tried out for the sprints. I figured that would help me be a better base-stealer. But I was too slow for the sprints.

I tried the half mile. It was too long to run full speed, and too short to run slow. I couldn't figure it out.

That's how I became a miler.

The really, *really* bad thing: One of the people that beat me was a girl! You know what I'm saying? A girl. G-I-R-L !

At first I wasn't too excited about it. I didn't see how running the mile was going to help me be a better shortstop. I was only doing it because the baseball coach was grooming me for next year.

Then I saw a mile race on TV. Some great miler from England was running, and as he finished each lap the announcer was screaming:

ASK Yourself

- Why does Jason end up on the track team?
Think about the problem he had making the baseball team.

"He's on a record **pace**! He's on a record pace!" Each lap the people in the stands went crazier. On one side of the screen they showed the world-record time, and on the other side they showed the runner's time. The whole stadium was standing and screaming, like they were pushing him with their voices, and even though it was the last lap, instead of going slower he was going *faster*. I couldn't believe it. The stadium was going bananas, and he was flying and the world-record time and his time were getting closer and closer and he broke the world record by 3/10 of a second. And even then he

didn't collapse, or even stop. He just kept jogging another lap around the track, holding his arms up and smiling and waving to the cheering crowd.

Even though it was Saturday, I went outside and ran ten times around the block.

I turned out to be a pretty rotten miler. We had our first time trials, and I came in dead last. My time was 6 minutes and 47 seconds. The guy that broke the world record did it in less than 3 minutes and 50 seconds.

To top it off, I threw up afterward.

And to top that off, the place where I threw up happened to be the long-jump pit. Which didn't make the long jumpers too happy, but which the coach thought was just fine. He said now they had a good reason to jump farther than ever.

But all that, it was nothing. It was all just peaches and cream compared to the worst part, the really, *really* bad thing: One of the people that beat me was named Marceline McAllister. The girl.

"I'm quittin'," I told Peter Kim, who was on the track team too. A half-miler.

"Why?" he said.

"*Why*? You see who I lost to in the time trials?"

"I wasn't watching."

"The girl."

"Which one?" he said. There're other ones on the team too, but she's the only miler one.

"McAllister," I said.

"Marceline?"

"Yeah. Her."

"The one who plays the trombone?"

"Yeah."

He shrugged. "So?"

"So?" I hollered. "Waddaya mean, so? She's a girl, man! You ever lose to a girl?"

He said maybe I had a cramp.

"I didn't have no cramp."

"Maybe you just had a bad day."

"So what?" I **screeched**. "How bad could it be? She's still a girl. I got beat by a girl. I'm quittin'."

Then he started talking to me. He reminded me that some of the other girls on the team were doing better than last too. In fact, one of them was the second-fastest sprinter in the one-hundred-pound class. He said he heard that at our age a lot of girls are better than boys, because they mature faster. He said in another couple years I'd probably beat her easy. And he reminded me that the baseball coach had his eye on me.

"Yeah," I said, "he's really gonna be **impressed**, watching me lose to a girl."

"He didn't tell you to beat anybody," Peter said. "He just said to keep in shape."

I tried to explain. "Peter, all that stuff doesn't make any difference. The thing is, she's a girl. And a girl's a girl. You know what I'm saying? A *girl*. G-I-R-L. You understand me?"

Peter's expression changed. "No," he said, "I don't understand. Do what you want." He turned and left.

"Okay," I said. "I won't quit." He kept walking. I called, "Just don't tell Dugan! Peter? Hear? Don't tell anybody!"

It was a long, long track season.

Every day we started with calisthenics. Then most days we ran around the whole school grounds. *Five* times. Some other days we did intervals. That's where you run real fast as hard as you can for a while, then walk for a while (a littler while), then run fast again. Run-walk-run-walk. You just listen for the whistle to tell your legs when to start or stop. You'll never know how cruel a whistle is until you're walking after your tenth interval, and you hear it blow again.

As much as I hated practice, there was one good thing about it: You weren't running *against* anybody. There were no places. No first. No last.

Words, WORDS, Words	pace: rate of speed
	screeched: made a high, unpleasant sound
	impressed: thought highly of something

That's why I **dreaded** the first meet. Ham, my stepfather, wanted to know when it was.

"Why?" I asked him.

"Mom and I thought we'd like to come see it."

"See me lose?" I said. I didn't tell them about the girl. "I toldja I'm just running to keep in shape for baseball."

"We just like to come and see you, that's all," he said. "We came to all your Little League games, didn't we?"

"That was different. I'm good at baseball."

"We don't care," he said. "We don't come to see you be a star. Just to play."

"Well, anyway," I said, "the meet's away."

Which was true. It was at Mill Township. I came in last. By a lot. But the thing was, it didn't really bother me. That's because on the bus over to the meet I all of a sudden realized something: Even though I was running, I wasn't really in the *race*. If all I was supposed to be doing was staying in shape for baseball, there was no use getting all uptight about where I finished. I was actually running for the baseball coach, not the track coach. I was a baseball player **disguised** as a track runner. I didn't really want to break the world record. I was no miler. I was a shortstop.

It was a big relief when I thought about all that. It still might look to some people like I was losing to a girl. But inside I knew the truth. You can't lose if you're not racing.

After the mile the coach called to me. "Herkimer? You okay?"

"Yeah," I said. I was still jogging. I was hardly puffing. I thought I'd do another couple laps around the grass. Really get in shape.

"Hold it," he said. He came over. "Nothing wrong? Muscle pull? Dizzy?"

"Nah," I told him. "I'm okay."

He looked at me funny. "So why were you taking it so easy?"

I told him the whole thing, which to be fair I probably should have done the first day of practice. I told him about the baseball coach. About being groomed for next year. About wanting to be a major league shortstop.

He was nodding his head while I said these things. When I finished, he still kept nodding, looking at me. Then he stopped. He bent over so his face was right opposite mine. He didn't blink. His voice was hoarse. Almost a whisper.

"What's your first name?"

"Jason."

"Jason? Jason, when you're on my team, you run. And you run as well as you can. I don't care if you're slower than a turtle, you'll try your best when you're on my team. You will

ASK Yourself

- What does Jason decide on the way to the Mill Township meet?

Put Jason's thoughts into your own words.

Then something happened that
made me try even harder.

run as hard as you can. Every step of the way. Do you understand?"

I nodded.

"And next time I see you dogging it, you are no longer on my team. Understood?"

I understood.

So much for taking it easy.

So I did my calisthenics and ran my five times around the school and did my intervals and I tried harder.

In the second meet I brought my time down to 6:30. I was still last. McAllister's time was 6:15.

In the next couple meets I kept improving. But so did she. Our best miler, Floatmeier, a ninth-grader, only talked to me once. He said, "When you gonna beat that girl?" I tried. But by the middle of the season she was still a good ten seconds faster.

Ham kept asking about the meets. I kept telling him they were away. After a while he got the idea and stopped asking.

Then something happened that made me try even harder.

We were racing Shelbourne, and they had a girl miler too—and *she* beat me.

The next day at practice I ran around the school six times. I did my calisthenics perfectly. Even after fifteen intervals I dared that whistle to blow again.

Next meet, for the first time, I didn't come in last. I beat somebody. A kid on the other team.

Peter saw I was trying harder. He started running with me at practice. (He takes track seriously, like I take baseball.) During my races he would stand at the last turn with a stopwatch, and at each lap he would call out my time and yell, "Go, Jason! Go! Go!" And on the last lap, coming off the final turn, he would yell at me, "Sprint! Now! All out! Sprint! Now! Now!" And he would be sprinting along on the grass with me.

My times got better. I broke the six-minute barrier with a 5:58. (In the meantime Floatmeier was running in the 4:50s.) McAllister kept getting better too. I was closing the gap on her, but the closer I got, the harder it got.

dreaded: was afraid of or unwilling to do something
disguised: changed one's appearance to hide something

I couldn't believe I would have to try so hard just to beat a girl.

Then, on the next-to-last meet of the season, going down the backstretch, I got closer to McAllister than ever before. I was so close I could feel little cinder specks that her spikes were flipping back. Her hands were tight fists. Her hair was flapping like mad from side to side and slapping her in the neck. I could hear her breathing. She was kind of wheezing. Grunting. And all of a sudden, right there on the backstretch, it came to me: *Marceline McAllister wasn't faster than me.* Not really. She was just trying harder. She was trying so hard it scared me.

I practiced hard in the days before the final meet. But not superhard. The problem wasn't in my legs. It was in my head. I knew I could beat her now, but I didn't know if I wanted to pay the price. And the price was pain. I found that out following her down the backstretch that day. I was really hurting. My legs felt like they were dragging iron hooks through the cinders. My head was flashing and thundering. But the worst part of all was my chest. It felt like somebody opened me up and laid two iron shot puts inside me, one on top of each lung, and each time I breathed out, the shot puts flattened the lungs a little more. By the last one hundred yards there was only about a thimbleful of air to suck from.

When I remembered all that pain, and realized it would have to get even worse for me to go faster, I wasn't sure beating her was worth it. I felt like somebody, somewhere, double-crossed me. I couldn't believe I would have to try so hard just to beat a girl.

The day before the meet, Floatmeier gave me a little punch in the shoulder. "Last chance," he said.

When they called the milers to the start, me and McAllister, as usual, being seventh-graders and the slowest, lined up at the back of the pack. Only this time somebody else lined up with us. It was Pain. He was grinning. I swore right there this would be the last race I ever ran in my life.

In all my other races, what I did was stay pretty far behind McAllister for the first two or three laps. That way I could save my energy and sprint after her on the last lap. But this time I stuck with her right from the start. Like a wart.

By the end of the first lap I was already blowing hard. My legs were getting a little heavy. Pain didn't touch me yet, but he was right beside me, still grinning. We were really smoking.

We kept it up the second lap. Didn't slow down at all. Her spikes were practically nicking my knees. Our breathing had the same **rhythm.**

At the half-mile mark things started to get a little scary. Never before, this far into the race, were we this close to the leaders. I was almost as tired already as I usually was at the end of a whole mile. Something had to give. Pain was right there, **stride** for stride, grinning away. Something was going to happen.

It did. Coming off the first turn into the backstretch of the third lap. The leaders started to go faster. McAllister sped up too. She was trying to stay with them. *She's crazy!* I thought.

I had no choice. I had to go too. I stepped on it, and all of a sudden Pain wasn't alongside me anymore. He was *on* me. He was beating up on my head. He was pulling on my legs. He speared a cramp into my side. He opened up my chest and dumped in those two iron shot puts.

Little by little McAllister pulled away: three yards . . . five yards . . . ten yards . . . When she leaned into the far turn I got a side view of her. She was running great. Long strides. Arms pumping. Leaning just a little forward. Keeping her form. Everything the coach told us.

A feeling I never expected in a million years came over me: I **admired** her. I was proud of her. I knew she was hurting too, maybe even as bad as me, but there she was, gaining on the guy in front of her. I wanted to be like her.

The gun went off: last lap. Four hundred forty more yards and my racing career would be over.

I reached out, like my own breath was a twisted rope, and pulled myself along. My lungs sagged under the shot puts. I tried to forget that. I shook my arms to relax. *Stride long. Head steady. Keep your form. . . .*

ASK Yourself

■ What is Jason trying to do differently in the last meet? Describe how Jason's attitude has changed.

I don't know whether she slowed down or I got faster, but the gap between us closed: ten yards . . . five yards . . . three yards . . . We were on the final backstretch, and I was where I started, nipping at her heels. *Now!* I thought. I pulled alongside her. Floatmeier and some others were already sprinting for the tape, but we were in our own private race, crunching down the cinders, gasping like asthmatics, side by side. We never turned to look at each other.

Words, WORDS, Words

rhythm: a regular beat
stride: a person's step
admired: liked and respected someone

Faces on the side lurched and swayed. The track wobbled under my feet.

Then, going into the final turn, she started to edge ahead. A couple inches. A couple feet. I went after her. My lungs disappeared. Only the shot puts now. And now they were doing something. They were getting warm. They were getting hot. They were burning.

I caught her coming off the final turn. Side by side again. There was no form now. No nice fresh strides. With every step we staggered and knocked into each other like cattle coming down a chute. I wished I had the shot puts back, because in my chest now was something worse: two balls of white-hot gas. Stars! A pair of stars in my chest. A billion degrees centigrade. And they were expanding. Exploding. Searing hot star gas scalding into my stomach and arms and legs, into my head. My eyes were star gas. Faces on the side lurched and swayed. The track wobbled under my feet. Elbows, shoulders, hips colliding. If Peter was running with me I didn't know it. I couldn't see. I couldn't hear. I couldn't breathe. I was dying.

I don't know when I crossed the finish line. I only know they stopped me and held me up and dragged me around with my arms draped over their shoulders.

Somebody came over and slapped me on the back. "Way to go!"

It was Floatmeier's voice.

"Why?" I gasped.

"You beat her, man!"

I opened my eyes. Floatmeier was grinning and holding out his hand. I was too weak to slap it. I sort of petted it.

Then there were hands coming down from everywhere. I did my best to hit them all. "Way to go, Herk," they kept saying. "Way to gut it . . . Way to run . . . Good race . . . Good race . . . Good race . . ."

Finally I plopped to the ground. Little by little I got my shoes off. My chest was returning to normal. The star gas must have gone out through my eyes: They were burning.

Another hand, palm up, in front of me. I slapped it. I looked from the hand to the face. It was McAllister. She looked sick. Her lips were bluish and wet and her mouth was crooked. But then it smiled.

"Good race," she said. ●

Jerry Spinelli

Jerry Spinelli dreamed of becoming a shortstop for the New York Yankees. Fortunately for his fans, he became a writer instead.

Growing up, Jerry Spinelli wanted to be a major league shortstop. He played baseball in junior high and high school. Although he loved it, he wasn't very good. So he gave up his dream of playing for the Yankees. Luckily, right around that time, he discovered something new—writing.

What made you decide to become a writer instead of a baseball player?

When I was sixteen, my high school football team won a big game. I was so excited— I wrote a poem about it. A local newspaper published the poem. That's when I decided to become a writer.

What is your favorite book that you've written?

I guess that would be my first published book, *Space Station Seventh Grade.*

What inspired you to write *Space Station Seventh Grade?*

I married my wife Eileen, a writer who already had five kids. One night, one of our little angels snuck into the refrigerator and swiped a piece of fried chicken I was saving for lunch. When I discovered the chicken was gone, I wrote about it. That piece of writing became *Space Station Seventh Grade.*

Are your childhood memories important to your writing?

When I was growing up, I didn't think my childhood was special. It was full of kid stuff: bike riding, flipping baseball cards, and catching poison ivy. It wasn't until I started writing about it that I realized what an adventure it had been! ●

Other Books by Jerry Spinelli

Maniac Magee

Jeffrey Lionel Magee is a living legend. Two Mills, Pennsylvania, has never seen anything like him.

There's a Girl in My Hammerlock

Maisie goes out for wrestling to get close to Eric, the boy of her dreams. However, she soon finds out that it's wrestling she loves.

Talk About It

Now that you've read *Miles* and the author profile, what do you have to say about these questions?

▶ Why do you think Jason is embarrassed to lose to a girl?

▶ Which is more important — trying or winning? Why?

Comprehension Check

Write your answers to the questions below. Use information from the novel and the profile to support your answers.

1. Why wasn't Jason on the baseball team?

2. How would you describe Jason's character?

3. What does Marceline help Jason to realize?

4. Did you want Jason to beat Marceline? Why or why not?

5. What does Jerry Spinelli have in common with Jason?

Vocabulary Check

Complete each sentence starter below. Before you answer, think about the meaning of the vocabulary word in bold.

1. The boy **screeched** when he saw . . .

2. For the costume party, he **disguised** himself as . . .

3. She **dreaded** going to . . .

4. If a song has a good **rhythm**, I might . . .

5. One thing I have always **admired** about athletes is . . .

Write About It

Choose one of the writing prompts below.

▶ Write a journal entry from Marceline's point of view. Tell what it was like to be on the track team with Jason.

▶ Write a short article for the school newspaper about the last mile race between Jason and Marceline. Use language that makes it sound exciting.

▶ Imagine you had a chance to interview the author. Create your own list of questions for Jerry Spinelli.

Fact FILE

Miles in History

As a miler, Jason's time of 6 minutes and 47 seconds would keep him way out of the record books. Today's fastest milers all clock in under four minutes. But it wasn't always that way. In fact, no one could beat the four-minute mile until 1954. That's when an English runner named Roger Bannister finally ran it in 3 minutes and 59 seconds.

Overnight, Bannister became world-famous. But he's not the guy Jason saw on television. That was probably Sebastian Coe. Coe, also English, set three world records for the mile in the 1970s and 1980s. More recently, Moroccan Hicham El Gerrouj set a new world record with a time of 3 minutes and 43 seconds in 1999.

Reading a Bar Graph

Did you ever get into arguments about your favorite sport? Perhaps you like baseball, and your friend likes basketball. A bar graph is an easy way to show what everyone likes.

Check out the one below. It shows the number of high school girls who participate in 11 different sports. Can you figure out which sports are the most popular?

Girls in High School Sports

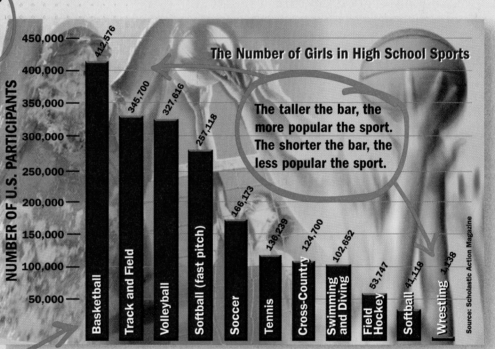

The vertical line shows how many girls play each sport.

The Number of Girls in High School Sports

The taller the bar, the more popular the sport. The shorter the bar, the less popular the sport.

NUMBER OF U.S. PARTICIPANTS

450,000
400,000
350,000
300,000
250,000
200,000
150,000
100,000
50,000

Basketball — 412,576
Track and Field — 345,700
Volleyball — 327,616
Softball (fast pitch) — 257,118
Soccer — 166,173
Tennis — 136,239
Cross-Country — 124,700
Swimming and Diving — 102,652
Field Hockey — 53,747
Softball — 41,118
Wrestling — 1,138

Source: Scholastic Action Magazine

The horizontal line gives the name of each sport.

"This chart includes exact figures. But some don't. How would you figure out these charts? Easy. Go to the top of the bar that says 'soccer.' Then trace a line straight across to the left. You can see that more than 150,000 girls play soccer."

Take the Bar Exam

Bar graphs are a quick way to compare things. Taller means more. Smaller means less. It's as simple as that. Take another look at the chart on the left. Review the tips, too. Then use them to answer the questions below. Write your answers on your own paper.

1. What is the most popular sport among high school girls? What is the least popular sport?

2. Where does soccer rank among the rest of the sports on the graph?
   a. most popular
   b. seventh most popular
   c. fifth most popular
   d. least popular

3. Which is more popular: tennis or cross-country?
   a. tennis
   b. cross-country
   c. They are exactly the same.

4. How much more popular is basketball than swimming and diving?
   a. They are about the same.
   b. Basketball is about twice as popular as swimming and diving.
   c. Basketball is about four times as popular as swimming and diving.

Raise the Bars

Suppose you want to update this graph. The WNBA has made basketball even more popular. Now 100,000 more girls are playing. The U.S. women's soccer team won the World Cup. So 200,000 more girls play soccer. Meanwhile, 60,000 girls have dropped volleyball. And there are now 280 girls playing football in the U.S. List the sports and their new numbers.

Graph It

Now take the list from above and redraw the bar graph.

" What else can you put in bar graphs? You can compare anything that is measured in numbers: the salaries of different jobs, the size of cities, the amount of rainfall in different years. "

Real-World Words

vertical: going up and down
horizontal: parallel to the ground
update: to make newer or more recent

Odd Jobs
by Pam Cardiff

Snake Scientist

To scientist Bob Mason, there's nothing creepy about these crawlers!

Picture a place where the ground is alive with snakes. Thousands of them are piled two feet deep. A nightmare, you say? To Bob Mason, it's a dream come true.

Actually, this scene isn't a dream at all. It takes place every spring at the Narcisse Wildlife Management Area in Manitoba, Canada. Each year people from all over the world come to see the red-sided garter snakes. One of these people is Bob Mason.

Bob is a zoologist at Oregon State University. A zoologist studies animals and animal life. This is something Bob has done since he was a boy.

Nature Boy

While growing up in Connecticut, Bob loved to watch nature shows. He also liked to bring home small creatures from the woods. Bob would observe the animals for a while. Then he would return them to where he found them. Sometimes the animals managed to escape. "Turtles and snakes would cruise around the house," Bob remembers. "They'd turn up in the washing machine! It was rough on my mom."

At Oregon State University, Bob is known as the Snake Scientist. A stuffed snake sits on top of his computer. Snake cartoons cover the door of his office. He wears a bracelet made of tiny snake bones.

If you think most *jobs* are boring, *think again!*

One of the many red-sided garter snakes at Narcisse.

For over fifteen years Bob has been asking questions about snakes. How do snakes choose their mates? How do snakes find their way back to the same area year after year? How can learning about snakes help humans in the future? Bob is finding some of these answers at Narcisse.

Snake Season

April and May are really "snaky" months at Narcisse. That's when you can see more snakes there than anyplace else in the world. "This is the most awesome, **remarkable** sight I've seen in my life!" says Bob. To him, Narcisse is a snake wonderland. You may wonder why so many snakes are in one place at the same time. To understand the answer, you have to learn a thing or two about snakes.

First of all, snakes are cold-blooded. This means that their body temperature is the same as the temperature of their **surroundings.** When the sun is hot, snakes warm up. When the temperature drops, snakes cool down. During the coldest months, snakes have to keep from freezing. They often crawl into basements or barns. Or, they dig warm little holes.

The land around Narcisse makes the perfect winter rest stop for snakes. Why? Beneath the topsoil is a deep layer of limestone. Limestone is a soft rock that **dissolves** easily. Over the years, lots of underground caves have formed in it. In some places the caves have **collapsed.** This forms holes that snakes can enter and leave easily. These holes are known as "sinks."

Bob Mason "bags" a snake to study.

Every September, red-sided garter snakes slither into these sinks. Thousands of snakes pile right on top of each other. Then they take a long and cozy winter nap—for about eight months! Their breathing and heart rate slow down. Their blood becomes as thick as ketchup. They don't eat or drink. Then, in April, the warm sun hits the ground again. Up come the snakes. They're ready to enjoy the lovely spring weather. And up to Canada comes Bob Mason. He's ready to make new discoveries about snakes.

Like a Puzzle

When Bob goes to Narcisse, he doesn't go alone. He brings a team of helpers. He also brings laptop computers, pens, and paper. And he brings thermometers, tape measures, and pillowcases. The pillowcases aren't used at bedtime. They're used to collect snakes to study. Bob and his team measure the snakes. They take their temperatures and mark them

with paint. Some of the snakes are released right away. Others are kept for a while so they can take part in experiments.

ASK Yourself

- What makes Bob Mason think that Narcisse is a snake wonderland?

Think about his job and what happens at Narcisse every spring.

Bob is excited by every bit of information he learns about snakes. "It's really fun," he says, "like a jigsaw puzzle. When a piece fits, it's tremendous."

Bob has made many important discoveries about snakes. He has learned that snakes use smells to communicate with each other. These smells help snakes choose their mates. Snakes also follow smells left by other snakes to help them get back to their dens each year.

There's lots more Bob has learned about snakes. He knows they can travel up to twenty miles. He knows they

usually live about nine years. And he knows that they like to eat frogs.

Save the Snakes!

However, there is still plenty for Bob to learn about snakes. He even hopes his snake studies could one day help people. "We're actually more similar to snakes than dissimilar," he says. "They have all the same organs we do. They have blood. They have lungs."

Bob thinks helping people would be great. But in the meantime, he tries hard to help the snakes. Several years ago, Bob discovered that there were fewer snakes than before. So he helped make snake collecting at Narcisse against the law. He also helped figure out ways to keep drivers in Narcisse from running over the snakes.

Through his work, Bob has gotten people to appreciate snakes. He thinks that's part of his job as a snake scientist. At Narcisse, Bob wants people to see that snakes can be fun. Says Bob, "having the snakes here can give them joy."

Words, Words, Words

remarkable: worth noticing
surroundings: the setting that a person or thing is in
dissolves: breaks up into small pieces
collapsed: fell or caved in

://internet_detective.

How do you catch a computer criminal? Just ask Tsutomu Shimomura. He's the expert!

It was Christmas day, 1994. Tsutomu Shimomura was in San Francisco. He was getting ready for a ski vacation. Then a well-known computer criminal broke into his computer. Valuable information was stolen. So Tsutomu went into action. He played a real-life game of cops and robbers. But this cops and robbers game was different from most. It was played on the Internet!

Tsutomu Shimomura helps keep information on the Internet safe.

Computer Wizard

Tsutomu won the game. But how did he do it? In person, he looks like an ordinary guy. He likes to wear sandals, shorts, and T-shirts. Two of his favorite activities are in-line skating and skiing. But behind this laid-back image is a computer **security** expert. Tsutomu's job is preventing computer break-ins. When Kevin Mitnick broke into Tsutomu's computer, he made a *big* mistake!

Tsutomu is a Japanese citizen. But he grew up in Princeton, New Jersey. His parents were both scientists. Tsutomu has always been a whiz at science as well. In fact, he got a job as a scientist right out of high school. It was at an important lab in New Mexico.

Eventually Tsutomu became interested in computer security. Since then he has designed a lot of security software. Some of it has been used by the FBI and the Air Force. His work has helped protect the privacy of Internet users.

America's Most-Wanted Hacker

A hacker is a person who illegally enters someone else's computer system. Usually hackers want to steal secret information or money.

They use the Internet to commit their crimes. In the 1990s, one of the best-known hackers was Kevin Mitnick.

Mitnick had a long history of computer crimes. He broke into the Los Angeles telephone system when he was only a teenager. That was just the beginning. Soon he was stealing credit card numbers. He also stole software. Mitnick was arrested several times. He went to jail. Then he got out. But he didn't stop hacking. By 1992, Mitnick was wanted again. This time, the FBI was looking for him. They suspected him of stealing computer files and credit card numbers. He had also broken into many telephone networks. And he was suspected of breaking into an important Internet computer.

"He was clearly the most-wanted computer criminal in the world," said Kent Walker, a U.S. attorney. "He **allegedly** had access to corporate secrets worth billions of dollars."

"He's a computer terrorist," said John Russell, a U.S. Justice Department spokesman.

By the time Mitnick broke into Tsutomu's computer, many people were already looking for him. So far, no one had been able to catch him. That is, until Tsutomu got on the case.

ASK YOURSELF

- Why do people break into computer systems?
Think about how the information found there might be used.

Busted

When Mitnick broke into Tsutomu's computer, he didn't know that Tsutomu had set up his computer in a special way. Tsutomu's computer was set up to give him an automatic warning that an attack was underway.

After the attack, Tsutomu discovered that the robber had stolen several important files. He **vowed** to catch the person who had done it.

Tsutomu first asked some other computer experts to help him. The group used the Internet to search for Mitnick. "We basically walked around on-line looking for clues," says his partner, Julia Menapace. It took about eight weeks for Tsutomu to track Mitnick down. During that time, Mitnick broke into even more computers. He used some of the files he had stolen from Tsutomu to help him.

Finally, Tsutomu and his team traced Mitnick to Raleigh, North Carolina. Tsutomu flew there from California. Then he led the FBI right to Mitnick's door.

So what do you do after you've caught America's most-wanted hacker? If you're Tsutomu Shimomura, you finally go skiing!

But that's not the end of the story. After serving almost five years in prison, Mitnick is now speaking out against hacking. He's even giving advice to companies so that they can protect themselves from cyber attacks.

WORDS, WORDS, WORDS

security: protection or safety from crime
allegedly: supposedly
vowed: promised

PUPPET MASTER

Imagine watching in terror as a herd of charging animals rushes straight at you. They race closer and closer. You cover your eyes in fear. Suddenly you hear clapping. The scary spell is broken. Soon you're clapping too. What's going on? You're watching a performance of *The Lion King*. It's the hit Broadway play based on the Disney movie.

Audiences agree that *The Lion King* is incredibly exciting. But most people don't know the person behind the scenes who made it all happen. That person is Julie Taymor. Julie is the play's director. That means Julie was in charge of how the play should look. She also designed all the costumes. And she helped design the play's amazing masks and puppets. They're

what make *The Lion King* such a special experience.

Finding a Director

The Lion King, as you may know, tells the story of a lion cub named Simba. After his father is killed, Simba goes on a quest to become the king of the jungle. He has lots of adventures along the way. *The Lion King* became Disney's most successful movie ever.

So the folks at Disney decided to turn *The Lion King* into a Broadway play. First, they had to find a director. They chose Julie Taymor. Julie had already created many other children's plays. She was known for using colorful masks and huge puppets. She based these unusual masks and puppets on ones she had seen in Africa, Japan, and Indonesia.

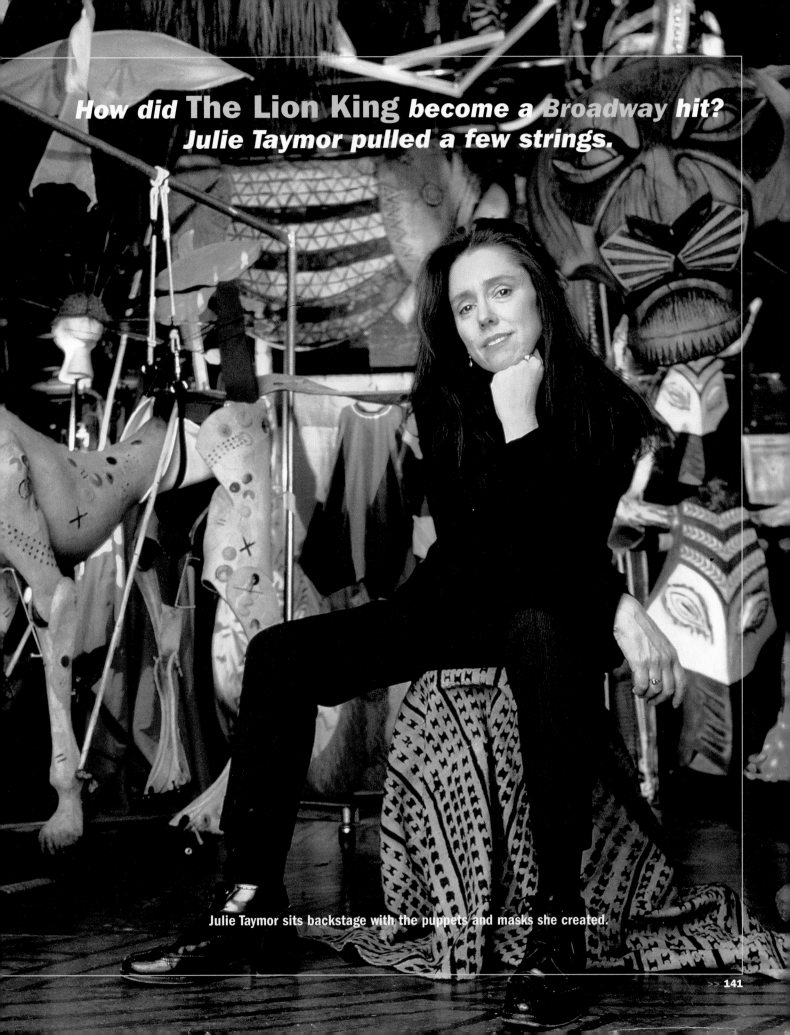

How did The Lion King become a Broadway hit?
Julie Taymor pulled a few strings.

Julie Taymor sits backstage with the puppets and masks she created.

Julie Taymor won a Tony Award for Best Director of a Musical.

When she was asked to direct *The Lion King*, Julie hadn't even seen the movie. She might have been the only person left in America who hadn't! But after watching it, she realized her challenge. How was she going to bring a movie starring cartoon animals to life?

Making Masks and Puppets

"How," she wondered, "do I deal with a story that is all animals, but is . . . a human story? Am I going to take great actors and hide them in animal suits?"

No, decided Julie. "I thought, what if I create these giant masks that really are clearly the characters? The human face is **revealed** below, so that you're not losing the human facial expression. And, you're not hiding the actor."

Julie worked with another designer to create African-style masks. In Africa, masks are an art form. But they are also useful. They play an important role in storytelling. Many of them are worn above the head instead of over the face. Julie decided that the masks in *The Lion King* would be worn that way.

Not all the actors in *The Lion King* wear masks, however. Some actors work with giant puppets. They control these puppets with rods and wires. This is known as Bunraku puppetry. Bunraku puppetry comes from ancient Japan. In Bunraku puppetry, the people controlling the puppets can be seen by the audience. Together, a person and a puppet work to bring a character to life.

The masks and puppets are exciting to watch on stage. But working with heavy masks and huge puppets isn't always easy. The actors can get sore backs and muscles from lugging them around. Julie **appreciates** how hard the actors work. "They have been unbelievably patient," she says. "No one has said, 'I can't do this.'"

Thrills and Chills

Julie doesn't just create incredible puppets and masks. She is also a whiz at special effects. The best example is the scary wildebeest scene. For this scene, Julie worked with another designer. Together, they built rollers with larger and larger rows of wildebeests on them. When these are moved, it looks like waves of wildebeests are running toward the audience. This scene always gets some frightened screams.

Theater Lover

How do you get a job directing such an exciting show? It probably helps to start young. Julie began putting on shows when she was a little girl in Massachusetts. She hasn't stopped since. In college she became interested in the theater of different **cultures** around the world. She became interested in shadow puppetry. Shadow puppets are flat. They're moved behind a screen so that they cast shadows. Shadow puppetry is very popular in Indonesia. So after college, that's where Julie went. It was in Indonesia that Julie formed her first professional theater group.

Since then, Julie has won many awards, including a Tony award. The Tony is the theater's most important award. Julie won a Tony for Best Director of a Musical. She was the first woman ever to win in that category.

Whenever she's working in the theater, Julie wants to give her viewers an unforgettable experience. "The most exciting thing," she says, "is to reach an audience that has never seen my work before." ●

ASK YOURSELF

- What was Julie Taymor trying to do when she designed the costumes?

Think about why the characters wear masks instead of animal suits.

WORDS, WORDS, WORDS

revealed: seen or shown
appreciates: values someone or something
cultures: groups of people that share the same way of life

Talk About It

Now that you've read "Odd Jobs," what do you have to say about these questions?

▶ What is more important—to make lots of money, to help others, or to love your job? Explain.

▶ Think of your interests and hobbies. Which do you think could be turned into a job? What job would that be?

Comprehension Check

Write your answers to the questions below. Use information from the profiles to support your answers.

1. Why are there so many snakes at Narcisse?

2. Do you think that Julie Taymor loves her job? Why or why not?

3. Why is hacking a crime?

4. Which of the three jobs did you find most interesting? Why?

5. What do you think most successful people have in common?

Vocabulary Check

Answer each question below with a complete sentence. Before you answer, think about the meaning of the vocabulary word in bold.

1. Which **cultures** do your favorite foods come from?

2. Who **appreciates** your jokes?

3. How would you describe your **surroundings**?

4. What's the most **remarkable** thing that's happened to you today?

5. What would you say to someone who **revealed** the ending of a movie you wanted to see?

Write About It

Choose one of the writing prompts below.

▶ Think of a story you know that might make a good play. Describe how you would want it to look. What would the costumes and scenery be like?

▶ Write an e-mail to Tsutomu Shimomura. In it, ask him at least three questions about the kind of work he does.

▶ Write a letter to Bob Mason asking at least three questions that you have about snakes.

Fact FILE

Dream Jobs

Are you tired of people asking you what you want to be when you grow up? These sites can help you come up with a great answer.

▶ **BLS Career Information**

http://stats.bls.gov/k12/html/edu_over.htm

Based on your interests now, you can find out about jobs you might want in the future. Click on math, science, music/arts, reading, social studies, or outdoors/physical education.

▶ **What Do They Do?**

http://www.webquarry.com/~lgfd/

Check out this site for a list of jobs from actor to zoologist. Is there a job that you've always thought might be right for you? Ever wondered what a volcanologist does? No problem. Click on the job title and read all about it.

Completing a Job Application

Are you eager to get your first part-time job? Before you do, you'll probably have to fill out a job application. It's not tough, but you have to do it correctly.

Here is a standard job application. Check it out. Think about what you would write on each line.

Write neatly. Try not to scratch out words. Make sure you read over the application before handing it in.

Fill in all the blanks neatly. If a question doesn't apply to you, write "NA" (not applicable). Amy wrote "NA" here because she is not yet in high school.

Here's where you would list any accomplishments, skills, or interests that would make you a good employee.

APPLICATION

IDENTIFICATION

(Print) First Name	Middle Name	Last Name
Amy	Louise	Choi

Date of Birth	Social Security Number		
December 21, 2081	555-555-5555		

Street Address and Number	City	State	Zip	Telephone No.
1525 NASA Way	Fort Lauderdale FL		55555	555.1234

Position Applying For	Date You Can Start
Cashier, Space Shuttle Dining Car	June 14, 2094

EDUCATION

School	Name and Location	Dates Attended		Degree Received
		From	To	
Middle School	Lunar Middle School, Ft. Lauderdale, FL	9/93	Present	NA
High School	NA			NA
College	NA			NA
Business or Trade	NA			NA

WORK EXPERIENCE

(List most recent employer first.)

POSITION	DATES		EMPLOYER Name and Phone #	RATE OF PAY	REASON FOR LEAVING
	From	To			
Dog walker	6/92 to present		Mr. James Hill, 555-1595	$7/hour	NA
Dishwasher	6/93 to 8/93		Space Burger, Ms. Maria Hernandez, 555-8282	$6.50/hour	Start of school

OTHER EXPERIENCE, SKILLS, OR INTERESTS

Co-Captain of field hockey team. Florida 12-and-under Jetboard champion, 2092. Enjoy space travel, computer programming, and pets.

Have you ever been arrested? ○ yes ⊗ no   If yes, explain on reverse.

Reference: Ms. Karen Barts

Telephone: 555-8213   Relationship to Applicant: Teacher

Signature of applicant: *Amy L. Choi*   DATE: 9/15/93

"A reference is someone the employer can call to find out if you're a good worker. It's a good idea to use an adult. Make sure you ask your reference if it's okay to use his or her name."

Get a Job

A job application may form your employer's first impression of you. It pays to make it a good one. Reread the application on the left. Check out the tips that go with it. Then answer the questions below. Write your answers on your own paper.

1. "NA" stands for "Not Applicable." What does that mean? Choose one of the following answers.
   a. never mind
   b. not again
   c. does not apply to me
   d. none of your business

2. What job does Amy hope to get?
   a. dog walker
   b. dishwasher
   c. cashier
   d. field-hockey coach

3. List three of Amy's interests or experiences outside of school.

4. Who is Ms. Maria Hernandez?
   a. Amy's former teacher
   b. Amy's former employer
   c. Amy's mother
   d. a former Jetboard champion

5. Do you volunteer, play a sport, or belong to a club? List two experiences to include in the "Other" section of a job application.

Be Prepared
When you apply for a job, you'll need information handy. On a sheet of paper, write down the names and addresses of your school, your employers, and your references.

Best Foot Forward
Why would you be a good employee? Write a paragraph describing your strengths as a worker. Be sure to back up your strengths with examples of things you have done.

"You usually need a Social Security number to get a job. If you don't have one, talk to a parent or guardian."

Real-World Words

applicant: a person who is trying to get a job
employer: a person who hires someone for a job
position: a job

play

Smiffy Blue Solves Two

ADAPTED FROM THE BOOK **BY WALTER DEAN MYERS**

Who's the thief? You may be confused. But just wait until *Smiffy Blue* starts chasing clues.

FAMOUS RUBY OF MORA MORA

DAVID SIMS '95

Smiffy Blue and the Case of the Missing Ruby

Cast of Characters

Narrator 1*

Narrator 2*

Smiffy Blue, famous crime fighter*

Jeremy Joe, Smiffy Blue's assistant*

Inspector Hector, the police inspector

Professor Lessor

Chubby Checkin, the hotel clerk

Peter Porgy, the fish man

Art Decoe, the paint man

Girard the Guard

starred characters are major roles

SCENE 1

Narrator 1: Smiffy Blue, famous crime fighter, sat in his small office. He was reading the local newspaper, the Doober City Gazette.

Narrator 2: Jeremy Joe, who often helped Smiffy Blue solve crimes, twirled his new umbrella.

Jeremy Joe: I wonder what keeps the raindrops up in the sky? Why doesn't it rain all the time?

Narrator 1: Smiffy Blue looked up from his paper.

Smiffy Blue: That is simple, my lad. It is the heat of the sun that keeps up the rain.

Jeremy Joe: How does it do that, Smiffy Blue?

Smiffy Blue: When it is cool, the rain falls from the clouds, and we get wet. But when the sun is very hot, it dries the rain before it reaches us. That is why it only rains on days when it is not sunny and warm.

Jeremy Joe: Oh.

Narrator 2: Suddenly, the telephone rang. It was Inspector Hector of the Doober City Police.

Inspector Hector: Come over to the museum right away. The famous ruby of Mora Mora has been stolen!

Smiffy Blue: I will leave right away.

Narrator 1: Smiffy Blue hung up the phone and put on his coat. Then he left the office, with Jeremy Joe and his dog, Dog, right behind him.

Narrator 2: Smiffy Blue and Jeremy Joe got on their bicycle and rode to the museum.

SCENE 2

Narrator 1: When they arrived at the museum, the first one to greet them was Professor Lessor. He looked very upset.

Smiffy Blue: What happened, Professor Lessor?

Professor Lessor: Girard the Guard was outside the door. But he did not see the thief.

Narrator 2: Suzette from the Gazette was taking pictures. Inspector Hector was there, too. He was examining the scene of the crime.

Professor Lessor: Oh me! Oh, my, my!

Narrator 1: Professor Lessor wrung his hands.

Professor Lessor: The ruby was in the crown of the king of Mora Mora. He lent it to us so that we could let the people of Doober City see it. Now the king will be furious.

Narrator 2: Smiffy Blue looked at the case. The crown was sitting on a velvet pillow. But where the ruby was supposed to be, there was just a big hole.

Smiffy Blue: When did you last see the ruby?

Professor Lessor: I checked it before I left last night, and then I locked the door. Suzette from the Gazette took a picture as I checked it.

Narrator 1: Suzette showed Smiffy Blue the picture.

Smiffy Blue: Were there any clues?

Inspector Hector: Only this empty notebook.

Smiffy Blue: Let me see it at once!

Narrator 2: Smiffy Blue looked at the book carefully. All of the pages were indeed empty. Smiffy Blue smiled. It was a shy smile. And a **sly** smile. It was the kind of smile that Smiffy Blue smiled when he had found a clue.

Jeremy Joe: Smiffy Blue has found a clue!

Smiffy Blue: Yes, I have! This is an address book.

Inspector Hector: But there are no addresses in the book.

Smiffy Blue: Exactly! Which means the thief doesn't know anyone around here. Therefore, he must be a stranger.

Jeremy Joe: That's a good clue.

Smiffy Blue: We must go to the Doober City Hotel. I have noticed quite a few strangers staying there lately.

Narrator 1: So Smiffy Blue and Jeremy Joe and Dog jumped upon their bicycle and hurried over to the Doober City Hotel.

SCENE ③

Narrator 2: At the Doober City Hotel, Smiffy Blue talked to Chubby Checkin, the hotel clerk.

Smiffy Blue: Do you have a stranger staying here today who looks as if he has just stolen a famous ruby?

Chubby Checkin: No. We have had very few strangers here lately. And the only one we did have left early this morning.

Smiffy Blue: We must search the room in which he stayed.

Narrator 1: So Chubby Checkin took Smiffy Blue and Jeremy Joe to the stranger's room. They looked all around. They looked under the rug and under the lamp. They looked in the closet and under the bed.

Jeremy Joe: There is nothing in the closet except this old newspaper.

Smiffy Blue: Let me see it.

Narrator 2: Smiffy Blue looked at the old newspaper. He rubbed it with his finger. He smelled it. He held it up to the light. Then Smiffy Blue smiled. It was a shy smile. It was a sly smile. It was the kind of smile that Smiffy Blue smiled when he had found a clue.

Words, **Words,** Words

sly: crafty and secretive
trained: taught a person or animal how to do something

Jeremy Joe: Ooh! Ooh! Smiffy Blue has found another clue.

Smiffy Blue: Indeed, I have. This is an old newspaper.

Jeremy Joe: I've got it! The thief likes to read old newspapers.

Smiffy Blue: NO! You use old newspapers to wrap up fish! The thief must have been to the fish market.

Jeremy Joe: I haven't got it.

Smiffy Blue: We must go quickly to the Doober City Fish Market.

Ask Yourself

- What's wrong with the clues that Smiffy Blue finds?

As you read, think about whether or not the clues make sense.

SCENE 4

Narrator 1: At the Doober City Fish Market, Peter Porgy, the fish man, asked Smiffy Blue what they wanted.

Smiffy Blue: Did a stranger, a stranger who looked as if he might steal a precious ruby, come here to buy a fish?

Peter Porgy: No. But yesterday a stranger did come here. He bought a lobster.

Smiffy Blue: A lobster?

Peter Porgy: Yes. And under his left arm was a can of gold paint.

Narrator 2: Smiffy Blue rubbed his chin. Then he paced up. Then he paced down. Then he scratched his ear. Then, slowly, slowly, Smiffy Blue began to smile. It was a shy smile. It was a sly smile. It was the kind of smile that Smiffy Blue smiled when he had found a clue.

Jeremy Joe: You have a clue, Smiffy Blue?

Smiffy Blue: Indeed, I have! The thief bought a lobster and he had gold paint. What he must have done was to paint the lobster gold. Then he must have **trained** the lobster to sneak into the museum and steal the crown. If someone saw the lobster in the case he would think it was part of the crown.

Jeremy Joe: That has to be one very smart thief.

It was a shy smile. And a sly smile. It was the kind of smile Smiffy Blue smiled when he had found a clue.

Smiffy Blue: Never fear. We will soon track him down. Let us go quickly to the paint store and find out who bought a can of gold paint.

Narrator 1: So Smiffy Blue and Jeremy Joe and Dog hopped on their bicycle and rode to the paint store as fast as Jeremy Joe's legs would go.

SCENE 5

Narrator 2: When they arrived at the paint store, Jeremy Joe was huffing and puffing.

Smiffy Blue: Did you sell a jar of gold paint to a stranger yesterday? A stranger who looked like he might steal a ruby from the king of Mora Mora's crown?

Art Decoe: Yesterday?

Narrator 1: Art Decoe, the paint man, scratched his head.

Art Decoe: Yesterday, I sold two jars of gold paint. One to a schoolteacher and one to a little man carrying a poodle. I also sold him a jar of red paint but no brush.

Smiffy Blue: Did you say no brush?

Art Decoe: I did.

Smiffy Blue: And did you say he was carrying a poodle?

Jeremy Joe: He said that, too, Smiffy Blue.

Narrator 2: Smiffy Blue brought his lips tightly together. Then he looked up at the ceiling. Then he shut his eyes as tightly as he could. But it was no use. Jeremy Joe saw that he was beginning to smile. At first it was just a very shy smile. Then it became a slightly sly smile. Then it became the smile that Smiffy Blue smiled when he had found a clue.

Jeremy Joe: Smiffy Blue has found another clue! He has found the best clue yet.

Smiffy Blue: And indeed, I have, my lad. First the thief came into the museum. Then he opened the back door and let in the poodle.

Jeremy Joe: The poodle stole the ruby!

Smiffy Blue: NO! The poodle carried the lobster to the crown.

Then the lobster grabbed the ruby, jumped back onto the poodle, and the poodle returned to his evil master.

Jeremy Joe: Ooh, Smiffy Blue. That is such a good clue, I think I'm going to cry.

Smiffy Blue: But now we must get back to the museum at once. Call Inspector Hector and Suzette from the Gazette. Tell Inspector Hector to bring his handcuffs and be ready to arrest the thief.

Ask Yourself

- Who do you think the thief is? Reread the story and look for your own clues.

SCENE 6

Narrator 1: By the time Smiffy Blue and Jeremy Joe and Dog got back to the Doober City Museum, it had started to rain. Jeremy Joe put up his new umbrella and held it over Smiffy Blue.

Narrator 2: Inspector Hector, Professor Lessor, and Suzette from the Gazette were all waiting at the museum for Smiffy Blue.

Professor Lessor: Have you found out who stole the ruby?

Smiffy Blue: No. But I know how it was stolen.

Jeremy Joe: The lobster did it, and the poodle did it, and a stranger, too.

Narrator 1: Jeremy Joe was very proud of himself. Professor Lessor looked confused.

Professor Lessor: I don't know what you are talking about.

Smiffy Blue: Let me look about the room once more.

Narrator 2: Smiffy Blue looked all over the room. He looked in the corners and on the floor. He looked at the ceiling and the walls. He scratched his head. He rubbed his chin.

Narrator 1: Then Smiffy Blue looked as if he were about to grin. But it wasn't exactly a grin. It was more of a smile. It was more of a shy smile, and a sly smile. It was more the kind of smile that Smiffy Blue smiled when he had found a clue.

Jeremy Joe: Oh! Oh! Smiffy Blue has found another clue.

Smiffy Blue: Better than that, my lad. I have found the thief!

SCENE 7

Narrator 2: Everyone waited to find out what Smiffy Blue was smiling about.

Jeremy Joe: How did you find the thief?

Smiffy Blue: The poodle carried the lobster into the museum. The lobster, carefully disguised as the royal crown of the king of Mora Mora, grabbed the ruby, then hopped upon the back of the poodle and took it to his master.

Inspector Hector: But how will we find his master?

Smiffy Blue: Very simply. The paint man said that he did not sell a paintbrush to the thief. Then how did the thief paint the lobster?

Suzette: How did the thief paint the lobster, Smiffy Blue?

Smiffy Blue: With his mustache!

Narrator: Smiffy Blue pointed toward Girard the Guard, who had a mustache.

Girard the Guard: Oh, no. The famous detective has found me out! I must get away!

Narrator 1: But it was already too late. Inspector Hector had put the handcuffs on him, and Suzette from the Gazette had taken his picture just as the ruby fell from his pocket.

Inspector Hector: You must now go to jail!

Girard the Guard: But I have no lobster, and I have no poodle.

Smiffy Blue: Mere details, my boy. Mere details.

SCENE 8

Narrator 2: Smiffy Blue and Jeremy Joe and Dog left the museum.

Jeremy Joe: That mustache was a wonderful clue. But I didn't get it.

Smiffy Blue: One day you will. It takes time to become a great detective.

Jeremy Joe: True, true, Smiffy Blue. True, true.

Narrator 1: Then Smiffy Blue and Jeremy Joe and Dog got on the bicycle and rode back to their office as fast as Jeremy Joe's legs could pedal.

Smiffy Blue and the Case of the Missing Formula

Cast of Characters

Narrator 1*

Narrator 2*

Smiffy Blue, famous crime fighter*

Jeremy Joe, Smiffy Blue's assistant*

Inspector Hector, the police inspector

Doctor Von Von, the scientist

Suzette, the photographer from the Gazette

Patty de Pate, the barber

Doctor Seymour Orless, the eye doctor

Stash McCash, the richest man in Doober City

Penny Stampp, the postal clerk

Bobbie Baddie, the janitor

*starred characters are major roles

SCENE 1

Narrator 1: Smiffy Blue, famous crime fighter, sat in his small office. He was reading the local newspaper, the Doober City Gazette.

Narrator 2: Jeremy Joe, who often helped Smiffy Blue solve crimes, sat at his own desk in the corner of the office. He was having his breakfast of donuts and milk.

Jeremy Joe: I wonder how they put the holes in these donuts.

Smiffy Blue: It's simple, my lad. They do not put the holes in the donuts. They wrap the donuts around the holes.

Jeremy Joe: Oh, I see.

Narrator 1: Jeremy Joe was pleased to have discovered the secret of making donuts.

Narrator 2: Suddenly, the telephone rang. It was Inspector Hector of the Doober City Police.

Inspector Hector: You must come over to the Acme plant right away. A top secret formula has disappeared.

Smiffy Blue: I'm on the way.

Narrator 1: Smiffy Blue hung up the phone and put on his coat. Jeremy Joe was right behind him. So was Smiffy Blue's brave and trusty dog, Dog.

SCENE 2

Narrator 2: The Acme plant was on the edge of town. Doctor Von Von, the scientist, met Smiffy Blue at the front gate.

Doctor Von Von: Yesterday we announced to everyone that we had invented two new secret formulas. One was a formula to un-pop popcorn. That one is still there. The other one was a top secret formula for turning people invisible. And now it is gone!

Narrator 1: Smiffy Blue looked into the safe. Doctor Von Von was right. The secret formula for making people disappear had disappeared.

Smiffy Blue: When did you first notice that the secret formula was missing?

Doctor Von Von: This morning when I came to work. I was about to help our Janitor, Bobby Baddie, clean the floor. He needs help because he has a broken arm. Then I noticed that the safe was open.

Smiffy Blue: Are you sure that the safe was locked last night?

Doctor Von Von: Yes, I am. Last night, after everyone had left, Suzette from the Gazette took a picture of me putting the formula into the safe and locking it.

Smiffy Blue: I must see those pictures. Jeremy Joe, we must go to the Doober City Gazette.

Narrator 1: Smiffy Blue and Jeremy Joe rode on their bicycle to the Doober City Gazette.

SCENE ③

Narrator 2: At the Doober City Gazette, Suzette showed them the pictures she had taken.

Suzette: Here are the pictures I took.

Narrator 1: Smiffy Blue looked at the pictures. In the corner of one picture, he saw a small bowl. On the side of the bowl were three letters: C-A-T.

Narrator 2: Smiffy Blue smiled. It was a slightly shy smile. And a slightly sly smile.

Ask Yourself

- Do you think the C-A-T bowl has anything to do with the thief?

Consider what a C-A-T bowl might really be used for.

It was the kind of smile that Smiffy Blue smiled when he had found a clue.

Jeremy Joe: Have you found a clue, Smiffy Blue?

Smiffy Blue: Indeed, I have. Do you see this bowl?

Jeremy Joe: Yes.

Smiffy Blue: Do you know what these letters stand for?

Jeremy Joe: Ooh! Ooh! I got it!

Narrator 1: Jeremy Joe's ears **twitched** with excitement.

Jeremy Joe: They stand for cat. A pussycat has stolen the secret formula.

Smiffy Blue: NO! It stands for Criminal and Thief.

Jeremy Joe: Oh, I didn't get it.

Smiffy Blue: This is the bowl from which the Criminal and Thief eats. But there is no fork or spoon about and no spots on the floor. How can the criminal eat from a bowl without a spoon and leave no spots on the floor?

Jeremy Joe: How did he do that?

Smiffy Blue: By catching the spots in his beard. The thief is a man with a beard! We must go to the Doober City barber and ask if she knows about a man with a beard.

SCENE ④

Narrator 2: Smiffy Blue and Jeremy Joe and Dog, the dog, went to the Doober City Barber Shop. There, they met Patty de Pate, the Doober City barber.

Smiffy Blue: Have you seen a man with a long beard come in here?

Patty de Pate: Only one. A tall man with a long beard and **squinty** eyes.

Smiffy Blue: Did you say squinty eyes?

Patty de Pate: I did.

Narrator 1: Smiffy Blue smiled. It was a slightly shy smile. And a slightly sly smile. It was the kind of smile that Smiffy Blue smiled when he had found a clue.

Smiffy Blue: That means the thief has misplaced his glasses. That is why he squints. The thief is a man with squinty eyes and a beard. He will probably go to the glasses store to buy a new pair of glasses. We must go there also.

Narrator 2: Doctor Von Von and Inspector Hector drive up in the Doober City police car. Smiffy Blue tells them about the man with the beard and squinty eyes.

Doctor Von Von: You have to find him quickly. For if he sells the secret formula to our enemies in Enemyville, we will be lost!

Words, Words, Words

twitched: made a small, jerky movement
squinty: with eyes nearly closed
keen: sharp

Smiffy Blue: Never fear. We will find him soon enough. Now, on to the glasses store.

Narrator 1: And off they went. Smiffy Blue's scarf flew behind him as Jeremy Joe pedaled the bicycle until he was quite red in the face.

SCENE 5

Narrator 2: At the glasses store, Smiffy Blue looked around carefully, letting nothing escape his **keen** eye.

Doctor Seymour Orless: Do you need glasses?

Smiffy Blue: Hardly. I am Smiffy Blue, the famous detective. And this is Jeremy Joe, who often helps me solve crimes. Have you seen anyone with a long beard and squinty eyes who looks as if he might have stolen a secret formula?

Doctor Seymour Orless: No. The only one who came in here today was a man wearing a nice blue suit and a blue silk tie.

Narrator 1: Smiffy Blue covered his mouth with his fingers. But Jeremy Joe could tell that he was smiling. It was a shy kind of smile. And a sly kind of smile. It was the kind of smile that Smiffy Blue smiled when he had found a clue.

Jeremy Joe: Smiffy Blue has found another clue!

Smiffy Blue: Indeed I have found a clue! Indeed I have!

Jeremy Joe: What is that clue?

Smiffy Blue: Why would the thief wear a blue silk tie?

Jeremy Joe: Ooh! Ooh! I've got it! He wears it because he likes that tie?

Smiffy Blue: NO! He wears the tie to cover up his beard! But we know that he must have a very long beard to catch any drops of gravy that fall as he eats.

Jeremy Joe: True, true, Smiffy Blue.

Smiffy Blue: Then he must have bought a very big tie. Which means he is a rich man. Therefore we must go to the Doober City Rich Man's Club at once!

SCENE 6

Narrator 2: The Doober City Rich Man's Club was the tallest building in Doober City. There, they met Stash McCash, the richest man in Doober City.

Smiffy Blue: Is there a tall, squinty-eyed rich man in the Rich Man's club who is wearing a blue silk tie and who looks as if he might have just stolen a secret formula?

Stash McCash: No, there is not. But just this morning, I saw a tall, squinty-eyed rich man headed toward the Doober City Post Office. He had a letter in his hand.

Smiffy: A letter, did you say? Then we must act quickly. Come, Jeremy Joe. We must hurry to the Doober City Post Office!

Narrator 1: So Smiffy Blue and Jeremy Joe and Dog hurried to the Doober City Post Office. They got there just before Penny Stampp, the mail clerk, was leaving.

Smiffy Blue: Quick! Tell me if you have seen a tall, bearded man with squinty eyes, wearing a blue silk tie today.

Penny Stampp: No. We had only one customer today. A man wearing a trench coat bought an envelope. He also had a **determined** look on his face.

Smiffy Blue: And did he also buy a stamp?

Penny Stampp: No.

Smiffy Blue: And the determined look—are you sure about that?

Penny Stampp: I am sure.

Narrator 2: Then Smiffy Blue smiled. It was a shy smile. And a sly smile. It was the kind of smile that Smiffy Blue smiled when he had found a clue.

Jeremy Joe: Smiffy Blue has found *another* clue!

Smiffy Blue: Yes. Indeed, I have. I know where the thief is going. Quick! Call Inspector Hector and tell him to meet me at the Acme plant. Also call Suzette from the Gazette so she can come and take a picture of the thief.

Narrator 1: Jeremy Joe called Inspector Hector and the Gazette's Suzette. Then he and Smiffy Blue got on their bicycle, with Dog on the crossbar, and rode as fast as Jeremy Joe's legs could pedal to the Acme plant.

- Do you think Smiffy Blue will catch the thief?

Think about what happened in the first play.

SCENE 7

Narrator 2: When they got to the plant, they found Inspector Hector, Suzette, and Doctor Von Von waiting for them. As they **gathered** around the safe, Bobby Baddie, the janitor, swept the floor.

"One day you, too, will be a great detective. . . . It takes time."

Jeremy Joe: Why do you think the thief will come back here?

Smiffy Blue: What did the thief steal?

Doctor Von Von: Why, everyone knows he stole the secret formula.

Smiffy Blue: But he made a mistake. It was the other formula that he wanted, not the one that made people disappear. And the determined look on his face meant that he was determined to come back and get the right formula this time.

Doctor Von Von: But the only one here is Bobby Baddie.

Smiffy Blue: Exactly! Arrest him at once!

Bobby Baddie: Curses!

Narrator 1: Inspector Hector grabbed Bobby Baddie. Suzette from the Gazette snapped his picture.

Bobby Baddie: How did you know it was me?

Jeremy Joe: Yes, how did you know that?

Smiffy Blue: Simple, my lad. I noticed a ticket to Enemyville sticking out of Bobby Baddie's pocket. He has a friend in another city but did not go there. In other words, he unvisited his friend. He also had a letter but he did not buy a stamp. So he un-mailed the letter. Now he has returned to get the secret formula that un-pops popcorn.

Jeremy Joe: Oh, you are such a great detective.

Smiffy Blue: One day you, too, will be a great detective. But it takes time, my son. It takes time.

Jeremy Joe: True, true, Smiffy Blue. True, true. ●

Words, **Words,** Words

determined: settled on an idea
gathered: stood together in a group

Talk About It

Now that you've read "Smiffy Blue and the Case of the Missing Formula" and "Smiffy Blue and the Case of the Missing Ruby," what do you have to say about these questions?

▶ Is Smiffy Blue a good detective? Why or why not?

▶ Do you think the Smiffy Blue plays are funny? Why or why not?

Comprehension Check

Write your answers to the questions below. Use information from the two plays to support your answers.

1. Why does Smiffy Blue think the ruby thief is a stranger?

2. What clues does Smiffy Blue use to track down the stolen formula?

3. How does the janitor's name give you a clue that he has stolen the formula?

4. Do you think a real detective would act like Smiffy Blue? Explain your answer.

5. What do you think the author's purpose was in writing about Smiffy Blue?

Vocabulary Check

Answer each question below with a complete sentence. Think about the meaning of the vocabulary word in bold, and use that word in your sentence.

1. How does a **sly** person act?

2. What trick might a **trained** dog perform?

3. Why might someone's eyes get **squinty**?

4. If a group of your friends **gathered** somewhere, what might be happening?

5. If someone told you that you had a **keen** mind, what would you say?

Write About It

Choose one of the writing prompts below.

▶ The characters in this play have names that give clues about their jobs. The eye doctor is called Seymour Orless (see more or less) and Penny Stampp is the postal clerk. Create three character names of your own.

▶ Write a short newspaper article about how Smiffy Blue caught Bobby Baddie.

▶ What does it take to be a real detective? Write a short job description of all the skills a real detective might need.

About the AUTHOR

Walter Dean Myers has written many books for children and young adults. And he has won many awards for his writing. He often writes about kids who face difficult problems.

The idea for the Smiffy Blue stories comes from a game the author played with his son. In this game, he made each story sillier than the next. Then he would ask his son to try and guess the ending.

Other Books by Walter Dean Myers:

Mouse Rap
Darnell Rock Reporting
Amistad: A Long Road to
    Freedom
The Journal of Joshua Loper:
    A Black Cowboy
Me, Mop, and the
    Moondance Kid

Analyzing Ads

Ads are created for one reason—to sell products. Smart shoppers know they must read carefully to find out what's really for sale.

Take a look at the ads below. Make sure you read the fine print. Are the products really as great as the advertisers make them sound?

Newspaper Ads

Watch out for contests. Winning is usually not as easy as it sounds.

Buy some refreshing Cool Cola now and win a cool $1 MILLION*

To enter our big-bucks sweepstakes send a card with a return address and proof-of purchase to P.O. Box 1234, Colaville, OH 12345

Cool Cola

* Odds for grand prize: 1: 2,350,000. Offer good only with purchase of 2-liter bottle of Cool Cola.

SassyStyles

Sale on Sweaters and Jackets

Get this year's hippest and trendiest styles at

Up to 70% off!

All last year's styles marked down 10-70%. Limited sizes available. All sales final.

The advertiser hopes you'll notice the really big words and ignore the really small ones.

"Want the facts about a product? Look for a label that tells what it's made of, how to use it, or what ingredients it contains."

HEALTHY FLAKES

HEALTHY FLAKES

Delicious wheat flakes with a light sugar coating.

The low-fat breakfast cereal for people who care about their health.

Read Between the Lines

Let's see if you're a smart shopper. Take another look at the ads. Make sure you read all the fine print. Is it all as good as it sounds? Use the ads to answer the questions below. Write your answers on your own paper.

1. What will happen if you buy a 2-liter bottle of Cool Cola now?
   a. You will win one million dollars.
   b. You will be able to enter a contest.
   c. You will get another bottle free.

2. **Write About It:** Do you think that you would have a good chance of winning the Cool Cola contest? Explain your reasons.

3. Which statement is true of the sale at Sassy Styles?
   a. All sizes are on sale.
   b. Some sizes are on sale.
   c. All sale items are 80% off.

4. The ad for Sassy Styles says that "all sales are final." That means that
   a. sale items will be on sale forever.
   b. you may return sale items if they don't fit.
   c. you may not return sale items.

5. What can you learn about Healthy Flakes by reading the ad for it?
   a. It's lower in fat than any other cereal.
   b. It's better for you than all other cereals.
   c. It contains sugar.

Describe It

Advertisers use lots of describing words—like *refreshing, healthy, hip,* and *trendy*—to make you think their products are really great. Think of a product. Imagine it's your job to advertise it. List five describing words you could use in your ad.

Ad Agency

Create an ad for the product of your choice. What will you say in big type? What will you say in small print? Trade ads with a partner. Would you buy your partner's product? Why or why not?

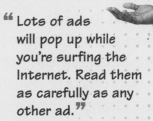

" Lots of ads will pop up while you're surfing the Internet. Read them as carefully as any other ad. "

Real-World Words

advertiser: a person or company that creates an ad
proof-of-purchase: a part of a label that you can use to show that you bought a product
sweepstakes: a big contest

Every Living Thing by Cynthia Rylant
Can a cat, a dog, and a hermit crab change lives?

Spaghetti

Gabriel wanted to live outside—all by himself. Would anything change his mind?

It was evening, and people sat outside, talking quietly among themselves. On the stoop of a tall building of crumbling bricks and rotting wood sat a boy. His name was Gabriel and he wished for some company.

Gabriel was thinking about things. He remembered being the only boy in class with the right answer that day. He remembered the butter sandwich he had had for lunch. Gabriel was thinking that he would like to live outside all the time. He imagined himself carrying a pack of food and a few tools and a heavy cloth to erect a hasty tent. Gabriel saw himself sleeping among coyotes. But next he saw himself sleeping beneath the glittering lights of a movie theater, near the bus stop.

Gabriel was a boy who thought about things so seriously, that on this evening he nearly missed hearing a cry from the street. The cry was so weak and faraway in his mind that, for him, it could have been the slow lifting of a stubborn window. It could have been the creak of an old man's legs. It could have been the wind.

But it was not the wind, and it came to Gabriel slowly that he did, indeed, hear something. And that it did, indeed, sound like a cry from the street.

Gabriel picked himself up from the stoop and began to walk carefully along the edge of the street, peering into the gloom and the dusk. The cry came again and Gabriel's ears tingled and he walked faster.

On the stoop
of a building
sat a boy.
His name was
Gabriel and
he wished for
some company.

He stared into the street, up and down it, knowing something was there. The street was so gray that he could not see. . . . But not only the street was gray.

There, sitting on skinny stick-legs, wobbling to and fro, was a tiny gray kitten. No cars had passed to frighten it, and so it just sat in the street and cried its windy, creaky cry and waited.

Gabriel was amazed. He had never imagined he would be lucky enough one day to find a kitten. He walked into the street and lifted the kitten into his hands.

Gabriel sat on the sidewalk with the kitten next to his cheek and thought. The kitten smelled of pasta noodles, and he wondered if it belonged to a friendly Italian man somewhere in the city. Gabriel called the kitten Spaghetti.

Gabriel and Spaghetti returned to the stoop. It occurred to Gabriel to walk the neighborhood and look for the Italian man. But the purring was so loud, so near his ear, that he could not think as seriously, as fully, as before.

Gabriel no longer wanted to live outside. He knew he had a room and a bed of his own in the tall building. So he stood up, with Spaghetti under his chin, and went inside to show his kitten where they would live together.

Stray

Doris didn't want to fall in love with the puppy. It just happened.

In January, a puppy wandered onto the property of Mr. Amos Lacey and his wife, Mamie, and their daughter, Doris. Icicles hung three feet or more from the eaves of houses, snow-drifts swallowed up automobiles and the birds were so fluffed up they looked **comic.**

The puppy had been **abandoned,** and it made its way down the road toward the Laceys' small house, its ears tucked, its tail between its legs, shivering.

Doris, whose school had been called off because of the snow, was out shoveling the cinderblock front steps when she spotted the pup on the road. She set down the shovel.

"Hey! Come on!" she called.

The puppy stopped in the road, wagging its tail timidly, trembling with shyness and cold.

Doris trudged through the yard, went up the shoveled drive and met the dog.

"Come on, Pooch."

"Where did *that* come from?" Mrs. Lacey asked as soon as Doris put the dog down in the kitchen.

Mr. Lacey was at the table, cleaning his fingernails with his pocketknife. The snow was keeping him home from his job at the warehouse.

"I don't know where it came from," he said mildly, "but I know for sure where it's going."

Doris hugged the puppy hard against her. She said nothing.

Because the roads would be too bad for travel for many days, Mr. Lacey couldn't get out to take the puppy to the pound in the city right away. He agreed to let it sleep in the basement while Mrs. Lacey let Doris feed it table scraps. The woman was sensitive about throwing out food.

By the looks of it, Doris figured the puppy was about six months old, and on its way to

Words, Words, Words

comic: funny
abandoned: left alone

Doris didn't name the dog. She knew her parents wouldn't let her keep it....

becoming a big dog. She thought it might have some shepherd in it.

Four days passed and the puppy did not complain. It never cried in the night or howled at the wind. It didn't tear up everything in the basement. It wouldn't even follow Doris up the basement steps unless it was invited.

It was a good dog.

Several times Doris had opened the door in the kitchen that led to the basement. The puppy had been there, all stretched out, on the step. Doris knew it had wanted some company. It had lain against the door, listening to the talk in the kitchen, smelling food, being a part of things. It always wagged its tail, eyes all sleepy, when she found it there. Even after a week had gone by, Doris didn't name the dog. She knew her parents wouldn't let her keep it. She knew also that her

father made so little money that any pets were out of the question, and that the pup would definitely go to the pound when the weather cleared.

Still, she tried talking to them about the dog during dinner one night.

"She's a good dog, isn't she?" Doris said, hoping one of them would agree with her.

Her parents glanced at each other and went on eating.

"She's not much trouble," Doris added. "I like her." She smiled at them, but they continued to ignore her.

ASK YOURSELF

- How do Doris's feelings about the puppy compare to her parents' feelings?

Pay attention to what each character says and does.

"I figure she's real smart," Doris said to her mother. "I could teach her things."

Mrs. Lacey just shook her head and stuffed a forkful of sweet potato in her mouth. Doris fell silent, praying the weather would never clear.

But on Saturday, nine days after the dog had arrived, the sun was shining and the roads were plowed. Mr. Lacey opened up the trunk of his car and came into the house.

Doris was sitting alone in the living room, hugging a pillow and rocking back and forth on the edge of a chair. She was trying not to cry but she was not strong enough. Her face was wet and red, her eyes full of **distress.**

Mrs. Lacey looked into the room from the doorway.

"Mama," Doris said in a small voice. "Please." Mrs. Lacey shook her head.

"You know we can't afford a dog, Doris. You try to act more grown-up about this." Doris pressed her face into the pillow. Outside, she heard the trunk of the car slam shut, one of the doors open and close, the old engine cough and choke and finally start up. "Daddy," she whispered. "Please." She heard the car travel down the road, and, though it was early afternoon, she could do nothing but go to her bed. She cried herself to sleep, and her dreams were full of searching for things lost.

It was nearly night when she finally woke up. Lying there, like stone, still **exhausted,** she wondered if she would ever in her life have anything. She stared at the wall for a while. But she started feeling hungry, and she knew she'd have to make herself get out of bed and eat some dinner. She wanted not to go into the kitchen, past the basement door. She wanted not to face her parents.

But she rose up heavily.

Her parents were sitting at the table, dinner over, drinking coffee. They looked at her when she came in, but she kept her head down. No one spoke.

Doris made herself a glass of powdered milk and drank it all down. Then she picked up a cold biscuit and started out of the room.

"You'd better feed that mutt before it dies of starvation," Mr. Lacey said.

Doris turned around.

"What?"

"I said, you'd better feed your dog. I figure it's looking for you."

Doris put her hand to her mouth. "You didn't take her?" she asked.

"Oh, I took her all right," her father answered. "Worst looking place I've ever seen. Ten dogs to a cage. Smell was enough to knock you down. And they give an animal six days to live. Then they kill it with some kind of a shot."

Doris stared at her father.

"I wouldn't leave an *ant* in that place," he said. "So I brought the dog back."

Mrs. Lacey was smiling at him and shaking her head as if she would never, ever, understand him.

Mr. Lacey sipped his coffee.

"Well," he said, "are you going to feed it or not?"

distress: sadness; worry
exhausted: really, really tired

Shells

Michael and his aunt are not getting along. How in the world could a hermit crab help them?

"You *hate* living here."

Michael looked at the woman speaking to him.

"No, Aunt Esther. I don't." He said it dully, sliding his milk glass back and forth on the table. "I don't hate it here."

Esther removed the last pan from the dishwasher and hung it above the oven. "You hate it here," she said, "and you hate me."

"I don't!" Michael yelled. "It's not you!"

The woman turned to face him in the kitchen. "Don't yell at me!" she yelled. "I'll not have it in my home. I can't make you happy, Michael. You just refuse to be happy here. And you punish me every day for it."

"*Punish* you?" Michael gawked at her. "I don't punish you! I don't care about you! I don't care what you eat or how you dress or where you go or what you think. Can't you just leave me alone?"

He slammed down the glass, scraped his chair back from the table and ran out the door.

"Michael!" yelled Esther.

They had been living together, the two of them, for six months. Michael's parents had died and only Esther could take him in—or, only she had offered to. Michael's other relatives could not imagine dealing with a fourteen-year-old boy. They wanted peaceful lives.

Esther lived in a condominium in a wealthy section of Detroit. Most of the area's residents were older (like her) and afraid of the world they lived in (like her). They stayed

ASK YOURSELF

- How do you think Michael feels about Aunt Esther?

Think how you might feel in his place.

> He thought maybe he was going crazy.
> His heart hurt him. He wondered if
> he would ever get better.

indoors much of the time. They trusted few people.

Esther liked living alone. She had never married or had children. She had never lived anywhere but Detroit. She liked her condominium.

But she was fiercely loyal to her family, and when her only sister had died, Esther insisted she be allowed to care for Michael. And Michael, afraid of going anywhere else, had accepted.

ASK YOURSELF

- How is Michael like Gabriel and Doris? How is Michael different?

Think about what you've learned about each character.

Oh, he was lonely. Even six months after their deaths, he still expected to see his parents—sitting on the couch as he walked into Esther's living room, waiting for the bathroom as he came out of the shower, coming in the door late at night. He still smelled his father's Old Spice somewhere, his mother's talc.

Sometimes he was so sure one of them was *somewhere* around him that he thought maybe he was going crazy. His heart hurt him. He wondered if he would ever get better.

And though he denied it, he did hate Esther. She was so different from his mother and father. Prejudiced—she admired only those who were white and Presbyterian. Selfish—she wouldn't allow him to use her phone. Complaining—she always had a headache or a backache or a stomachache.

He didn't want to, but he hated her. And he didn't know what to do except lie about it.

Michael hadn't made any friends at his new school, and his teachers barely noticed him. He came home alone every day and usually found Esther on the phone. She kept in close touch with several other women in nearby condominiums.

Esther told her friends she didn't understand Michael. She said she knew he must grieve for his parents, but why punish her? She said she thought she might send him away if he couldn't be nicer. She said she didn't deserve this.

But when Michael came in the door, she always quickly changed the subject.

One day after school Michael came home with a hermit crab. He had gone into a pet store, looking for some small living thing. And hermit crabs were selling for just a few dollars. He'd bought one, and a bowl.

Esther, for a change, was not on the phone when he arrived home. She was having tea and a roll and seemed cheerful. Michael wanted

Esther told her friends that she didn't understand Michael.

He didn't want to, but he hated her. And he didn't know what to do except lie about it.

badly to show someone what he had bought. So he showed her.

Esther surprised him. She picked up the shell and poked the long, red, shiny nail of her little finger at the crab's claws.

"Where is he?" she asked.

Michael showed her the crab's eyes peering through the small opening of the shell.

"Well, for heaven's sake, come out of there!" she said to the crab, and she turned the shell upside down and shook it.

"Aunt Esther!" Michael grabbed for the shell.

"All right, all right." She turned it right side up. "Well," she said, "what does he do?"

Michael grinned and shrugged his shoulders. "I don't know," he answered. "Just grows, I guess."

His aunt looked at him.

"An attraction to a crab is something I cannot identify with. However, it's fine with me if you keep him, as long as I can be assured he won't grow out of that bowl." She gave him a hard stare.

"He won't," Michael answered. "I promise." The hermit crab moved into the condominium. Michael named him Sluggo and kept the bowl beside his bed. Michael had to watch the bowl for very long periods of time to catch Sluggo with his head poking out of his shell, moving around. Bedtime seemed to be Sluggo's liveliest part of the day, and Michael found it easy to lie and watch the busy crab as sleep slowly came on.

One day Michael arrived home to find Esther sitting on the edge of his bed, looking at the bowl. Esther usually did not **intrude** in Michael's room, and seeing her there disturbed him. But he stood at the doorway and said nothing.

Esther seemed perfectly comfortable, although she looked over at him with a frown on her face.

"I think he needs a companion," she said.

"What?" Michael's eyebrows went up as his jaw dropped down. Esther sniffed.

"I think Sluggo needs a girlfriend." She stood up. "Where is that pet store?"

Michael took her. In the store was a huge tank full of hermit crabs.

"Oh my!" Esther grabbed the rim of the tank and craned her neck over the side. "Look at them!"

Michael was looking more at his Aunt Esther than at the crabs. He couldn't believe it.

"Oh, look at those shells. You say they grow out of them? We must stock up with several sizes. See the pink in that one? Michael, look! He's got his little head out!"

Esther was so dramatic—leaning into the tank, her bangle bracelets clanking, earrings swinging, red pumps clicking on the linoleum—that she attracted the attention of everyone in the store. Michael pretended not to know her well.

He and Esther returned to the condominium with a thirty-gallon tank and 20 hermit crabs.

intrude: to come in uninvited
inherit: to be given something after someone has died
overwhelmed: having too many feelings; not able to take action
distinguish: to be able to tell one thing from another

> ## Aunt Esther, who had not embraced anyone in years, gently put her arm about his shoulders.

Michael figured he'd have a heart attack before he got the heavy tank into their living room. He figured he'd die and Aunt Esther would **inherit** 21 crabs and funeral expenses. But he made it. Esther carried the box of crabs.

"Won't Sluggo be surprised?" she asked happily. "Oh, I do hope we'll be able to tell him apart from the rest. He's their founding father!"

Michael, still in a shock over his Aunt Esther's purchase of 20 hermit crabs, wiped out the tank, arranged it with gravel and sticks (as well as the plastic scuba diver Aunt Esther insisted on buying). And he assisted her in loading it up, one by one, with the new residents. The crabs were as **overwhelmed** as Michael. Not one showed its face.

Before moving Sluggo from his bowl, Aunt Esther marked his shell with some red fingernail polish so she could **distinguish** him from the rest. Then she flopped down on the couch beside Michael.

"Oh, what would your mother *think,* Michael, if she could see this mess we've gotten ourselves into!"

She looked at Michael with a broad smile, but it quickly disappeared. The boy's eyes were full of pain.

"Oh, my," she turned her head away.

Aunt Esther, who had not embraced anyone in years, gently put her arm about his shoulders.

"I am so sorry, Michael. Oh, you must hate me."

Michael sensed a familiar smell then. His mother's talc.

He looked at his aunt.

"No, Aunt Esther." He shook his head solemnly. "I don't hate you."

Esther's mouth trembled and her bangles clanked as she patted his arm. She took a deep, strong breath.

"Well, let's look in on our friend Sluggo," she said.

They leaned their heads over the tank and found him. The crab, finished with the old home that no longer fit, was coming out of his shell. ●

ASK YOURSELF

■ How do you think Michael feels about Aunt Esther now?

Think about how you might feel if you were in his place.

Talk About It

Now that you've read "Spaghetti," "Stray," and "Shells," what do you have to say about these questions?

▶ Which story could you relate to the most? Why?

▶ Have you ever had or wanted a pet? Tell about that experience.

Comprehension Check

Write your answers to the questions below. Use information from the three stories to support your answers.

1. Who is the main character of each story? What animal is each person involved with?

2. The story doesn't say, but why do *you* think that Gabriel wants to live outside on his own?

3. What reason did Doris's dad give for bringing the puppy back home?

4. Do you think Michael and Aunt Esther's relationship will change now? Why do you think so?

5. In these stories, do the animals help people? Explain your answer.

Vocabulary Check

Answer each question below with a complete sentence. Before you answer, think about the meaning of the vocabulary word in bold.

1. Why do you think that some animals are **abandoned**?

2. If someone is in **distress**, what kind of sign or signal can he or she give to let you know?

3. If you were **exhausted**, what would you do?

4. Tell about a time that you felt **overwhelmed**.

5. What would you say to someone who was about to **intrude** on a conversation you were having?

Write About It

Choose one of the writing prompts below.

▶ What do you think Doris should name the stray? Write a letter to Doris, giving her your suggestion. Then explain why you chose that name.

▶ Have you ever had an experience with a pet that changed your life? Write a short story that tells about it.

▶ Which kind of animal do you think makes the best pet? State your opinion. Then give at least three reasons to back it up.

More to READ

Are you an animal lover? If so, then check out these books. You won't be disappointed!

Stone Fox
By John Reynolds Gardiner

It's sad. It's scary. It's exciting. It's everything you want in a book. A boy and his dog must race against some of the best dogsled racers in the world—including the unbeatable Stone Fox.

The Secret of the Seal
By Deborah Davis

Young Kyo lives in a small, quiet Eskimo village. His only friend is a seal named Tooky. But now Tooky may have to go and live in a zoo far away. Can Kyo protect Tooky from life in a zoo?

A to Z Mysteries: The Falcon's Feathers
By Ron Roy

Josh and his friends have discovered a nest of young falcons. That's the good news. The bad news is that someone is clipping the falcons' wings. Can they figure out what is going on before it is too late?

Following a Recipe

You've promised to make dessert for your class picnic. How hard can it be? Not hard at all, as long as you have a recipe!

Check out this recipe. It lists the ingredients and step-by-step instructions for making brownies. Can you figure it out?

Brownie Recipe

Recipes sometimes use abbreviations for quantities— "oz." stands for *ounce*; "tsp." stands for *teaspoon*.

The steps in a recipe are often numbered. Follow the steps in order.

Brownie Bonanza

Ingredients

1/2 cup butter
4 oz. unsweetened chocolate
4 eggs
1/4 tsp. salt
2 cups sugar
1 tsp. vanilla
1 cup sifted all-purpose flour
Optional: 1 cup chopped nuts
Yield: About 30 brownies

Directions

1. Preheat oven to 350°F.
2. Melt butter and chocolate in a pan over low heat. Let cool.
3. In a new bowl, beat together the eggs and the salt.
4. Slowly add the sugar and vanilla. Beat until creamy.
5. Mix together the mixture from Step 4 with the melted-chocolate mixture.
6. Slowly add the flour.
7. If you'd like, stir in the chopped nuts.
8. Grease a 9" x 13" baking pan.
9. Pour brownie mixture into pan.
10. Bake in preheated oven about 25 minutes.
11. Let cool. Then cut into squares.

Here's the number of brownies that you'll make with this recipe.

" Before you begin any recipe, read it completely. Make sure you have all the ingredients and equipment. "

Reading Recipes

Grab your apron—it's time to bake. Reread the recipe and the tips that go with it. Use the recipe to answer these questions. Write your answers on your own paper.

1. Your teacher estimates that about 25 people will stop by the class picnic. If you follow this recipe, will you have at least one brownie per person?

2. Which ingredient can you add if you want to, but leave out if you prefer?
   a. vanilla
   b. nuts
   c. salt

3. *Preheat* means "to heat ahead of time." The recipe says to preheat the oven to 350°F. What does that mean?
   a. Turn off the oven right now.
   b. Set the oven to 350° after you put the brownies in.
   c. Set the oven to 350° before you put the brownies in.

4. Which do you make first—the melted-chocolate mixture or the egg mixture? How do you know?

5. List three pieces of equipment you need to make these brownies.

Wish List
Would you like to be a great cook someday? Make a list of five dinners you would cook . . . if you could!

Write a Recipe
Think of some food or drink you know how to prepare—like a sandwich, chocolate milk, or even a bowl of cereal. List all the ingredients, tools, and equipment you need to prepare it. Then write the recipe.

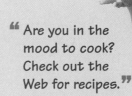

" Are you in the mood to cook? Check out the Web for recipes."

Real-World Words

ingredients: the items that something is made of
instructions: directions on how to do something
optional: not necessary or required

Tarzan ®

A classic tale retold by ROBERT D. SAN SOUCI

IN 1888, LORD AND LADY GREYSTOKE WERE SAILING TO AFRICA. IN THE MIDDLE OF THE NIGHT, A REBELLIOUS CREW TOOK CONTROL OF THE SHIP. THE YOUNG COUPLE WERE LEFT ON A LONELY SHORE WITH SOME FOOD AND TOOLS. JOHN GREYSTOKE BUILT THEM A CABIN AND PROTECTED THEM FROM WILD ANIMALS. ALICE AWAITED THE BIRTH OF THEIR FIRST CHILD. BUT SOON AFTER THE BABY BOY ARRIVED, LADY GREYSTOKE DIED. . . .

In the forest lived a tribe of great apes, ruled by cruel, foul-tempered Kerchak. One day Kerchak, followed by two males, approached the curious nest where strange white apes lived. Behind came Kala, a young female. Before, the apes had been driven off by the thunder-stick the male carried. It always roared out death for a member of the tribe. But though the door was open, the white ape did not appear with the stick.

Kerchak peered in. The strange male sat weeping beside a bed on which the female lay dead. From a cradle came the wail of a babe.

John Greystoke barely had a chance to look up before Kerchak attacked and finished him. Then the ape turned to the cradle—but Kala snatched the baby and fled to a high tree. There she quieted and tended the tiny child.

Kerchak started to follow her, but then he spotted the thunder-stick. The child forgotten, he turned the stick this way and that. It fired! KERCHOOM! Terrified, the apes fled. In their clumsy haste the door closed, and the sturdy latch dropped into place.

In the years that followed, Kala protected the human child from Kerchak's rages and the jungle's other dangers. By the age of ten—when great apes were fully grown—Kala's adopted child was still a boy. But he was clever and intelligent.

ASK YOURSELF

- How would you describe Tarzan's jungle home?

Look at the pictures and think about the details in the story.

HE WAS STRONG AND COULD SPEED FROM BRANCH TO BRANCH.

He was strong, too, and could speed from branch to branch.

But he was unhappy because he was different. When he saw his reflection in a pool, he felt ugly compared to his hairy fellows. The tribe called him "Tarzan," meaning "white skin."

He was also unlike the apes in his eagerness to learn. When the tribe wandered near the sealed cabin, his companions **ignored** the place. They hunted for food, **roughhoused**, groomed themselves, or slept. But Tarzan would pat and poke and pry at the walls and roof for hours, seeking a way in. At last he figured out how to undo the latch.

He ignored the two skeletons as he explored. His best discovery was a hunting knife. He cut his fingers several times before he learned to hold it properly. Just as exciting were books filled with colorful pictures. For hours he looked at the pictures and the letters. He thought the letters looked like bugs crawling on the page. Some drawings were things he knew: Sabor, the lioness; Tantor, the elephant; and Bara, the deer. Others were **baffling**, for he had never seen such things.

WORDS, WORDS, WORDS

ignored: did not pay attention to something
roughhoused: played at fighting
baffling: confusing

When he left, he latched the door, taking only the knife to show his fellows. Suddenly, Bolgani the gorilla charged at him from the green shadows. Recalling how the knife had hurt him, Tarzan thrust it at his giant enemy. The wounded gorilla fought **fiercely**, but Tarzan finally **slew** him.

All the other apes were amazed by this feat—and more so by the knife Tarzan carried everywhere. Even Kerchak eyed him with respect.

Returning often to the cabin, Tarzan learned the secret of the "bugs" on each page. By age 15, he recognized the words that went with each picture. When he found some pencils, he copied the "bugs" and so began to write.

He no longer felt shamed by his hairless body or different features, for now he understood that he was of another race. He was H-U-M-A-N; his companions were A-P-E-S. He knew that Sabor was a L-I-O-N-E-S-S; Tantor, an E-L-E-P-H-A-N-T; and Bara, a D-E-E-R. And so he learned to read.

But he was still part of the tribe. One night he joined in a Dum-Dum ceremony to celebrate the victory of Kerchak's tribe over enemy apes that had invaded their territory. While the females beat on a huge mound of earth with knotted branches, the males danced and roared beneath the rising moon.

Suddenly, Kerchak was seized with madness and rage. His fury turned upon Tarzan, who danced like a great ape but whose

TARZAN LEARNED THE SECRET OF THE "BUGS" ON EACH PAGE.

hairless skin gleamed in the moonlight. With a screech, Kerchak launched himself at Tarzan. The drumming stopped. The other apes froze. Tarzan, with his knife ready, faced the king.

Kala, his foster mother, leaped snarling at Kerchak. But the huge male knocked her aside. Then Tarzan charged. His blade cut Kerchak's arm. Making a noisy show of **defiance**, the old ape king backed away.

Tarzan helped Kala to her feet. Raising his eyes to the full moon, he voiced the blood-chilling cry of the great apes. Staring into Kerchak's wicked red eyes, he shouted, "I am Tarzan. I am a great fighter. Let all respect Tarzan of the Apes and Kala, his mother. There is none among you as mighty as Tarzan. Let his enemies beware."

Kerchak thumped his chest and yelled his own cry. Then he turned away. But the tribe sensed that someday the two would meet in deadly **combat**.

ASK YOURSELF

- What has the relationship between Kerchak and Tarzan been like so far?

Reread the parts of the story that include them both.

WORDS, WORDS, WORDS

fiercely: in a strong and powerful way
slew: killed
defiance: a challenge or dare given to an opponent
combat: a serious fight or struggle

In the days that followed, Tarzan grew stronger and wiser. He learned many amazing things from his books. Beyond the J-U-N-G-L-E or across the O-C-E-A-N, many H-U-M-A-N-S lived in a C-I-T-Y, a place of strange nests as big as mountains.

He carefully studied pictures of wrestlers and swimmers, and learned their skills. Guided by the books, he fashioned a bow and arrows, a loincloth, and a sheath for his knife.

One day Kala, now grown old and careless, was busy digging grubs from a tree stump. She did not notice Sabor, the lioness, stalking her. Too late, Kala drew herself up and faced her enemy with a bellowing cry. A moment later she fell to Sabor's paw.

Tarzan, answering Kala's cry, found the lioness **crouched** over the body of his foster mother. He was filled with grief and anger. He roared out his challenge and beat his fists on his great chest. He fitted an arrow to his bowstring. Then he boldly dropped to the ground, not twenty paces from Sabor.

The lioness's great yellow eyes fixed upon the ape-man with a wicked gleam. Her red tongue licked her lips. She tensed, ready to spring. But when she leaped, Tarzan's arrow caught her in mid-air. At the same instant Tarzan jumped to one side. As the great cat struck the ground beyond him, another arrow sank deep into her side.

With a mighty roar the beast turned and charged once more, only to be met with a deadly third arrow. But this time she was too close for the ape-man to sidestep her. Tarzan of the Apes went down beneath the great body of his enemy. He lay **stunned** for a moment. Then he realized that Sabor was dead.

Later, seated upon a broad tree limb, Tarzan proudly showed Sabor's skin to the great apes. "Look! Apes of Kerchak," he cried, "see what Tarzan the mighty hunter has done. He has slain the killer of his mother, Kala. Tarzan is mightiest among you for Tarzan is no ape. Tarzan is—"

He stopped, because the apes had no word for human and Tarzan could only write the word, he could not say it.

The tribe had gathered to listen. Only Kerchak held back. Suddenly, something snapped in the ape. With a frightful cry, the huge beast sprang at Tarzan, who was just out of reach.

"TARZAN IS THE MIGHTIEST AMONG YOU FOR TARZAN IS NO APE. TARZAN IS—"

ASK YOURSELF

- How did finding the cabin change Tarzan's life?

Think about the things he found inside the cabin.

WORDS, WORDS, WORDS

crouched: bent over
stunned: shocked

"Come down, Tarzan, great killer," Kerchak **taunted**. "Come down and feel my fangs. Mighty fighters do not hide in trees."

As the other apes watched, Tarzan leaped down and faced the leader. His knife was drawn. The struggle was fierce. Tarzan's knife helped balance Kerchak's greater bulk and strength.

Then Kerchak smashed Tarzan's knife hand, sending his weapon spinning. But the ape-man managed to get behind Kerchak. Using a wrestling hold learned from one of his books, Tarzan locked an arm across Kerchak's throat, then tightened his grip. It was now in his power to break his enemy's neck.

If I kill him, thought Tarzan, it will rob the tribe of a great fighter. If he is alive, he will always be an example of my power to the other apes.

"*Ka-goda*?" hissed Tarzan. "Do you **surrender**?"

Kerchak growled and struggled harder. Tarzan added pressure, which forced a grunt of pain from the beast.

"*Ka-goda!*" cried Kerchak, defeated.

Tarzan relaxed his hold. "I am Tarzan, King of the Apes, mighty hunter, mighty fighter. In all the jungle there is none so great. You have said *Ka-goda* to me. All the tribe heard. I am king now. Do you understand?"

But when Tarzan released him, the ape turned upon him. As they struggled, it seemed that Kerchak was winning. But Tarzan once

THE HARSH JUSTICE OF THE JUNGLE HAD BEEN SERVED.

again used his wits as well as his strength to catch Kerchak in a death grip. This time, the new king of the apes showed Kerchak no mercy. Nor did Kerchak seek it. He was still snarling and snapping and scratching at his captor. Tarzan jerked his arm suddenly. Kerchak shuddered, then his body stiffened; a moment later, he sank lifeless to the ground. The harsh justice of the jungle had been served.

So Tarzan became the **undisputed** ruler of the apes. But he soon tired of kingship. It left him little time to visit the cabin and study his books. He was growing further apart from the apes, who had no interest in such things and who were impatient to move into the deep forest.

One dawn Tarzan called the tribe together. "Tarzan is not an ape," he said. "His ways are not your ways. Tarzan goes to seek his true tribe. You must choose a new king, for Tarzan will not return."

So saying, the ape-man strode boldly into the breaking day and toward his **destiny**. ●

WORDS, WORDS, WORDS	**taunted:** teased in order to make someone angry **surrender:** to give up **undisputed:** agreed upon without argument **destiny:** fate, or future events to come

The Many Faces of TARZAN

by Michael Dahlie

▲ This cast was the fans' favorite. It included Johnny Weissmuller (as Tarzan), Maureen O'Sullivan (as Jane), Johnny Sheffield (as Boy), and Cheeta.

▲ Olympic athlete Glenn Morris starred in *Tarzan's Revenge*. Jane was also played by an Olympian—Eleanor Holm, champion backstroke swimmer.

▲ Ron Ely was injured 17 times when he played Tarzan. He broke his nose in a water fight. He cracked three ribs while swinging from vines. And he got seven stitches in his head after a lion bit him.

▲ One of the nice things about the making of Disney's animated *Tarzan* was that no one got hurt. The first film-makers in 1917 were so afraid of the real jungle that they shot their movie in a Louisiana swamp.

Tarzan first came to life in 1912 in a short story published in *The All-Story* magazine. It became so popular that the author, Edgar Rice Burroughs, decided to write more. Pretty soon, magazines all across the country were printing tales of the famous King of the Jungle. In 1914, Burroughs made Tarzan the main character of a book. He called it *Tarzan of the Apes*.

But Burroughs didn't stop there. Soon he started thinking about making a Tarzan movie.

At first, no one else seemed interested in the idea. Movie producers thought filming in the jungle would be too hard. But Burroughs wouldn't take no for an answer. He spent five years convincing people that Tarzan should be in the movies. And in 1917, he was finally able to begin filming.

Out of Control

Unfortunately, the movie did not go as Burroughs hoped. In order to raise money for the movie, he had to agree to changes in Tarzan's story. The directors and producers had their own ideas about how Tarzan should look and act.

Burroughs didn't like how the movie turned Tarzan into a wild man. Burroughs had imagined that Tarzan was smart enough to educate himself. The directors weren't interested in a smart Tarzan. Burroughs couldn't do a thing about it. He signed a contract that gave away his creative control over the story.

In the years to come, Burroughs fought for his kind of Tarzan. Every time a new comic book or movie came out, he'd fight with the artists and actors. Many times he lost. But that's not so bad for Tarzan fans. Some of the greatest Tarzan stories were *not* told by Burroughs.

Live Action Ape-Man

The first eight Tarzan movies were silent. They were wildly popular. The first one, *Tarzan of the Apes,* made over one million dollars—a huge amount for a movie in 1918. The seven silent films that followed were also hits. But no one could ever decide on the right actor for the part. Five different actors played Tarzan in the first eight movies.

When "talking pictures" came along, Burroughs and the other filmmakers chose the actor Jack Merrill. He had been Tarzan in the last silent movie. This was a great decision. Merrill was an excellent gymnast and could perform amazing stunts. In fact, he was the first Tarzan to swing from vine to vine. More important, Jack Merrill came up with the famous "ape-man yell." Can you imagine Tarzan without his jungle scream?

Olympic Tarzan

Of all the actors to play Tarzan, Johnny Weissmuller is the most famous. He was a swimmer who won five gold medals in the Olympics! But Tarzan was Weissmuller's ticket to stardom.

Weissmuller was the perfect Tarzan. He was strong and athletic but also kind and gentle. The only person who didn't like Weissmuller was Tarzan's creator. Burroughs thought the actor made Tarzan look stupid. As Tarzan, Weissmuller didn't get many lines. He just grunted a lot. The producers thought his voice wasn't deep enough. They didn't think he sounded like the King of the Apes.

Eventually, Weissmuller stopped playing Tarzan. The producers couldn't afford to pay him anymore. He was a big star and too expensive. However, Weissmuller made the most of his role as King of the Apes. He opened a chain of jungle-style restaurants and clothing stores.

Buff and Tough

In the past 80 years, 20 actors have starred in over 40 Tarzan movies. Though Weissmuller was the most popular, each one added something unique to the story.

After Weissmuller left, an actor named Gordon Scott took over. Scott was a body-builder with huge muscles. He made Tarzan look buff. Scott was also the first Tarzan to appear in "living color."

Mike Henry was the Tarzan of the 1960s. He had great hair and a "groovy" look. He's often called the James Bond Tarzan.

Ron Ely played Tarzan in the first Tarzan television show. Ely looked like a game show host. In fact, that's the job he got after his Tarzan show ended.

In the 1990s, Tarzan's big change had to do with his hair. He grew it long. Filmmakers said that it was more realistic for the Jungle King to have long hair. But really it was just a sign of the times. It was cool to have long hair in the 1990s.

Tarzan Today

Actors and filmmakers are not the only people to tell Tarzan's story. He has appeared on radio shows, on CDs, in video games and cartoons, in comic books, and on lunch boxes. In fact, Tarzan has been plastered across everything you can think of.

And then there are Tarzan spoofs. The biggest hit was Brendan Fraser's movie *George of the Jungle*. Fraser plays a guy who looks a lot like Tarzan. But he calls himself George. And he's not very good at swinging through the jungle.

Basically, people seem to love anything that has to do with Tarzan. Whether it's a movie, a TV show, or a board game, people want as much Tarzan as they can get. People love him! And that's why his story keeps getting told. ●

People seem to love anything that has to do with Tarzan.

Talk About It

Now that you've read *Tarzan* and "The Many Faces of Tarzan," what do you have to say about these questions?

▶ Why do you think people enjoy the story of Tarzan again and again?

▶ Do you have a favorite Tarzan? Explain.

Comprehension Check

Write your answers to the questions below. Use information from the tale and the article to support your answers.

1. How did Tarzan end up in the jungle?

2. Why do you think Kerchak disliked Tarzan?

3. In your opinion, could the story of Tarzan have ever really happened? Why or why not?

4. What was Edgar Rice Burroughs always fighting for?

5. Do you think Edgar Rice Burroughs would have liked the version of the story that you read? Why or why not?

Vocabulary Check

Answer each question below with a complete sentence. Before you answer, think about the meaning of the vocabulary word in bold.

1. What does it feel like to be **ignored**?

2. If someone told you a **baffling** story, what would you say?

3. What have you heard or seen that has **stunned** you?

4. Why might a baseball player be **crouched** over the ball?

5. What would happen if you pedaled your bike **fiercely**?

Write About It

Choose one of the three writing prompts below.

▶ You have the chance to direct your own Tarzan movie. Write a short description of what your version of Tarzan will be like.

▶ Is Tarzan a hero? Write a short essay that states your point of view. Give reasons to support your opinion.

▶ How do you think Tarzan felt after leaving the jungle? What do you think he saw? Write a diary entry as if you were Tarzan. Explain what happened after leaving the jungle.

Fact FILE

There's No Town Like a Tarzan Town

No, we're not kidding. Tarzan's creator, Edgar Rice Burroughs, loved the ape-man so much that he named a town after him. He called the town Tarzana, and about 45,000 people live there today.

Tarzana is in southern California, just north of Los Angeles. And it's pretty much like any other American town. There's no jungle. There are no apes. People don't live in tree houses. But everybody knows who the town is named after. And everyone has his or her favorite story about the King of the Jungle.

You can learn more about Tarzana by checking out the Web site:

www.tarzana-chamber.org

Reading Editorial Cartoons

Most cartoons are meant to make you laugh. Editorial cartoons are meant to make you think, too. You won't find them in the comics section of the newspaper. They're on the editorial page because they express the cartoonists' points of view.

Check out the cartoon below. Do you get the point?

An Editorial Cartoon

First, look at the art. Who's causing the traffic jam in this picture? Then read the caption. What issue does the cartoon address?

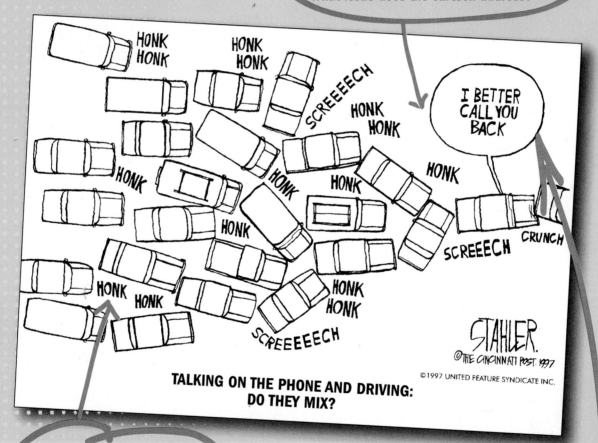

TALKING ON THE PHONE AND DRIVING: DO THEY MIX?

Some cartoons use words as "sound effects." These sound effects let you know the drivers aren't just parked. They're honking at each other and slamming on their brakes.

No phones can be seen in this cartoon at all. But this speech bubble tells you the driver is using one.

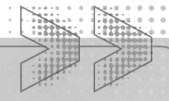

Get the Point?

What is the cartoonist saying about driving and mobile phones? Take another look at the cartoon. Reread the tips that go with it. Then use the cartoon and tips to answer the questions below.

1. The cartoon shows a picture of
   a. cars parked in a parking lot.
   b. drivers running a red light.
   c. cars in a traffic jam.

2. What is causing the problem in the cartoon?
   a. A fallen tree is blocking the road.
   b. Someone is using a mobile phone instead of paying attention to the road.
   c. Someone is listening to music instead of paying attention to the road.

3. Which driver is talking on the phone? How can you tell?

4. The cartoon's caption asks
   a. if all drivers should have mobile phones for emergencies.
   b. if it's a good idea to honk your horn in a traffic jam.
   c. if it's a good idea to talk on the phone while you drive.
   d. if cars should be banned.

5. How do you think the cartoonist would answer the question in the caption? Write one or two sentences explaining your answer.

Write About It
The cartoonist seems to think that talking on the phone and driving do not mix. Do you agree with the cartoonist? Why or why not? Write a short paragraph explaining what you think.

Express Yourself
Think of an issue that you feel strongly about. How could you express your opinion in a drawing? Create an editorial cartoon that depicts your point of view.

" Check the Web for your local newspaper. There's probably a collection of editorial cartoons. "

Real-World Words

cartoonist: a person who creates a cartoon
depicts: shows in words or pictures
editorial: expressing an opinion or a point of view

Dr. Pedro José Greer Jr.

Doctor
to the
Homeless

Dr. Pedro José Greer Jr. used to stay away from homeless people. Then something happened to change that.

In June 1984, Dr. Greer walked into Jackson Memorial Hospital in Miami. In Bed 9, he found a man who could barely breathe. The man had tuberculosis. This disease is rare in the United States. That's because doctors can prevent and cure it. How could this happen? Dr. Greer saw that the man's hospital bracelet said "No address."

Dr. Greer couldn't help but wonder who this man was. Was he someone's father? Someone's brother? Someone's son? He decided to try to find the man's family before it was too late. He searched the poorest sections of Miami, Florida, where many homeless people live. He never did find the man's family. But what Dr. Greer *did* find shocked him.

"I saw people living under a bridge. They had borrowed clothes and old worn-out shoes. I saw homes made of cardboard boxes. They had nothing," says Dr. Greer. "I couldn't believe what I was seeing. I couldn't believe people were living this way in a rich country like the United States."

A Man With a Mission

Dr. Greer decided to do something. He went to a local homeless shelter. It was called Camillus House. There, he volunteered in the soup kitchen and gave out clothing. By the third visit, he had a better idea: He took over a tiny office at the shelter and began providing free medical care.

But the patients who needed the *most* care didn't come to the clinic. So Dr. Greer went looking for them. He searched the poorest areas of Miami, looking for the sick and the homeless. He walked the streets and searched under freeways.

But Dr. Greer wasn't always welcome. Some people didn't trust this stranger in a white lab coat. They called him nasty names. One man threatened him with a weapon. But Dr. Greer kept coming back. He refused to be scared off. Little by little, homeless people began to trust the doctor.

Dr. Greer gave his one-room clinic a name—Camillus Health Concern. Soon, some medical students began to volunteer. As people heard about Dr. Greer's work, donations of money and medicine began to come in. The clinic grew.

Today the Camillus Health Concern is one of the nation's largest clinics of its kind. It treats more than 10,000 men, women, and children each year for free. Nearly all the patients are homeless. They arrive with all kinds of problems—large and small. "People come here because they know they'll be cared for and won't be judged," says Dr. Greer.

ASK Yourself

- How did the homeless respond to Dr. Greer at first? Later?

Explain what happened in your own words.

Good Examples

Dr. Greer knows what it's like to be judged unfairly. Dr. Greer's parents were immigrants. They moved to Miami from Cuba. One day he was riding a bike and someone called him an ugly name.

"I was an immigrant kid," says Dr. Greer. "My hair wasn't blond. My eyes weren't blue. I looked different."

Dr. Greer's mother taught him to be proud of who he was. His mother's attitude was simple. "It didn't matter if a person was Hispanic, black, or whatever. A person is a person. Period. My mother also taught me to stick up for the underdog," says Dr. Greer.

Dr. Greer's father, a doctor, **inspired** him as well. His father was the first person in his family to graduate from high school. He was the first to go to college and the first to go to medical school. Dr. Greer's father set another important example. He also made time to care for the poor. "Growing up, my father never talked about money," says Dr. Greer.

"Today people are so **concerned** about money and things. Sure it's nice to have a boat or a fancy car—let's not kid ourselves," he adds. "But if you don't love your life, these other things won't make it better. Living well and doing the right thing, that's what really matters."

To do both, Dr. Greer has two jobs. One is a private practice he shares with his father. Those patients pay for their care. Dr. Greer's other job is caring for people who can't afford to pay. That one he does for free.

The Work Gets Harder

For this second job, Dr. Greer has become something of a local hero in Miami. He's won many honors, including a presidential award. But the number of homeless people continues to rise, so Dr. Greer's work is getting even harder.

Dr. Greer published a book recently to inform others about the problems that homeless people face—not only getting medical help, but getting the community to care. "People feel uncomfortable with the homeless because of the way they smell, dress, and look," says Dr. Greer. "There's a lot of **prejudice.**"

Dr. Greer hopes people will understand that the homeless are human beings. They have feelings just like anyone else. Homelessness can happen to anyone.

The Rewards

Dr. Greer has learned a lot working with the homeless. "My work has given me a great life," Dr. Greer says. "Nobody said it would be easy, and at

Words, Words, Words

inspired: influenced or encouraged someone
concerned: worried about
prejudice: an unfair opinion based on race, religion, or culture
complicated: difficult; complex
satisfaction: a good feeling that comes from getting something done

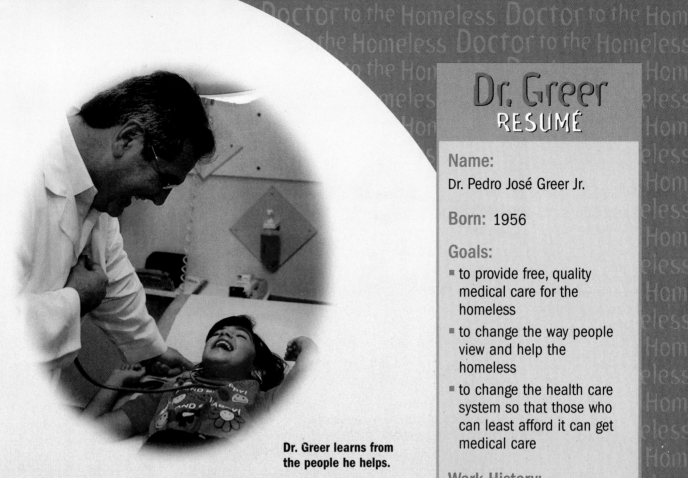

Dr. Greer learns from the people he helps.

times it hasn't been. It's been fun though, doing good stuff. Helping to make people feel better. Helping to make people smile. How can that not be fun? To me it's all about people."

He still remembers one homeless boy he met at the clinic. "I gave him a sandwich because he was very hungry. He took two bites and put it back in the bag," Dr. Greer says. "I asked, 'Why?' He said, 'I've got two brothers. They're hungry too.' I learned more from that kid than I could ever imagine. Although he was hungry, he wasn't just thinking of himself. What an incredible lesson for all of us."

Dr. Greer hopes his efforts will inspire people—especially young people—to help others. Helping doesn't have to be hard or **complicated,** he adds.

"It can be as simple as helping your mom. Maybe she's working two jobs. Wash the dishes for her. Or maybe you can help neighbors with their chores," Dr. Greer says. "You'll get the **satisfaction** of knowing you've helped somebody. One day that individual might help somebody else—and that person might be you." ●

Dr. Greer
RESUMÉ

Name:
Dr. Pedro José Greer Jr.

Born: 1956

Goals:
- to provide free, quality medical care for the homeless
- to change the way people view and help the homeless
- to change the health care system so that those who can least afford it can get medical care

Work History:
- Founder and medical director of the Camillus Health Concern
- Assistant Dean, Homeless Education, University of Miami

Education:
- attended medical school in the Dominican Republic

Major Achievements:
- winner of the President's Service Award, 1997
- winner of the MacArthur Foundation "Genius" grant, 1993
- author of *Waking Up in America: How One Doctor Brings Hope to Those Who Need It Most,* 1999

Lennie: In His own Words

Lennie is 12 years old. Except for not having a permanent home, is he really so different from most kids?

These photographs were taken by Lennie.

My life is lots of fun, but it is hard to be moving a lot and lose touch with my friends. I have been to so many schools and met so many people. I guess my home is in Minneapolis because we spend a lot of time there, but we also stay in lots of other places. We are leaving for Oklahoma soon. We have lived in South Dakota, Oklahoma, and Minnesota, and even on reservations a few times. We move a lot.

My mother has told me we have to go where we can find work or get some money or stay with people we know. I know other kids who have to

do this, too. I think that because we have to move around so much, I get to see many things that people who don't travel so much probably don't get to see.

Most of the time I live with my mother and brothers and sisters, and once I lived with my aunt for a few months. I ran away two times but only for a little while. I was scared and missed my family. I met some nice kids, though.

We lived in our car many times and in parks and a few times in abandoned buildings.

I am part Indian but we really don't have much contact with other Native Americans because we are never in one place for very long. We know some people on reservations and have some relatives there, but mostly we are around white people. I've gone to pow-wows and they are lots of fun. The kids dance and wear these really great clothes with feathers and beads.

I'm lucky because I have met people who are from many backgrounds, like Native Americans, Asian Americans, and African Americans. We lived for a while in St. Paul and I met some Hmong kids and hung out with them. The family of one of the kids sold vegetables at a market every week. I liked going there, but I don't get to see them now because we moved away.

I really want to have a big house someday and not have to move all the time. The house would be big and white with a fence around it and a dog in the backyard.

I think I would like to be a photographer someday and show how people are and how they live, so other people could learn. I love to read and take pictures. I might even like to write, but pictures are more fun. I like to photograph houses, and cars, and boats, and kids, and costumes, and dream catchers, and things at powwows.

In the city there are things to photograph that you don't see in the country or on reservations, like a stop sign that had writing, maybe from a gang, all over it. Cities are scary sometimes because there are too many fights and gangs and drugs. My mother says this is a problem for everyone.

Everyone should be able to have money and not have to sleep in cars and parks. They should have houses. Families are very important and should be able to stay together all the time. I met a woman with a dog, and all her things were in a shopping cart. She smiled at me and we talked, but I don't think she should have to always be outside without a house. ●

Talk About It

Now that you've read "Dr. Pedro José Greer Jr." and "Lennie," what do you have to say about these questions?

▶ How do you think a person might become homeless?

▶ Who do you think should help homeless people?

Comprehension Check

Write your answers to the questions below. Use information from the profile and the personal narrative to support your answers.

1. What did Dr. Greer learn from the boy who shared his sandwich with his brothers?

2. How do you think Dr. Greer feels about his father?

3. How would you describe a person like Dr. Greer?

4. What does Lennie want to be when he grows up?

5. What do you think Dr. Greer might be able to learn from Lennie?

Vocabulary Check

Complete each sentence with the correct vocabulary word.

prejudice   inspired   concerned
complicated   satisfaction

1. I was _____ about the man sleeping in the alley.

2. Dr. Greer wrote his book to help stop the _____ that exists toward homeless people.

3. The math problem was more _____ than I thought.

4. I was _____ by a newspaper article about Dr. Greer.

5. It gave me a feeling of _____ to help teach my sister to read.

Write About It

Choose one of the writing prompts below.

▶ Create a journal entry that Lennie might have written after moving again.

▶ Write a poem about what the idea of home means to you.

▶ Do you think Dr. Greer is a hero? Write one paragraph explaining your opinion.

Take ACTION

Want to know how you can help? Here are some ideas. First, look in the phone book for local organizations that help the homeless. Then you can:

1. **Collect Toys and Games for Donations**
Don't let old books and toys gather dust on a shelf. Sort through things you don't use anymore and donate those that are not too worn. Collect toys, games, and books from your friends, too.

2. **Donate Admission Fees From an Event**
Does your school charge money for plays, ball games, or dances? Find out if admission to one or more of these events can be donated to an organization that helps the homeless. Or suggest that instead of admission, people donate cans of food.

For more ideas on how you can help the homeless, go to http://earthsystems.org. Your local Boy Scout or Girl Scout troop or YMCA may also have some ideas.

Prioritizing Tasks

You've got homework to finish, a class party to attend, neighbors to help, and chores to do at home. You don't know where to start. What should you do? Prioritize!

Read this list of things to do. Can you figure out which tasks should be done right away?

Jorge's To-Do List

Jorge has organized his tasks under several headings. The first two headings are "For School" and "For Home."

When making your list, include due dates to show when things must be completed. Then you can plan to do the tasks in the order that they are due.

School and home aren't the only places where Jorge has responsiblities. He also does chores for other people. He has listed them here.

For School
- study for algebra test (on Tuesday)
- make posters for basketball rally (on Friday night)
- make cookies for class party (on Friday)
- finish history report (due Thursday)
- read assigned English book (by next Wednesday)

For Home
- organize garage
- make dinner for Mom's birthday (Mon.)
- clean my room
- mow the lawn

For the Smiths
- walk and feed the dog (M–F)
- pick up the mail
- water the plants
- set out recyclables (pick-up on Wed.)

For Mrs. Sanchez
- buy groceries (Sat.)
- take out trash (pick-up on Tues.)
- mow the lawn (Sat.)
- return library books (due Thurs.)

Get Your Priorities Straight!

Now it's time to prioritize! Review Jorge's to-do list and the tips that go with it. Then answer the questions below. Write your answers on your own paper.

1. It's Monday. Look at Jorge's school activities for the week. What should he do first?
   a. make posters for the rally
   b. study for the algebra test
   c. make cookies for the party

2. Which task for home must Jorge do on a certain day?
   a. make dinner for his mother's birthday
   b. organize the garage
   c. mow the lawn

3. It's Monday, and Jorge is going to the Smiths' house. Which task must he do that day?
   a. mow the lawn
   b. set out the recyclables
   c. feed and walk the dog

4. Look at the tasks Jorge must do for Mrs. Sanchez. Which task must he do early in the week?
   a. buy groceries
   b. mow the lawn
   c. take out the trash

Schedule It
Look again at Jorge's list. Create a calendar for Jorge's week. Write down each day of the week. Then write down what Jorge must remember to do that day. Put stars next to the important activities for each day.

Try It!
Make your own to-do list for the next week. Before you begin, think about how you might organize your tasks. Write down headings like "School" and "Home." Then fill in your tasks under each heading.

" A great way to keep track of all the things you have to do is to write them in a daily log or on a calendar. As you complete each activity, check it off! "

Real-World Words

due date: when something must be completed or accomplished
prioritize: to do things in order of importance
priority: something that is more important than other things

GREATEST MOMENTS

OF THE NBA

from the book by Bruce Weber

You've probably seen an NBA game on TV. Maybe you've been lucky enough to attend one. You've seen the huge, talented players. You've heard the screaming fans. You've felt the thrill of victory . . . and the pain of defeat. There's no doubt about it— the NBA has helped to make basketball an extremely popular sport.

The NBA produces great moments every game. If this time line included *every* great moment from the past 55 years, you'd never be done reading it. So, on the following pages, you'll find some of the biggest moments in NBA history.

THE BUZZER HAS SOUNDED! BEGIN READING...

LET THE GAME BEGIN!

The date was November 1, 1946. The Toronto Huskies were hosting the very first professional basketball game—against the New York Knicks. They were both teams of the BAA—the Basketball Association of America.

The BAA of 1946 was nothing like the NBA of today. There was no shot clock. Players were shorter and slower than they are today. And coaches encouraged players to shoot with both feet planted firmly on the ground. (There were no "Air Jordans" flying through the air with amazing shots!)

More than 7,000 fans showed up for the opening night. The Knicks **dominated** the first half. The Huskies briefly led in the second. But New York stayed tough and pulled off a 68-66 victory. The new league was on its way.

The Toronto Huskies never made it to the second season. Other teams came and went as the league grew. Two years later, the BAA **merged** with another league. This new league became the NBA. The rest, as they say, is history!

Professional basketball has come a long way since this first game in 1946.

WORDS, WORDS, WORDS

dominated: controlled or ruled
merged: joined together
crisis: a time of difficulty

THE MAGIC CLOCK

Teams couldn't be allowed to hold the ball forever.

By the early 1950s, the NBA was having problems. The league had made rules to speed up games, but coaches and players found ways to get around them. The games were slow and boring. And thanks to lots of late-game fouls, the games were really long, too. If that continued, the league—and maybe even the game of basketball—could be in big, big trouble.

Then Danny Biasone came along. Biasone could possibly be the NBA's all-time superstar—without ever scoring a single basket. Here's the explanation: Biasone was the owner of the Syracuse Nationals. He realized that the game was in **crisis** and went to work on the problem.

Biasone figured a clock might do the trick. Teams couldn't be allowed to hold the ball forever. They would have to shoot within a certain period of time. Biasone watched a few films, played with a stopwatch at some games, and decided the proper amount of time would be 24 seconds.

The results of the Biasone clock were immediate. The year before the clock, average per-team scoring was 79.5 points per game. In the clock's first season, the average jumped to 93.1. That's exactly what Biasone had in mind. And ever since then, Biasone's magic clock has been ticking away at every NBA game.

ASK YOURSELF

- Which happened first: the addition of the shot clock or the first BAA game?

Use the time line to help you figure out the order of events.

TICKETS, PLEASE!

In the first season of the NBA, players were paid about $5,000 for the season. That's about what a superstar gets for one minute today! Of course, lower player salaries made for lower ticket prices. For the league's first game, the highest-priced seat at Maple Leaf Gardens cost only **$2.50.** You could get in for as little as 75 cents.

And if you were taller than the Huskies' tallest player, 6'8" George Nostrand, you got in free!

GAME OF THE CENTURY

There were 4,124 fans at the Hershey Arena in Pennsylvania on March 2, 1962. Another 100,000 or so claim to have been there. All of them say they saw the greatest one-game performance in the history of the NBA. That was the night Wilton Norman Chamberlain of the Philadelphia Warriors scored 100 points.

Playing against the Knicks, Chamberlain tossed down 23 points in the first quarter. In the second, he scored 18. By the end of the third, he had a total of 69 points. And a few minutes into the fourth quarter, he had broken the NBA single-game scoring record of 78 points. Whose record did he break? His own! He had set that record himself in a game earlier that season.

But that wasn't enough, for Wilt or the fans. Finally, with 46 seconds to go, he hit a short shot. Bang! 100 points! The fans raced out of their seats and onto the floor.

Wilt wound up the season averaging 50.4 points per game. He became the only player in NBA history to score more than 4,000 points in a single season!

Wilt Chamberlain scores 100 points in a single game.

WILT CHAMBERLAIN

THE LIMPING HERO

The Knicks' captain came limping from the locker room. But could he play?

May 8, 1970. It was Game 7 between the New York Knicks and the Los Angeles Lakers. The experts said the Knicks didn't stand a chance. Two games earlier, the Knicks had lost their captain, Willis Reed, to a badly torn muscle in his right thigh. And the Knicks couldn't win without Reed.

But one minute before tip-off, as the players came onto the court, the Knicks' captain came limping from the locker room. Quickly, every eye in the building turned to the 6′10″, 240-pound superstar. *Would* he play? *Could* he play?

Reed could hardly lift his right leg. When he ran, he dragged the **injured** leg behind him. But he was determined to help his team win the championship.

In the Knicks' first possession, they worked the ball to their captain, who tossed in a 21-footer to give New York a 2-0 lead. The place went wild. The next time up the court, Reed hit another 20-footer. Swish! Two shots, four points. The roof practically came off the building.

Reed would score no more that night. But his teammates were so **uplifted** it didn't matter. The Knicks coasted to an amazing 113-99 victory.

ASK YOURSELF

■ Why do you think Reed tried to play with a hurt leg?

Think about how his effort made his teammates feel.

WORDS, WORDS, WORDS

injured: hurt
uplifted: inspired

THE DOCTOR IS IN

Erving had been Michael Jordan before there was a Michael Jordan.

From the moment Julius Erving—or Dr. J as he was called—arrived in pro basketball, everyone knew he was special. But after several years he still didn't have a championship ring. His team, the Philadelphia 76ers, had come close several times, but they lacked a big man to complete their game.

Luckily, just before the 1982–83 season, they got the big man they needed: Moses Malone, the NBA's Most Valuable Player. Malone gave the team a big body who could score and rebound. Moses took pressure off the Doctor—and helped make the Sixers a championship team.

They **romped** through the regular season. Their 65-17 record was the league's best. And when the playoffs started, Coach Billy Cunningham and the Sixers were more than up to the task. With Dr. J and Malone in top form, it turned out to be easy.

The New York Knicks went down in four straight games in the opening round. Then in the Conference Finals, the Milwaukee Bucks actually won a game. But Philly took the series, four games to one. Then, in the NBA Finals, it was the Sixers over the Lakers in four straight.

It was the perfect cap to a great career. Erving had been Michael Jordan before there was a Michael Jordan. He had moves on the court that no one had ever dreamed of. People everywhere watched the Sixers play just to get a **glimpse** of their whirling, hang-in-the-air Doctor. And in the end, the Doctor finally got his ring.

WORDS, WORDS WORDS

romped: played in a carefree and lively way
glimpse: a brief look
rivalries: competitions between two opponents
critical: very important

MAGIC'S MOMENT

When you talk about great NBA **rivalries**, it's hard to find one that tops the rivalry between Larry Bird and Magic Johnson.

It began in their college days. The 1979 NCAA Championship Game matched Johnson of Michigan State against Bird of Indiana State. When Magic's team pulled out the victory, the rivalry was born.

The rivalry got really intense when the two met in the NBA Finals for the first time in 1984. Bird's Boston Celtics won in seven games and Larry was the series MVP. Round two went to Bird.

They were right back at it in 1985. This time it was Magic's turn. The Los Angeles Lakers won in six games. Two years later, these superstars would get one more chance to settle the score.

In Game 1 of the 1987 series, Magic came close to a triple-double with 29 points, 13 assists, and 8 rebounds as L.A. won by 13. In Game 2, Johnson was even better, leading L.A. to a convincing 141-122 win.

Boston won Game 3, making Game 4 **critical**. But Boston didn't have a chance. And when Magic tossed in a running hook shot to give L.A. a 107-106 victory, hardly anyone was still seated.

The Celtics won Game 5. But that was their last gasp. In Game 6, the Lakers put the finishing touches on their spectacular season with a runaway 106-93 victory. At game's end, the MVP was strictly no contest. Magic Johnson had done it again!

ASK YOURSELF

■ When did the rivalry between Bird and Magic begin?

Look for dates in the text. They can help you figure out when an event took place.

Larry Bird and Magic Johnson settle the score.

SHE'S GOT GAME

The 1996 Olympics changed everything. Twelve women stood on a **podium** with gold medals around their necks and smiles on their faces. They had made their country proud. And they changed basketball forever.

Women's basketball had been gaining in popularity for years. College games were drawing more fans than ever before. The NCAA Final Four was selling out months in advance. It was clear that an audience was building.

But U.S. women college players had no place to go after college. No place in the United States, that is. The most talented players were forced to play overseas in countries such as Italy, Spain, Japan, and Israel.

Then in 1997, a new league formed: the Women's National Basketball Association (WNBA). Finally, women would get the chance to play basketball professionally for their own country. The new league has been more successful than its **founders** had ever dared to hope.

Players like Lisa Leslie, Sheryl Swoopes, Nikki McCray, and Rebecca Lobo have been on magazine covers and grabbed newspaper headlines. It seems like people can't get enough of these stars. During the first season, more than a million fans attended WNBA games. Millions more watched on TV.

These exciting players showed the fans how much they loved the game by working hard and playing hard. This young league is still growing by leaps and bounds. Women's basketball is definitely here to stay.

ASK YOURSELF

▪ Why do you think the WNBA was created?

Think about what women's basketball was like right before the league got started.

The U.S. Olympic team helps inspire a whole new league— the WNBA.

MICHAEL'S LAST SHOT

Michael Jordan left a **legacy** of great shots, great defense, and tremendous victories. But he may have saved his very best for his last game ever.

The Bulls were barely hanging on to a three-games-to-two lead in the 1998 NBA Finals. With less than a minute to go in Game 6, Utah held a three-point lead. A Utah win would tie the series.

That's when Michael took over. He scored on a typical M.J. drive to the basket, cutting the Jazz's lead to one. Then Utah drove to the Chicago end. But Michael stripped the ball from Jazz star Karl Malone. It was Chicago's ball again.

The clock was ticking. Ten seconds to go, nine, eight. Jordan brought the ball up the court. There wasn't a question about what the Bulls were going to do.

Jordan drove to the hoop, but Utah's Byron Russell blocked M.J.'s path to the bucket. So Michael stopped in his tracks. Suddenly, Jordan had what basketball players call "a look." The clock continued to click. Eight seconds, seven.

Twenty feet from the basket, down by one point and with the championship on the line, he fired.

The ball took what seemed like forever to reach its target. But when it got there, it was nothing but net. The Bulls led by one. The clock read 5.2 seconds. All that was left was for Chicago to play defense.

Michael's last NBA shot gave his Bulls their title. This, his final field goal, will be remembered forever. ●

Michael Jordan is one of the greatest players in the history of the game.

WORDS, WORDS WORDS

podium: an elevated platform or stage
founders: people who begin an organization, club, company, etc.
legacy: something to be remembered by in the future

HOOPS

Robert Burleigh
Illustrated by
Stephen T. Johnson

It's only a
game—Or is it?

Hoops.
The game.
Feel it.

The rough roundness.
The ball
like a piece
of the thin long reach
of your body.

The way it answers whenever you call.
The never-stop back and forth flow,
like tides going in, going out.

The smooth,
skaterly glide
and sudden swerve.

The sideways slip
through a moment of narrow space.

The cool.

The into
and under
and up.

The feathery fingertip roll
and soft slow drop.

Feel your throat on fire.
Feel the asphalt burning beneath your shoes.
The two-of-you rhythm.
The know-where-everyone-is
without having to look.

The watching
and waiting
to poke
and pounce.

The fox on the lurk.

The hunger.

The leap from the pack.

The out-in-the-clear
like a stallion
with wind in your face.

The bent legs tense
as the missed shot swirls
and silently spins.

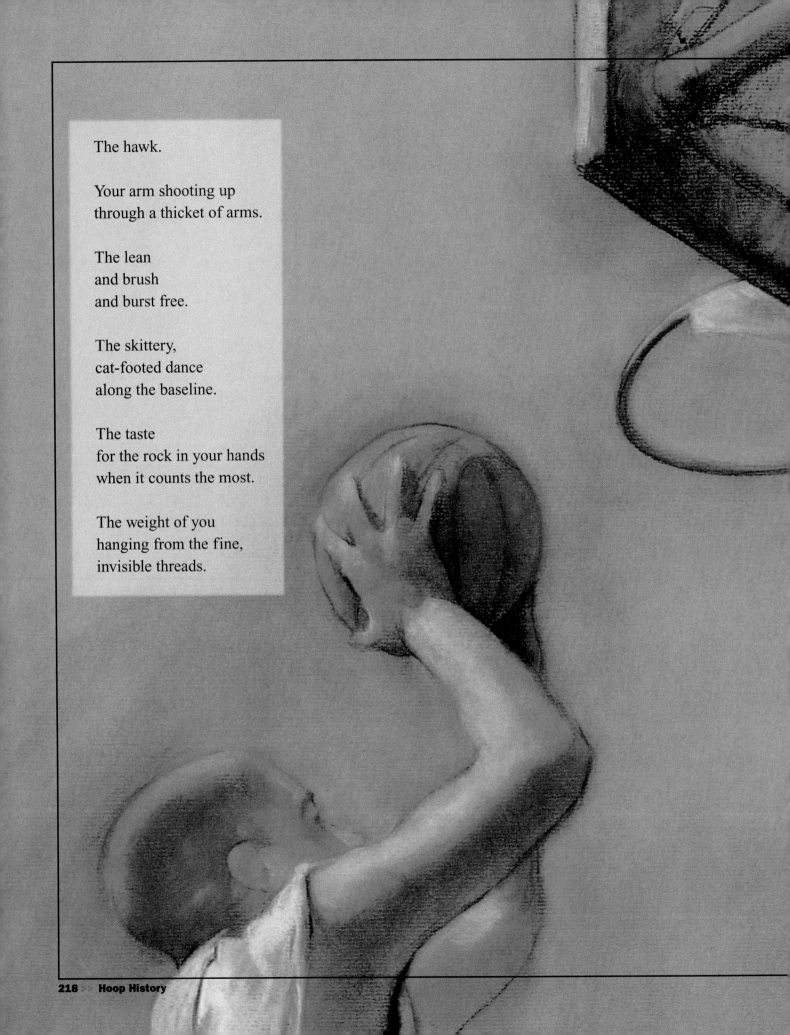

The hawk.

Your arm shooting up
through a thicket of arms.

The lean
and brush
and burst free.

The skittery,
cat-footed dance
along the baseline.

The taste
for the rock in your hands
when it counts the most.

The weight of you
hanging from the fine,
invisible threads.

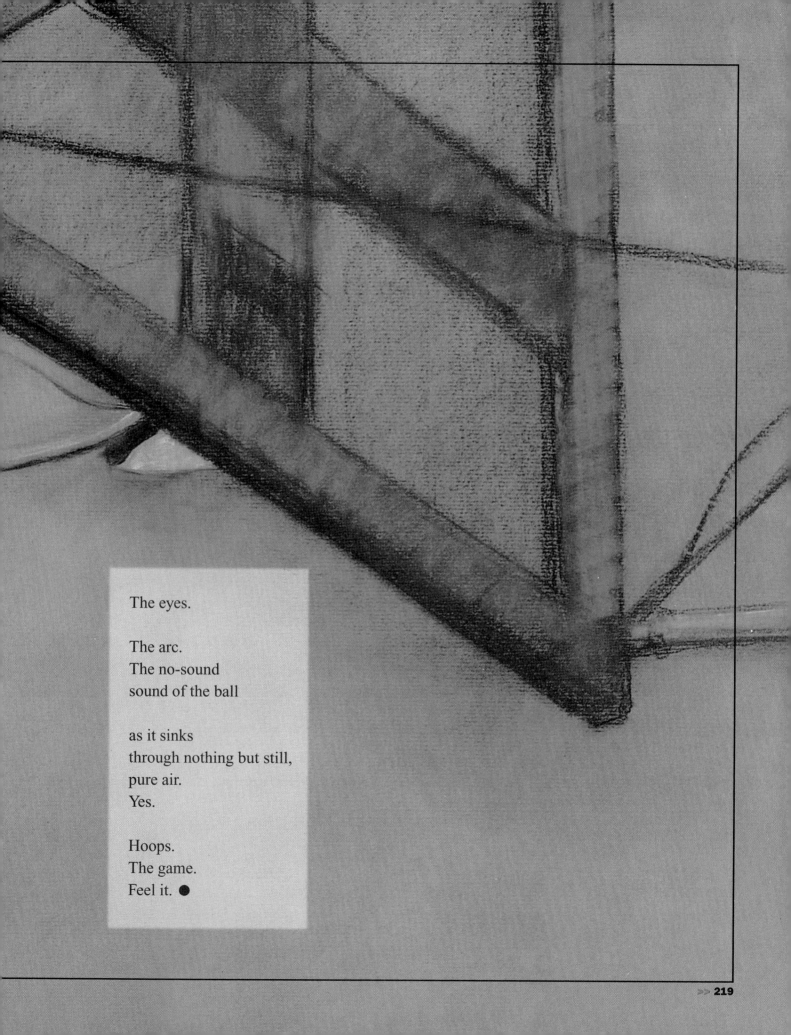

The eyes.

The arc.
The no-sound
sound of the ball

as it sinks
through nothing but still,
pure air.
Yes.

Hoops.
The game.
Feel it. ●

TALK ABOUT IT

Now that you've read *Greatest Moments of the NBA* and "Hoops,"
what do you have to say about these questions?

▶ Why do you think basketball is such a popular sport in this country?

▶ Which is your favorite sport to play? to watch? Explain.

COMPREHENSION CHECK

Write your answers to the questions below. Use information from the
time line and the poem to support your answers.

1. Why did Biasone invent the shot clock?

2. Why do you think Magic Johnson and Larry Bird competed so hard
   against each other?

3. Why do you think the writer says: "Women's basketball is definitely
   here to stay"?

4. In the poem "Hoops," what does "the two-of-you rhythm" mean?

5. Do you think that great basketball players feel the same
   way as the poet who wrote "Hoops"? Explain.

VOCABULARY CHECK

Answer each question below with a complete sentence. Before you answer, think about the meaning of the vocabulary word in bold.

1. Why are some **rivalries** so intense?

2. What makes you feel **uplifted**?

3. How do you usually react in a **crisis**?

4. What is **critical** to your happiness?

5. What would you do if the same person always **dominated** class discussions?

WRITE ABOUT IT

Choose one of the writing prompts below.

▶ Write a short newspaper article describing the time Wilt Chamberlain scored 100 points. Pretend you were a reporter watching the game.

▶ Create a list of five interview questions that you would like to ask Michael Jordan (or any of the other basketball stars).

▶ Write a short speech about why you support women's sports organizations like the WNBA. Give three reasons to back up your opinion.

More to READ

If you want to read more about basketball, you may enjoy:

Greatest Moments of the NBA
by Bruce Weber

Check out this book for even more highlights. Read about the Lakers winning their 33rd straight game. Check out how the Twin Towers of Texas (Tim Duncan and David Robinson) helped San Antonio win its first NBA Championship. Can't get enough of Michael Jordan? Find out how he and Scottie Pippen led the Chicago Bulls to win 70 games in one season!

She's Got Game: 10 Stars of the WNBA
by Michelle Smith

This book celebrates ten of the top women basketball players in the world. Do you know which player says that being a mom is the greatest job in the world? Or which player can rap and sing in Italian? You will after you read this insider's guide to the WNBA.

Comparing Prices

Many products in the grocery store come in several different brands and sizes. How can you find the best deal?

You need to check out each product's unit price. That's how much it costs per pound, ounce, liter, or other unit of measure. Look at the unit-price label and the chart below.

Unit Prices

```
BRAND:                      TOTAL
LARRY'S        ITEM:        WEIGHT:
LONG GRAIN     RICE         5 LBS.

UNIT PRICE: $1.50
YOU PAY: $7.50
```

Many grocery stores figure out unit prices for you. Look for a label like this on the shelf beneath each product.

"It's not hard to figure out unit prices. Divide the total price of the item by the number of units in the package. For example, the unit price of Sip 'n' Sup cups is $5.00 ÷ 20 cups. That's $.25 per cup."

Item	Size	Price	Unit Price
Basim's Basmati Rice	3 lb.	$6.00	$2.00/lb.
Jolie's Fancy Jasmine Rice	1 lb.	$2.30	$2.30/lb.
Larry's Long Grain Wild Rice	5 lb.	$7.50	$1.50/lb.
Cool Cola	1 liter	$1.09	$1.09/liter
Tropical Beach Cola	2 liters	$2.10	$1.05/liter
Tangy Tingle Cola	3 liters	$3.00	$1.00/liter
Sip 'n' Sup Plastic Cups	20 cups	$5.00	$ .25/cup
Picnic Pride Plastic Cups	50 cups	$7.50	$ .15/cup
Plain Ol' Plastic Cups	100 cups	$17.00	$ .17/cup

Larry's rice costs $1.50 per pound. Compare it to the unit prices of other brands to find out which is cheapest.

Dig for Deals

Are you ready to shop? Review the unit-price label and the chart, and reread the tips that go with them. Then use the label, chart, and tips to answer these questions. Write your answers on your own paper.

1. What is the unit price of Tropical Beach Cola?
   a. 2 liters
   b. $1.05/liter
   c. $1.09/liter
   d. $2.10

2. The largest package of plastic cups is the cheapest per cup.
   a. true
   b. false

3. Which brand of cola is the cheapest per liter?
   a. Cool Cola
   b. Tropical Beach Cola
   c. Tangy Tingle Cola

4. What is the most expensive brand of rice per pound? How much would you pay for five pounds of this rice?

5. Your supermarket carries a huge, family-size bag of Basim's Basmati Rice. It weighs 10 pounds. It sells for $8.00. What is its unit price?
   a. $8.00
   b. $1.00/lb.
   c. $.80/lb.
   d. $.80 per grain of rice

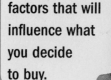
" Don't assume that the biggest package is the cheapest. Do the math, and you'll know for sure. "

Stock Up

You're in charge of beverages for a picnic. You need 45 cups and 12 liters of cola. Which brands will you buy? How much will you buy? What is the total amount you will spend?

Be a Smart Shopper

Imagine you have to do your family's grocery shopping. How will you decide what to buy? Will you just pay attention to cost? What about quantity? Make a list of three important factors that will influence what you decide to buy.

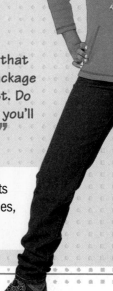

Real-World Words

liter: a measurement for liquids that is equal to about 1.1 quarts
unit of measure: one ounce, one pound, one liter, etc. Sometimes, an item such as one cup is a unit of measure.

LISTEN EAR

by Paul Jennings

Tell one little lie to your parents and you are history.

1

"Brad," said Dad, "Never, ever, ever touch this." In his hand he had the most fantastic compass you have ever seen. Not the type that shows you where to go, but the sort you draw circles with.

It was silver and had little metal bolts and a point as sharp as a needle. Instead of a pencil it had a little piece of lead held in a tiny screw-on top.

I whistled. "Wow," I said, "I bet it's worth a fortune."

"It is," said Dad. "And I need it for my work. *So don't touch it.*" He put it in the top drawer of the dresser in his bedroom and shut it before I could even get a good look.

Jeez, I longed for that compass. Just to hold it, I mean. Not to steal it or use it or anything like that. Just hold it. That's all I wanted to do.

That compass called to me. "Brad," I could hear it saying, "come and get me. Aren't I great? Pick me up. Look at me. Try me out."

It didn't really say that. But in my mind it did. All I wanted was a hold, one dinky little hold.

After tea, Mom and Dad and my little sister, Sophie, went into the living room to watch TV. It was my turn to do the dishes. Rats. I hate doing the dishes. It is so boring.

"Come and hold me," called the compass. "Brad, Brad, Brad."

I had to go. I just had to. All I wanted was a look. That's all. Just a look. With the dish

towel still in my hand I crept up the stairs. *Click*. I turned on the bedroom light. Softly, softly, I tiptoed across the room. Gently, gently, I pulled open the drawer. There it was. Dad's compass in all its glory. It sparkled; it twinkled; it was great.

"Pick me up," it called. "Pick me up. Just once." I rubbed my glasses with a dirty finger and stared down at the compass.

It was more than flesh and blood could stand. I put the dish towel down on the floor and picked up the compass with trembling fingers. It was much heavier than I expected. I opened it up and pretended to draw a little circle in the air.

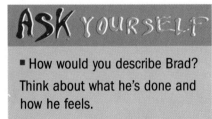

■ How would you describe Brad? Think about what he's done and how he feels.

Just then I heard a sort of **scuffling** noise. It was almost as if someone was watching. Oh no. Dad would kill me if he caught me with the compass. I dropped the compass into the drawer, turned, and ran.

As it turned out, no one was coming. Mom and Dad and Sophie were still watching TV. Maybe the noise was a rat or something.

I walked into the living room and sat down with the others. "Bedtime," said Mom. "I'll finish the dishes."

I snuggled down into bed. Something was wrong. The compass was going to cause trouble. I just knew it was. I couldn't get to sleep no matter how hard I tried. I always seemed to break things. I mean, it isn't my fault. Mostly it is bad luck.

But parents don't understand about accidents. They still think it's your fault. That's why Dad didn't want me to touch the compass. But what could go wrong? I mean I didn't break the compass, did I? It was safely back in the drawer.

I tossed and turned for a couple of hours until something terrible made me jump up. A yell filled the air. It was Dad. I could hear every word even though he was upstairs. "The compass," he screamed. "It's gone." I could hear footsteps coming my way quickly. I closed my eyes and pretended to be asleep. Maybe they would leave me alone until morning.

Fat chance. Dad ripped the covers back off the bed. "Don't try that one," he said. "I know you're awake." Boy, was he mad.

"Brad," he said. "This time you've really gone too far. Where's my compass?"

"I don't know," I said truthfully. "I haven't touched it. Sophie must have taken it."

"Sophie would never take it," said Mom.

"Neither would I," I said.

Mom and Dad both looked at me in silence. I knew they were remembering all the bad things I had done, like eating Sophie's chocolate Easter bunny one night. Well, she didn't want it. It was five months old and starting to turn white. You know what it's like. You just start by nibbling a tiny bit off the ear where it won't be noticed. Then, before you can blink, the whole ear has gone. So then you might as well **wolf** down the whole thing because you are going to get caught anyway.

"Did you go in our bedroom?" said Mom.

"No," I said.

"Did you open the drawer?" asked Dad.

"No," I answered.

"The drawer was open when we went up to bed," said Dad.

They both looked at me with cold eyes. I felt sick in my stomach. I must have forgotten to close the drawer.

"And you didn't go into our room?" Mom asked again.

"No," I said. I know I shouldn't have lied, but someone stole the compass and it wasn't me. I didn't want to get the blame for something I didn't do.

"Well," said Mom. "If you didn't go into the room, how come this was there?" She held up the wet dish towel that I had been using to dry the dishes. I suddenly went cold all over. Now they would never believe that I hadn't taken the compass.

Well, talk about trouble. They went on and on and on. They wouldn't believe me, just because I told one little lie. I was grounded until the compass was returned. They wouldn't even let me go to the movies with them the next night, even though they had promised to take me. And the worst of it was that Sophie got to go. And it must have been her who took the compass.

That's how I happened to be home on my own. Late at night.

2

"The baby-sitter will be here in half an hour," said Mom.

"I don't need a baby-sitter," I said. "I'm not scared. And anyway, she just sits on the phone

talking to her boyfriend all night."

"Where does he live?" said Dad. He was always worried about people making long-distance calls.

"Darwin," I said.

"He does not," said Mom. "He lives right here in Melbourne."

Dad looked at me with a bit of a smile but he soon lost it when Mom opened up. "Brad, I really thought you'd have learned not to tell lies by now," she said.

"It was just a joke," I said.

The three of them hurried out to the car and drove off.

I locked the front door and stared out the

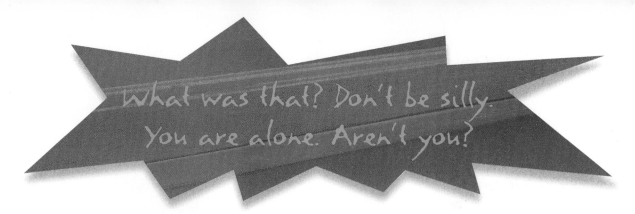

What was that? Don't be silly. You are alone. Aren't you?

window. It was growing dark. And it was raining. The clock ticked loudly in the hall. It felt as if I was the only person in the world. I started to feel sorry for myself. It wasn't fair. Okay, I did tell a couple of **fibs** but I didn't steal the compass. I really wanted to go to the movies and now I was being punished for something I didn't do.

I went over and looked at my face in the living-room mirror. My **reflection** stared back at me. My face looked mean. I just stared and stared into my own eyes. Suddenly I got the creeps. It was as if the reflection wasn't me. As if it was someone else. I gave a shiver and turned on the television.

Where was that baby-sitter? She should have been here already. Outside, it was black and cold. I tried to watch the television but my mind just wasn't on it.

Boomp, scroffle, scraffle. What was that? A sound upstairs. Rats. The rats were in the roof again. Or were they? A little shiver ran down my neck.

Maybe the baby-sitter had crashed her car. I decided to call and see if she was okay. June, that was her name. But what was her other name? Dalton. That's it. June Dalton.

Suddenly something terrible happened. The picture on the television zapped itself into a tiny square and disappeared. At the same time the lights went out. Oh no. A power failure. The lines were down again.

I ran to the phone. Nothing. Just a low, whistling noise coming down the line.

The house was silent. Where was the baby-sitter? I knew, deep inside, that she wasn't coming. It was going to be a long night.

Boomp, scroffle, scraffle. There was that noise again. This time from downstairs. Rats. Of course it was rats. No one would want to get in and get me. Would they?

The hairs started to stand up on the back of my neck.

There was only one thing to do: Go to bed and fall asleep as quickly as possible. I couldn't spend all night scared out of my wits. I felt my way along the hall and into my bedroom.

I pulled off my shoes, took off my glasses, and jumped into bed with my clothes on. Then I closed my eyes and tried to sleep, but sleep wouldn't come.

3

So here I am, surrounded by the sounds of the night.

Houses make a lot of noise when you are the only person in them. *Squeak. Creak. Rustle. Rumble.* What was that? Don't be silly. You are alone. Aren't you?

Who would want to get you? You're just

a boy, just an ordinary boy. Okay, so I told a couple of lies, but I'm not really mean. I don't deserve to die. I'm quite a nice person, really.

What if there was someone under the bed? What if a hand slowly started to pull the blankets down. Until I was uncovered? A horrible, cold hand with gray fingers. Go away. Go away, if you are there. Leave me alone. I won't tell any more lies, God. I promise. And I'll do the dishes on my own. Every night.

Well, nearly every night.

Where did that shadow in the corner come from? It looks like a man with a hat. Standing. Staring. Who's that breathing so loudly?

Me, of course.

Only me. I am alone. I hope. I try to breathe softly. Just in case there is someone creeping around looking for me. They won't know where I am. Unless I make a noise.

The room starts to become lighter. It's funny that—how you can see better in the dark after a while. It is not a man in the corner. It is just my robe hanging on a hook.

But what is that lump on the wall? That wasn't there yesterday. A small bump in the plaster. It must be my **imagination.** I can't see a thing without my glasses. I reach out and put them on, then I take another look. Yes, it is a lump on the wall. Where did that come from? It looks like a table-tennis ball half-buried in the wall. I stare and stare at it.

It's weird how your mind plays tricks on you. I could swear that the lump is bigger than before. I could swear that it is growing.

Aaaaaaaaagh. It is growing. I can see it wobbling and moving. I can't take my eyes off it. I am **hypnotized** by it: a horrible, swelling growth on the wall.

"Mom," I want to scream. But I am too frightened. The word is frozen in my throat.

I am trembling with fear. I am too scared to run. And too scared to stay. Help. Help. Someone. Anyone. Please. Make the lump go away. Come and save me. I need help.

It is wiggling. The ear is wiggling.

The ear?

Yes. Oh, horrible, horrible, horrible. The lump is in the shape of an ear. A wiggling, disgusting, plaster ear on the wall. It is listening. Listening. Listening.

It is the ear of the house. I bet it heard me tell Mom lies. It is the ear that hears all. Knows all. Understands all. Sneaky. Snaky. Snoopy. It is looking for liars.

Well, listen, ear. Just see what you think of this. I take a deep breath. I fill up my lungs. I'm terrified but I must be brave. I

ASK YOURSELF

- Do you think the ear is going to hurt Brad?

Think about whether the ear is real or something that Brad is imagining.

WORDS, WORDS, WORDS

fibs: small lies
reflection: an image thrown back by a surface
imagination: the ability to form pictures in your mind of things that are not real
hypnotized: unable to stop staring at something

yell as loud as I can.

"Get lost, ear."

The sound echoes around the empty rooms. But the ear does not get lost. It just wiggles a little bit. Like a worm on the end of a hook.

4

All is silent again. *Tick, tick, tick. Rustle, rustle.* Breathe in. Breathe out. Silently. Quiet.

Wiggle, wiggle. There it goes again. Don't annoy it. Don't shout. Don't even look. Pretend it is not there.

The ghastly ear on the wall.

Oh, oh, oh. No. It isn't. Not another lump. It can't be. I sneak a look through half-closed eyelids. Another foul lump is swelling out of the plaster. Yes, oh yuck. Another ear. A pair of ears wiggling on the wall. Stop, stop, stop.

Be a dream. Be a nightmare. Don't be real. *Please* don't be real.

I look at the wall. But the ears are still there. This is not a dream. This is real. The ears are still there in the wall. One of them has an earring. Just like mine but made of plaster.

The ears are living, wriggling plaster.

There is more movement. It is as if the plaster is growing a mole. Or bubbling like thick soup in a dark pot. Bits are boiling and growing.

Oh, what's this? A nose. And eyes. And a chin. A face grows like a flower opening on fast-forward.

A face in the wall. The white eyes roll around. The nose twitches. The mouth opens and closes but it says nothing. It is like the television with the sound turned down. The eyes stare at me. They see me hiding there under the covers, trying not to look.

I have seen this face before. But where? Whose face is this?

What can I do? I can't stay here with the **fiendish** face. I will run for it. Down to the kitchen. I will wait in the kitchen until Mom and Dad come home.

The face is still boiling and bubbling. What? It has grown glasses. They are just like mine but made of plaster.

I stare at the face. It stares back at me. Blinking with plaster eyes.

I know where I have seen this face before. I have seen it in the mirror.

It is my face.

I scream. I jump out of bed. I race along to the kitchen and slam the door. I fall panting to the floor. I am never going in that bedroom again.

Oh, Dad, Mom, Sophie, baby-sitter, where are you? Come home, come home, come home.

I can't bear to look at the walls. Or go near them. So I sit on the floor with my back against the fridge. It is cold on the tile floor, but I am going to stay there until someone comes home.

I lean my head back on the fridge door and close my eyes. The metal is cold and hard against my head. And it is moving. Like worms crawling in my hair. For a moment I just sit

> *I jump up and roar out of the room.*
> *I am running away from myself.*
> *No one can do that.*

there, frozen. Then I scream and scramble across the floor.

The face has erupted in the door of the fridge. Only now it is a horrible, horrible steel face with shiny white skin and lips and eyes. Its glasses are also white steel.

The face, my face is trying to talk. Its lips are moving, but nothing is coming out. What is it trying to say?

It is me. I know that it is me. It is my own **conscience.** Telling me not to tell lies.

"Leave me alone," I scream. "Leave me alone." I bolt into the living room and crouch behind the sofa.

But it has followed me.

There it is on the window. Now the face is made of glass. I can see right through its dreadful, moving lips. Is it calling me a liar? What is it trying to say? What is it doing? Why is it after me? Why? Why? Why?

I jump up and roar out of the room. I am running away from myself. No one can do that.

5

I bolt into Dad's study. The walls are all made of wood. The face can't get me here. I am safe.

Outside, the rain has stopped. The moon is playing hide-and-seek behind the clouds. How I wish I was on the moon. I stare up but then look away. Even the moon has a face.

The moonlight shines on the dark, wooden panels. The grain makes strange shapes like whirlpools in a rotting swamp. The lines begin to swirl and run like a crazy river.

My heart starts to beat faster and faster. I can feel the blood running beneath my flesh. Sheer **terror** is washing within me.

The **fearsome** face has made itself in a panel.

ASK YOURSELF

- How does Brad feel about telling lies?

Think about what the face is trying to tell Brad.

My awful reflection glares down at me through its wooden glasses. Its mouth opens and shuts without a sound. It is trying to say something. But what?

It is no use running. The face can turn itself into plaster and steel and glass. And wood. There is no escape.

A saying that I once heard is stirring in the back of my mind. What is it? I know. "The best form of defense is attack."

Could I attack the face? It might grab me and pull me into the wall. Never to be seen

WORDS, WORDS, WORDS

fiendish: evil or wicked
conscience: a person's knowledge of right or wrong
terror: very great fear
fearsome: frightening

again. But I can't keep running. If I go outside, it might appear on a tree. Or the footpath. There is nowhere to run. Nowhere to go. No escape.

I must beat it at its own game. Think, think, think. What is its weakness? It is my face. How can I outsmart it?

I am breathing so heavily that my glasses start to fog up. I give them a wipe. I can't see a thing without my glasses. If I lose them, I am gone.

The face still mouths silent words. And peers at me through its wooden glasses.

Okay. It is risky. It is a chance. But I have to take it. On hands and knees I crawl toward the grained face in the wood. Behind the sofa. Alone. I must keep my head down. I must get close without it knowing what I am up to.

I crouch low behind the sofa like a cat waiting for a bird. I can't see the face, and it can't see me. Unless it has moved.

Now. Go, go, go.

I fly at the face like an arrow from a bow.

Snatch. Got them. Got them. I can't believe it. I have grabbed the wooden glasses. The face is horrified. Its mouth opens in a silent scream. Its eyes are wide and staring. It rushes blindly around the walls. Like a rat running under a sheet, it shoots across the floor.

Its features change as it rushes to and fro. Glass, wood, plastic. It bubbles across the floor. Searching, searching, searching. Its mouth snaps and snarls. Its eyes **gape** and glare. But without the glasses it cannot see. Oh, what will it do if it catches me?

Flash. A blinding light fills the room. What? I blink in the glare. Oh, yes, yes, yes. The power has come back on. I have light. Now maybe the fiendish face will go back where it came from.

But no. In the light it is more fearsome than ever. More real. I am so scared. My knees are shaking so much that I can hardly move.

Suddenly from the living room I hear— voices. A woman's voice. And a child's. They are home. "Mom," I scream. "Mom, Mom, Mom." I race into the hall toward the living room, and the face follows my voice. But I don't care. They are here. Help has arrived. I am saved.

I rush into the room and then freeze. There are people there, all right. But they won't be any use to me. They are on the television. The television has come back on with the power. It is my favorite show.

6

I run out of the room and up the stairs. The face follows the sound of my thumping feet. Now it is made of carpet. A carpet face flowing up the stairs after my footsteps.

I run into Mom and Dad's room and slam the door.

Fool. Fool. What a mistake. The face heard the door slam. It bulges out onto the door. Staring. Searching. It knows I am in the room. I climb carefully onto the bed and try to breathe quietly. It can't find me. Not without the glasses. Not unless I make a noise. Don't move. Don't make the bed squeak.

The face starts to search. Up and down each wall. Across the ceiling. Under the bed. Its lips are pulled down in an unhappy **pout.** It circles the bed like a shark around a boat. It knows where I am.

"Listen," I yell. "I am sorry I told a lie. I'm sorry, sorry, sorry. Okay?"

This is weird. I am telling myself that I am sorry.

The face suddenly smiles. It is happy. Its mouth is making silent words. What is it trying to say? One word. It is saying the same word over and over again.

It is hard reading lips. But suddenly I know what the word is.

"Glasses," I yell at the face.

The face nods. Up and down with a limp smile. What is it about these glasses? I take my own glasses off and carefully put the wooden ones on my own face. Straight away, everything changes. The whole house is different. I can see through the walls and the ceiling. The house is a ghost house and I can see right through it.

Wires and building materials. Nails. Trash. An old newspaper. A soda bottle left by the builders. A rat's nest underneath the dresser. A rat scurrying away through a hole in the wall.

This is amazing. I can see into all the rooms from where I am standing. It is like X-ray vision.

gape: to open widely
pout: the act of pushing out your lips to show anger or disappointment

My mind starts to turn over. Somewhere in all this is the answer to a puzzle. The rat's nest. I stare and stare at the rat's nest. All of this started with rats scuttling around in the wall. I stare into the nest. Then I smile.

So does the face. It is happy, too.

I do not know if the face is my conscience. Perhaps it is the best and the worst of me. It has chased me around and made me feel guilty. And now it has helped me out.

I step down from the bed. I walk over to the grinning copy of myself and put the glasses on its cheeks. It blinks. "Thank you," I say. "You can go now."

Slowly, slowly, with just the hint of a smile, the face melts back into the wall. I know that it is happy.

Downstairs a door bangs. "Mom," I yell. "Dad. Sophie." I rush happily down the stairs.

"The baby-sitter called the cinema," says Mom. "Her car broke down. And the phones weren't working. Are you okay?"

"Sit down," I say. "You are not going to believe this." They sit down and don't say a thing while I tell them the story. I tell them everything and don't leave out one little detail.

I am right about one thing, though. They do not believe me.

"It was a dream," says Mom.

"It was a lie," says Dad.

They think I am still lying. They won't believe me. "It's the truth," I yell. "It is, it is, it is."

"There is one way to prove your story," says Dad. "We will move the dresser and see if there is a rat's nest underneath. Then we will know for sure."

We all walk up to the bedroom and Dad tries to move the dresser. It is very heavy, so the whole four of us join in and help. In the end we lift it into the middle of the room.

There against the wall is a rat's nest. There is no rat in it. It has run away because of all the noise. There is no rat. But there is a compass. Right there where the rat carried it.

"Now do you believe me?" I say.

I look at Mom and Dad and Sophie. Their mouths just open and shut, but no sound comes out.

No sound at all. ●

Calvin and Hobbes

by Bill Watterson

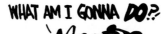

TALK ABOUT IT

Now that you've read "Listen Ear" and the Calvin and Hobbes
comic strip, what do you have to say about these questions?

▶ Is there ever a time when telling a lie is okay? Explain.

▶ How can a guilty conscience help you do the right thing?

COMPREHENSION CHECK

Write your answers to the questions below. Use information from
the short story and the comic strip to support your answers.

1. How do Brad's parents know that he touched the compass?

2. Why do you think Brad sees his face in the wall?

3. If you were Brad, would you have acted differently? Explain.

4. What happens to Calvin's father's binoculars?

5. What do Brad and Calvin have in common?

VOCABULARY CHECK

Complete each sentence starter below. Before you answer, think about the meaning of the vocabulary word in bold.

1. The sound of **scuffling** was caused by . . . .

2. It takes a lot of **imagination** to . . . .

3. I was gripped by **terror** after reading . . . .

4. My little brother began to **pout** when . . . .

5. Having a **conscience** is a good thing because . . . .

WRITE ABOUT IT

Choose one of the writing prompts below.

▶ Write a new ending for this story that tells what happens after Brad's parents find the rat's nest and the compass.

▶ Do you think that Brad should apologize to his parents? Do you think Brad's parents should apologize to Brad? Write a letter of apology that you think should be sent.

▶ Write a short story about a lie. You can invent the story from your imagination. Or, you can think of a situation that really happened and write about that.

About the AUTHOR

Australian writer Paul Jennings is known for writing spooky, funny, and wacky stories. His books have been read and loved by millions.

It all began in 1985 when his book *Unreal!* was published. It topped the best-seller lists in Australia. His stories have been turned into popular television shows in Australia and England.

More than three million copies of Paul Jennings' books have been sold throughout the world. He receives thousands of fan letters every year and replies to them all—as long as they include a return address.

Write to him at:
P.O. Box 1459
Warrnambool, Victoria 3280
Australia

Or visit his Web site:
www.pauljennings.com.au/

Interpreting Labels

You just washed your new shirt—and it came out a different color! To avoid future disasters, you need to read the care labels on your clothing.

Check out the labels below. Are you ready to do some laundry?

Sample Care Labels for Clothing

Felix's Fashions
Size XL
100% polyester
Machine wash cold.
Do not bleach.
Do not dry clean.

Look-Good Styles
Size L
100% wool
Dry Clean only.

Cool Dudz
Size M
60% cotton
40% polyester
Machine wash warm,
with similar colors.
Tumble dry, no iron

Snazzy Shirts
Size M
100% silk
Hand wash cold.
No bleach
Line dry.
Do not wring or twist.

Most washers have three or more temperature settings. Your clothing may shrink or fade if you choose the wrong setting.

Before washing, separate your laundry by color. The dye from dark-colored garments can "bleed" onto lighter-colored garments and ruin them.

" What happens if a label says 'Dry clean only'? Don't wash the garment— not even by hand. Take it to a dry-cleaning shop. If you don't like to spend money at the cleaner's, be sure to read labels before you buy. "

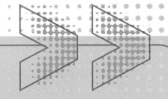

Read the Label!

It's time to wash your favorite shirt! But first, reread the labels and the tips that go with them. Then use them to answer the questions below. Write your answers on your own paper.

1. Which is the correct way to wash the shirt from Felix's Fashions?
   a. in the washing machine with warm water and bleach
   b. by hand
   c. in the washing machine with cold water and no bleach

2. You're going to a party tonight, but all your shirts are dirty. You don't have time to go to the dry cleaners. Which shirt should you forget about wearing?
   a. Cool Dudz
   b. Look-Good Styles
   c. Felix's Fashions

3. Your mom is doing a load of wash in warm water. Which shirt could you throw in with the load?

4. You're doing a load of laundry and adding bleach to the load. Which shirt should NOT go in the wash?
   a. Snazzy Shirts
   b. Felix's Fashions
   c. both of the above

Recommend It

You work in a clothing store. Choose a shirt from page 238 for each of these customers. Steve hates to spend money at the cleaner's. Tonya never wears polyester. Brett won't buy anything that isn't machine washable.

Explain It

How would you wash what you're wearing today? Without looking at the label, write down instructions for cleaning one of the garments you have on. Then if possible, check the label to see how well you did.

" Many Web sites offer tips for clothing care. You might check the Web if you know what a garment is made of, but you do not know how to care for that particular fabric. "

 **Real-World Words**

dry clean: to clean clothes using chemicals instead of water
fabric: the material an item is made from
garment: an item of clothing

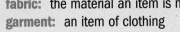

Three Voices

But you know what I think?
I think war makes people crazy

Kids from rich families and poor
families are the same.

10¢
UNITED STATE

So why do
I have to make
my bed?

Jazzimagination

by Sharon M. Draper

Dear Friend,

    I write in my journal every day—not boring stuff, like what color sweater I wore to school today, but thoughts that have been floating in my mind. I grab the thoughts and toss them into this book, where they wait for me to read again when I want to.

    I'm going to let you read my journal because maybe you've had some of the same kinds of thoughts, and maybe it will help you to know that you're not the only one who feels that way.

Love,
Jazzy

Family

Sometimes my mother really gets on my nerves. She'll decide that my room is a mess or I've been on the phone too long and start yelling at me for no reason at all. And just because I'm the kid around here, I have to get off the phone right away—even if I'm in the middle of a really important call with this boy from the bus stop who finally called me—and do something stupid, like clean my room. Why do I have to make my bed in the morning? Nobody is going to see it all day. And when I get home from school the first thing I want to do is get back in bed and rest a few minutes before starting my homework.

So why do I have to make my bed? Must be for the dog, I guess. We've got a cocker spaniel that I love to pieces. She sleeps on my bed while we're gone. She doesn't think I know, but I came home early once and her spot by my pillow was still warm. She looked at me with those big eyes as if she felt guilty. She knows Mama would never allow it. When I'm sick, I let her get up on the bed with me anyway. Mama doesn't like it, but she lets it slide because I'm feeling bad. I guess she really is okay as a mom, but I wish she wouldn't yell so much.

Daddy is tall and skinny and laughs all the time. He likes to tell funny stories. He works at an office downtown. I don't think he likes his job much. He'd much rather be outside in the woods, collecting bugs and leaves. I like to walk in the woods with him. The leaves are crunchy under our feet and the sun seems to shine brighter because he's whistling and happy.

In my family, if I want to find a quiet spot to think my own private thoughts, I can do it. My brother, Devin, is a pain sometimes, but he loves me. He'll tease me until I cry, but then he'll hug me and tickle me until I'm laughing again. He's going away to college next year. It scares me to think he won't be around. Who will answer my silly questions? Who will drive me to the mall?

ASK yourself

- In what ways are Jazzy's mom and dad different?

Reread what she says about each of them.

Names

I love my name. *Jasmine* rolls off my tongue like music. Jasmine is a flower that grows wild and beautiful. Jasmine is not a smell but a **scent** that whispers in the memory. My name is like a poem to me— I can sing it, sigh it, and feel it. It's my name and my poem.

When I whisper my name into the darkness at night, I feel special and warm and okay. And when I tell someone I've just met what my name is, I feel proud and pretty, even if my hair is all messed up. My name is both a weapon when I need it and a shield from the world around me. It protects me, because it is me.

When I was in third grade and the teacher finally let us write in cursive, my favorite letter was the capital *J*. I used to fill whole pages with my lovely, wonderful initials. I think my mama must have been in a really mellow mood when I was born, to give me a name that sounds so good and looks so good on a piece of paper. She gave me Joy as my middle name because she said that she knew I would be a joy in her life. (Some days, when I'm feeling grumpy and not acting very joyful, I bet she wonders if she did the right thing!) At any rate, I always get joy from writing my name and seeing it on paper. Jasmine Joy Jeffries! Even my friends think it's a slick name.

Some of my friends have wonderful, unusual names. There's a boy at my school whose name is LaDonTon—no kidding! I think it sounds like an African drum. His best friend is a boy named Eagle. I think it's wonderful when people are creative with names. It gives style and **individuality** to the person. But sometimes it goes too far. There's a boy at school whose last name is Topp and his first name is Table. I feel a little sorry for him. But he likes it, so who am I to **criticize**? We are what we are what we are.

Words, WORDS, Words

scent: a nice smell
individuality: the things that make a person different from others
criticize: to point out what another person has done wrong

The Air Down Here

by Gil C. Alicea with Carmine DeSena

Here are some of Gil C. Alicea's deepest thoughts. Gil lives in the South Bronx—a tough New York City neighborhood. How much do you have in common? Maybe it's more than you think.

Keeping Secrets

My dad doesn't keep secrets from me 'cause he doesn't want me to keep secrets from him. He tells me everything and wants me to do the same. Even if it's something bad, he just wants me to tell him the truth so I won't have to go through something even longer. The truth makes a bad thing end sooner 'cause eventually it comes out. So it's better to deal with it. I don't always do it, even though I know my dad is right.

Being Materialistic Is Not Everything

Kids from rich families and poor families are the same. There's no difference, except rich kids have money to get what they want.

Being **materialistic** is okay, until you feel you got to have something you can't— you feel you need it. People believe that if they don't have a certain type of sneakers or pants, that their whole life ends there. That they can't go outside anymore. Especially for a holiday or the first day of school. On the first day of school you have to have new sneakers and new clothes. You have to. It's **mandatory**. I don't know why or where it comes from, but it's the way it is! So some kids feel a lot of pressure to have things they can't afford.

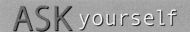
ASK yourself

- Do you think that kids feel pressure to have certain things, like sneakers and clothes?

Think about how you feel.

A Coin for Your Thoughts

I started a coin collection. I have **foreign** coins from Iran, Russia, and the Dominican Republic. It's fun to collect things. You won't get bored 'cause you have things to learn about. You can even get books to learn more about the stuff you have. Now I have new things to talk about with friends or anybody. I have more to talk about than if I'm doing the usual things. It's like, now I have different interests, that I can share. Other people will want to share their interests with me.

Words, WORDS, Words

materialistic: concerned with money or the objects it can buy
mandatory: necessary; important
foreign: from another country

The Media Ghetto

The news shows housing projects burnt down or messed up with garbage everywhere. Like this reporter who came to take pictures. He was telling me to go through these fields to show all the garbage. So people see the pictures he took and say, "Wow." He told me to walk through this street that I would never walk down in my life and dribble my basketball. He thought it would be good. Why would it be good for people to see garbage on the floor, fields of dirt, and stripped cars in the background? Why not show the good parts? If I'm living here, why do I have to go to this block, that I would never in my life go to, and take pictures? I just let it be.

The press looks at people from my neighborhood as being in gangs, not good with money, and a lot of bad stuff. They show people not having anything, not being organized, or always being behind on things.

Like the reporter asked me what would I do with money—buy a pair of sneakers? I thought, a pair of sneakers, what are you talking about? It's kind of dumb. They always have a picture in their head before they do their story. I have other things to think about than a pair of sneakers.

It's like the press thinks everyone where I live is the same. They put us in a **category**, and that's where we stay. It's **negative**, 'cause they think everyone is doing everything wrong just 'cause some people do.

If a news show comes to where I live, it's to put more dirt on our grave. Just to tell people, "Look at this problem or that problem."

Words, WORDS, Words

category: a class or group of things that have something in common
negative: bad; depressing

I Want to Do Something

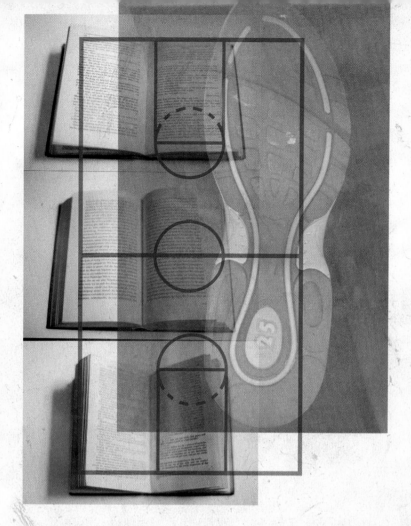

I want to be a professional basketball player. I want to do something. I just want to be famous. I would live in a house with a built-in basketball court, a full court. I want to give the neighborhood something I would have wanted when I was a kid, that no one ever thought of giving us—like indoor basketball, a batting cage, and a swimming pool. Then kids could say, "Why should I hang out on the corner when I could swim or play basketball?" A lot of kids would like it, but they don't have it.

So kids who can't play baseball outside can go indoors to use the batting cage and practice. Then, when they start to get good at it, they'll start to want to be into sports. They would meet friends there and say things like "This guy's good. You should play him." The peer pressure would change to competition—not drugs and stealing.

If I were famous, I would like to share with the neighborhood the things that helped me.

ASK yourself

- How are Gil and Jazzy alike? How are they different?

Think about what you've learned about each of them.

Told What I Already Knew

My dad said Mom was getting sick. I had figured it out on my own but didn't say anything. I was hoping it would go away. But she was losing weight and not doing things the way she used to. She liked the house to be perfect. Now she needed everything done for her. It made me grow up. I want to be more committed to my mom. I think about her now more than myself. I keep hoping that she'll get better, but for now I'll just be with her.

Letter From a
Concentration Camp

by Yoshiko Uchida

Jimbo's letter tells what it feels like to be a Japanese-American kid during World War II. At that time, America was at war with Japan. And Japanese Americans were forced to live in camps. How would you feel if something like this happened to you?

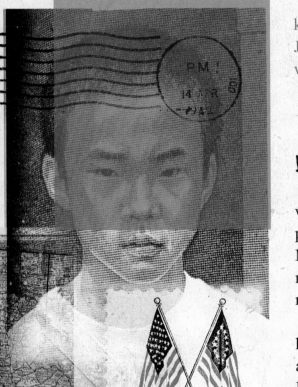

May 6, 1942

Dear Hermie:

Here I am sitting on an army cot in a smelly old horse stall, where Mama, Bud, and I have to live for who knows how long. It's pouring rain, the wind's blowing in through all the cracks, and Mama looks like she wants to cry. I guess she misses Papa. Or maybe what got her down was that long, muddy walk along the racetrack to get to the mess hall for supper.

Anyway, now I know how it feels to stand in line at a soup kitchen with hundreds of hungry people. And that cold potato and weiner they gave me sure didn't make me feel much better. I'm still hungry, and I'd give you my last nickel if you appeared this minute with a big fat hamburger and a bagful of cookies.

You know what? It's like being in jail here—not being free to live in your own house, do what you want, or eat what you want. They've got barbed wire all around this racetrack and guard towers at each corner to make sure we can't get out. Doesn't that sound like a prison? It sure feels like one!

What I want to know is, What am I doing here anyway? *Me*— a genuine born-in-California citizen of the United States of America stuck behind barbed wire, just because I *look* like the enemy in Japan. And how come you're not in here too, with that German blood in your veins and a name like Herman Schnabel?

We're at war with Germany too, aren't we? And with Italy? What about the people at Napoli Grocers?

My brother, Bud, says the U.S. government made a terrible mistake that they'll **regret** someday. He says our leaders **betrayed** us and ignored the Constitution. But you know what I think? I think war makes people crazy. Why else would a smart man like President Franklin D. Roosevelt sign an executive order to force us Japanese Americans out of our homes and lock us up in concentration camps? Why else would the FBI take Papa off to a POW camp just because he worked for a Japanese company? Papa—who loves America just as much as they do.

Hey, ask Mrs. Wilford what that was all about. I mean that stuff she taught us in sixth grade about the Bill of Rights and due process of law. If that means everybody can have a hearing before being thrown in prison, how come nobody gave us a hearing? I guess President Roosevelt forgot about the Constitution when he ordered us into concentration camps. I told you war makes people crazy!

Well, Hermie, I gotta go now. Mama says we should get to the showers before the hot water runs out like it did when she went to do the laundry. Tomorrow she's getting up at 4:00 A.M. to beat the crowd. Can you imagine having to get up in the middle of the night and stand in line to wash your sheets and towels? By hand too! No **luxuries** like washing machines in this dump!

Hey, do me a favor? Go pet my dog, Rascal, for me. He's probably wondering why I had to leave him with Mrs. Harper next door. Tell him I'll be back to get him for sure. It's just that I don't know when. There's a rumor we're getting shipped to some desert—probably in Utah. But don't worry, when this stupid war is over, I'm coming home to California and nobody's ever going to kick me out again! You just wait and see! So long, Hermie.

Your pal,
Jimbo Kurasaki

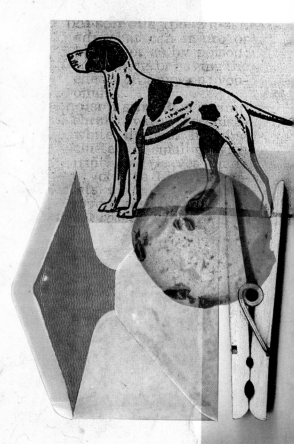

Words, **WORDS**, Words

regret: to be sorry for something
betrayed: failed to help in a time of need
luxuries: things that aren't needed but bring comfort or pleasure

Talk About It

Now that you've read "Jazzimagination," "The Air Down Here," and "Letter From a Concentration Camp," what do you have to say about these questions?

▶ Have you ever kept a journal? Why or why not?

▶ If you were going to write about your life, what subjects would you focus on—friends, family, school, interests, feelings? Explain.

Comprehension Check

Write your answers to the questions below. Use information from the journal entries, essays, and letter to support your answers.

1. Who are the members of Jazzy's family?

2. How does Jazzy feel about her name?

3. Do you agree with Gil that the media shows only negative images of some neighborhoods?

4. Why was the boy in "Letter From a Concentration Camp" sent to live at an abandoned racetrack?

5. How is journal writing different from letter writing?

Vocabulary Check

Complete each sentence with the correct vocabulary word.

**criticize   regret   scent
mandatory   materialistic**

1. The _____ of the apple pie in the oven is making us all hungry.

2. Does liking expensive clothes make a person _____?

3. I _____ that I won't be able to come to your party.

4. When people _____ me, my feelings get hurt.

5. Attendance is _____, which means we have to go.

Write About It

Choose one of the writing prompts below.

▶ Write a letter back to Jimbo Kurasaki. Describe how you feel about what happened to him.

▶ Use Jazzy's journal entries as a model for one of your own. Write a journal entry that tells how you feel about your name.

▶ Gil had some serious ideas. Write a paragraph describing one change that you would like to make in the world. Explain how your idea would make the world a better place.

More to READ

If you enjoyed reading this selection, you might also like:

For Your Eyes Only!
by Joanne Rocklin

A new teacher requires everyone in Lucy Keane's sixth-grade class to keep a journal. In hers, Lucy talks about her feelings about her divorced parents, her best friend, and the problems she has with a boy named Andy. Little does she know that something unusual is about to draw Andy and her together.

Mostly Michael
by Robert Kimmel Smith

When Michael Marder receives a diary for his eleventh birthday, he's disappointed. What a dumb present! But as he starts to write in it, Michael comes to like his diary very much. It's the one place where he can put down his private feelings. But the biggest change is yet to come!

Reading a Mall Directory

You're going to the grand opening of a music store at the mall. How can you find out where the store is? Look at the mall directory! It shows the building's floor plan and lists all the stores in the mall.

Check out the directory and floor plan below. Can you find your way around the mall?

This picture is a floor plan. You read it like you would a map.

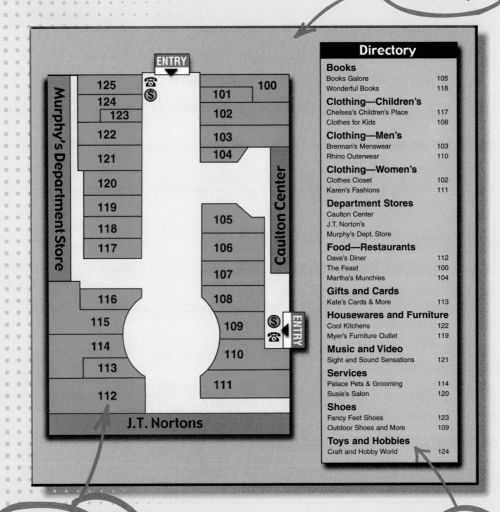

ENTRY

125	100
124	101
123	102
122	103
121	104
120	
119	105
118	106
117	107
116	108
115	109
114	110
113	111
112	

Murphy's Department Store

Caulton Center

ENTRY

J.T. Nortons

Directory

Books
Books Galore   105
Wonderful Books   118

Clothing—Children's
Chelsea's Children's Place   117
Clothes for Kids   108

Clothing—Men's
Brennan's Menswear   103
Rhino Outerwear   110

Clothing—Women's
Clothes Closet   102
Karen's Fashions   111

Department Stores
Caulton Center
J.T. Norton's
Murphy's Dept. Store

Food—Restaurants
Dave's Diner   112
The Feast   100
Martha's Munchies   104

Gifts and Cards
Kate's Cards & More   113

Housewares and Furniture
Cool Kitchens   122
Myer's Furniture Outlet   119

Music and Video
Sight and Sound Sensations   121

Services
Palace Pets & Grooming   114
Susie's Salon   120

Shoes
Fancy Feet Shoes   123
Outdoor Shoes and More   109

Toys and Hobbies
Craft and Hobby World   124

To locate a store, find the store name and number on the directory. Then locate the number on the floor plan.

The directory lists the stores in the mall. The stores are grouped into categories, then listed in alphabetical order.

What's the Plan?

Now it's time to hit the mall! See how well you can follow the floor plan. Review the mall directory and the tips that go with it. Then answer the questions below. Write your answers on your own paper.

1. Where is Sight and Sound Sensations located?
   a. space 101
   b. space 121
   c. space 100

2. You're looking for a store that sells couches. Under which category on the mall directory would you look?
   a. Gifts and Cards
   b. Services
   c. Housewares and Furniture

3. You're going hiking and you need some new shoes. Which store should you check first?
   a. Fancy Feet Shoes
   b. Outdoor Shoes and More
   c. Clothes Closet

4. As you leave Murphy's Department Store, which way would you turn to get to Kate's Cards & More?

5. You're in front of Books Galore and need a snack. Where is the nearest place to get food?
   a. The Feast
   b. Dave's Diner
   c. Martha's Munchies

Map it Out

Look again at the floor plan and directory on page 252. Imagine you're heading to this mall today. List three places you'd like to go. Tell where they're located and how you'd get there.

Write It!

Imagine you're a tour guide at a real or imaginary mall. Write a paragraph that highlights the stores and services at the mall.

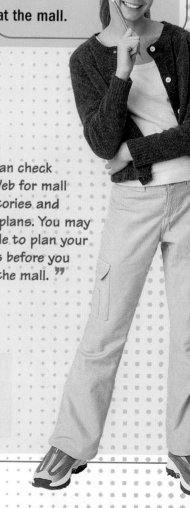

" You can check the Web for mall directories and floor plans. You may be able to plan your stops before you visit the mall. "

Real-World Words

entry: the point at which people can enter a building
directory: a list of names and locations for a specific area
floor plan: a diagram that shows the location of places on one level of a building

WILDFIRES

by Seymour Simon

Over one-third of Yellowstone was going up

A raging wildfire is a frightening thing. Living trees burn as fast as cardboard boxes in a bonfire. Flames race through the treetops, sometimes faster than a person can run, burning at temperatures hot enough to melt steel. A wildfire can be a major disaster, capable of destroying hundreds of homes and costing human lives.

But not all fires are bad. Fires in nature can help as well as harm. A burned forest allows young plants to begin growing. And fire is necessary for some trees, such as sequoias, to release their seeds.

Every year wildfires strike Yellowstone National Park. When this happens, park officials must consider both the needs of the natural world and the danger to human beings.

Yellowstone's forests depend on wildfires to strip away dead trees and renew the soil. But wildfires are a serious threat to tourists and the people who live near the park. In 1988, a series of wildfires took over one-third of Yellowstone. Officials had to act quickly. Turn the page to find out what they did.

in flames. Who could stop the raging fires?

The summer of 1988 was hot and dry in Yellowstone National Park. Almost no rain fell, less than in any year for the previous hundred years. On June 23, a flash of lightning started a fire near Shoshone Lake in the southwest part of the park. In a few weeks, a total of eight major fires were burning. Six of these fires were caused by lightning and were allowed to burn. The other two fires were caused by human carelessness and were fought from the beginning.

Since 1972, Yellowstone Park officials had allowed fires started by lightning to burn themselves out unless they **threatened** structures built by people. In the next sixteen years, there had been over two hundred such natural fires. But as the fires and smoke drove tourists from the park in the summer of 1988, officials changed their minds. In mid-July, they ordered fire fighters to attack the Shoshone fire, which was coming close to the park buildings at Grant Village. Finally the officials abandoned their policy of letting lightning fires burn naturally. They **launched** what was to become the greatest fire-fighting effort in the history of the United States.

The Battle Begins

Hundreds of fire fighters were sent to battle the eight major blazes. But by then, more than fifty smaller ones had started, most from new lightning strikes. The old fires continued to spread, while the small fires raced toward one another and merged into even bigger fires. Giant lodgepole pines and spruce firs burst into flames like matchsticks. Boulders and rocks exploded in the heat of the flames.

There was more bad news. On August 19, gale-force winds gusted to sixty miles per hour, blowing hot embers a mile downwind and starting new fires. The winds also whipped the flames forward and fed them oxygen. Some of the fires moved through the trees at speeds of up to five miles per hour, much faster than most forest fires and as fast as a person can run. On August 20, known as Black Saturday, 165,000 acres of forest, an area more than twice the size of the entire city of Chicago, were burning. But the worst was still ahead.

Flames Threaten a National Park

By early September, most of the fires in the park were completely out of control. Thick clouds of bitter black smoke covered the Yellowstone valley. One of the major fires, the North Fork, was racing toward Old Faithful, the famous geyser. The geyser couldn't burn, but the nearby Old Faithful Inn— the world's largest log cabin, and as **flammable** as a huge tinderbox—was directly in the fire's path.

Weary fire fighters tried to wet down the roof and walls of the inn, but it seemed hopeless. The fire was just too strong. Sparks and glowing embers shot over the cabin and set fire to the trees at the other end of the parking lot. It seemed as if the inn would soon be consumed by flames.

WORDS, WORDS, WORDS

threatened: put in danger
launched: started
flammable: easy to burn

More than 25,000 fire fighters helped save Yellowstone.

ASK YOURSELF

- What caused the fires in the summer of 1988?

Remember that fires need several things to start and grow.

A Change in the Weather

Suddenly, at the last moment, the winds shifted and the fires turned away from Old Faithful. On Saturday, September 10, heavy rains began to drench the area around the inn. The next morning, it snowed. While some fires in the park would continue to burn until November, the worst was over. More than 25,000 fire fighters had been called in to help. They had used more than one hundred fire engines and an

By the time the fires had all died out, over one million acres had burned.

equal number of planes and helicopters to drop millions of gallons of water and chemicals to slow the advancing flames. But it was the weather, not human beings, that finally ended that summer of fire.

By the time the fires had all died out, about 800,000 acres inside the park had burned, along with another 600,000 acres in the national forests and other lands nearby. About 65 buildings had been destroyed, and two people died in the fires. To many people watching on television, it seemed as if the park had been scorched by the flames and would never recover. But that was not so. Nearly two-thirds of the park had not been touched by fire, and even the one-third that had burned was starting to recover.

Some places looked like green islands in a sea of black trees.

Making a Comeback

The wind-driven fires of 1988 left a mosaic of green and black patches in the forests of Yellowstone. Depending upon the extent of the fires, some places looked like green islands in a sea of black trees, while others looked like black tar on a green carpet.

After a fire, burned areas quickly burst into life. In fact, when the ground is still warm from the fires, ants, wood beetles, millipedes, and centipedes are busy. Fire beetles actually seek out fire to breed and lay their eggs in charred logs. The first plants that appear are those whose roots and seeds were there before the fire. But soon new seeds are carried in by the wind and on the fur of animals or in their droppings.

ASK YOURSELF

- Which three states is Yellowstone in?

Look up Yellowstone in an atlas to find the answer.

The green-and-black mosaic favors newly arrived plants and animals. Hawks and owls hunt for food in the opened spaces. Tree-drilling woodpeckers hunt for insects beneath the bark of fallen trees. The dead trees also make good nesting sites; bluebirds and tree swallows move in. The fields of new grasses and wildflowers attract grazing animals, and birds come from all over to catch insects in the meadows.

A New Forest Begins

The forests of Yellowstone are mostly lodgepole pine trees. Many of the lodgepoles were several hundred years old at the time of the 1988 fire. As a lodgepole ages, it doesn't produce enough resin, or sap, to stop insects from **boring** into its bark, which eventually kills the tree. In very old lodgepole forests, many of the standing trees are dead. Fire removes these dead trees, making room for new ones.

Fire also helps the lodgepole reproduce. This tree has two kinds of cones. One opens normally, over time, and its winged seeds whirl to the forest floor. That is how lodgepoles usually sprout. The other kind of seed is **sealed** in a rock-hard pine resin that opens only when

WORDS, WORDS, WORDS

boring: drilling or digging
sealed: closed up

the heat of a fire melts and burns away the resin.

Following the Yellowstone fires, seed counts in burned lodgepole stands were very high, ranging from fifty thousand to one million seeds per acre. All had come from sealed pinecones that were opened by the fire. Most of these seeds would be eaten by chipmunks, squirrels, birds, and other small animals, but some seeds would sprout, starting a new cycle of life in the forest.

The Story Continues

Just two years after the 1988 fires, burned areas had sprouted new plants of all kinds. The pink flowers of fireweed soon appeared. Asters, lupine, and dozens of other kinds of plants grew among the burned trees. Insects returned in great numbers and began to **feast** on the plants. In turn, the insects became food for birds and other insect eaters. Elk and bison grazed on the plants. Chipmunks gathered seeds, and small rodents built nests in the grasses.

The young lodgepole pines are now waist high, and many different kinds of plants surround them. Before the fire, the towering older trees blocked sunlight from the forest floor, allowing only a few other species of plants to flourish there. Without **periodic** fires, low-growing plants that have survived in the park for thousands of years would die off completely.

In fifty to one hundred years, the lodgepoles will again be tall enough to **deprive** other plant species of the light they need to grow. The forest will become mostly pines. Then the fires are likely to return, and the cycle of burning and rebirth will continue.

ASK YOURSELF

- Why are some wildfires good for forests?

Reread to see how wildfires help plants and animals.

Today

Yellowstone is still renewing itself. Burned trees are losing their blackened bark and turning a silvery gray. Meadows are growing around them. The burned areas are slowly fading away. Meanwhile scientists still have a lot to learn about what happens to a forest after a huge fire. One question they ask: How often does an area burn naturally?

The time between natural fires varies, depending upon climate and tree life. In Yellowstone's lodgepole pine forests, the interval between large natural fires is three hundred to four hundred years. In Florida's slash pines, the interval is only seven years. And it is as short as two to five years in the open ponderosa forests of northern Arizona. In the cedarspruce forests of western Washington State, two thousand years can pass between fires!

Wildfires are neither good nor bad. In forests and grasslands, they are part of the endless cycle of change. ●

WORDS, WORDS, WORDS

feast: to eat with great pleasure
periodic: happening from time to time
deprive: to deny or take away

The flame from a single match can start a forest fire.

WHAT IS FIRE?

A fire is a chemical reaction, and it needs three things to burn: fuel, oxygen, and heat. During a fire, energy is released as heat and light, which is why fires are so hot and so bright. When a fire is done, there is nothing left but ash. Ash is the form the fuel takes after the chemical reaction of fire is over.

Fires not only release heat, they are also caused by heat. A fire can be caused by a burning match, a flash of lightning, or a glowing ember in a dying camp fire. Once a fire starts, the heat from the fire can cause other fires to start in nearby materials. A burning leaf can set fire to a nearby leaf without touching it, just from the intense heat. The flaming leaves can then set fire to a branch, which can set fire to the whole tree. In a short while, a fire can leap to another tree, and then another and another. A whole forest can be set ablaze from a tiny fire no bigger than the flame from a match.

SMOKE JUMPER

Does parachuting into a burning forest sound crazy?
These people do it for a living.

by June A. English

Some fire fighters don't arrive by truck—they just jump in.

Smoke jumpers are a special kind of fire fighter. They battle blazes in places that regular fire fighters can't get to. Fires can start in the middle of a wilderness or on the side of a mountain. Fire fighters can't drive to these places in a fire truck.

So, smoke jumpers drop from an airplane close to the fires using parachutes. Dropping from a plane allows them to get to the fire area quickly. But parachuting into forest areas is tricky, especially near raging fires.

Sometimes smoke jumpers get hung up in a tree or smash into a boulder. Jumpers can easily break a leg or arm coming down to the ground. Wind gusts can land them in the wrong place. They may

A super-heated tree can explode without warning.

drop right into the middle of a fire. Occasionally parachutes fail. Then the jumper has to use her emergency chute to keep from crashing to the ground.

Smoke jumping is hard physical work. Jumpers have to be in top shape. Because they work in remote areas, they have to carry tools with them. These can include pickaxes, chain saws, and a digging tool called a pulaski. After fighting a fire, a smoke jumper has to hike out of the area. This can mean traveling miles with a hundred pounds of supplies on her back.

Danger on the Job

Working around any kind of fire is dangerous. Tree fires are especially unpredictable. A super-heated tree can explode without warning. Burning trees can fall on fire fighters, killing or injuring them.

Fires can also spread with lightning speed. Fire fighters have to be sensitive to changes in the wind that can start cross fires. They have to notice changes in temperature. This could mean flames are moving their way.

Flames can spread around fire fighters, trapping them in an inferno. So it's important that they figure out safe zones to work in. They need escape routes in case the fire becomes too fierce for them to stay.

Sometimes smoke jumpers can't escape from a blaze. So they have to try to survive inside it. They drop flat to the ground. Then they cover themselves with special flame-resistant blankets until the fire passes over them. This is a last resort though. Only a lucky few will survive in the middle of a raging forest fire.

One of the Few

Smoke jumper Tiffan Thoele worked on a fire-fighting crew for six seasons. "Most of the training was physical," says Tiffan, who lives in Oregon. "We learned how to jump out of a heavy plane, how to do landing rolls, and how to get out of trees."

Tiffan also learned first aid and worked her way through a heavy-duty exercise program. Smoke jumpers also need a good basic education. But their instincts and drive are just as important. "A good fire fighter needs to be able to think in stressful situations," says Tiffan. "And they need a little bit of healthy fear. Every fire has the potential to be harmful."

There are fewer than 400 smoke jumpers in the United States. Tiffan is glad that she's one of them. For her, the thrill of the job includes the great people she gets to work with. The beautiful natural scenery she sees also makes her job special. "Few people," says Tiffan, "get to do what I do and see what I see." ●

Talk About It

Now that you've read *Wildfires* and "Smoke Jumper," what do you have to say about these questions?

▶ What do you think is the most frightening thing about a wildfire?

▶ What does the force and power of wildfires teach you about nature?

Comprehension Check

Write your answers to the questions below. Use information from the article and profile to support your answers.

1. Why did park officials decide to put out the fires in Yellowstone?

2. What would happen if people put out all wildfires?

3. Do you agree with the decision to fight the fires at Yellowstone? Why or why not?

4. Why does a smoke jumper need to be in top physical shape?

5. How might smoke jumpers help fight fires at Yellowstone?

Vocabulary Check

Complete each starter sentence below. Before you answer, think about the meaning of the vocabulary word in bold.

1. My lunch is **sealed** in a . . .

2. An example of something **flammable** is . . .

3. At Thanksgiving, my family likes to **feast** on . . .

4. I noticed that insects were **boring** into . . .

5. The teacher made **periodic** checks of . . .

Write About It

Choose one of the writing prompts below.

▶ Imagine you're a fire fighter and have just spent a week fighting a blaze. Write a letter home telling what you've seen and done. Remember to use lots of details.

▶ Whether you arrive by truck or parachute, fighting fires is a dangerous job. Do you think you'd like a job fighting forest fires? Write a paragraph telling why or why not.

▶ Have you ever lived through a disaster—a hurricane, tornado, or earthquake? What was it like? Write a short description of what happened.

Fact FILE

The best way to learn about Yellowstone National Park is to go there. If you're lucky enough to make the trip, here are some things you might see:

Geysers There are hundreds of geysers, but the most famous is "Old Faithful." It shoots water over 100 feet high and erupts (faithfully) about every two hours.

Wildlife There are over 400 kinds of animals, including moose, trumpeter swans, coyotes, and grizzly bears.

Hot Springs These are nature's own hot tubs. But be careful. Some hot springs are much too hot for humans.

Waterfalls There are over 40 waterfalls, including Fairy Falls, Mystic Falls, and Tower Falls. The pools below are great places to fish.

Can't make it to the park in person? Try checking out Yellowstone on the Web at this address: www.nps.gov/yell/home.htm

Following a Bus Map

You and a friend want to go to the movies, but you don't have a ride. Why not take the bus? It will take you right to the theater. All you have to do is figure out the bus map.

Check out this bus map. Are you ready to travel across town?

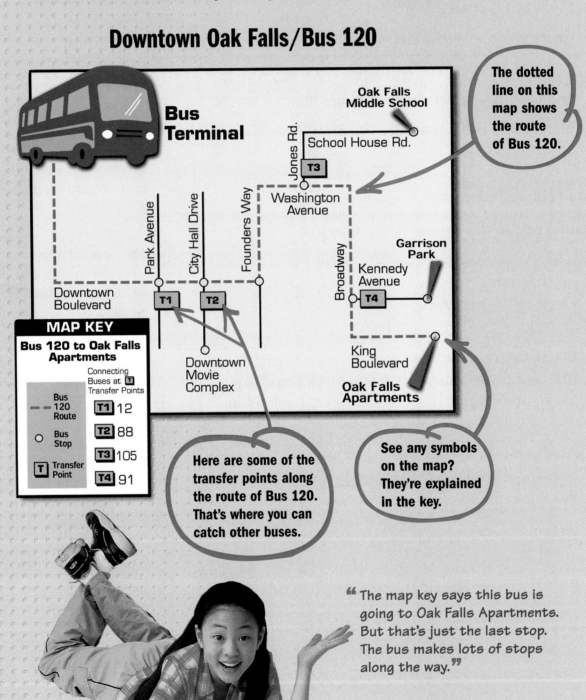

Downtown Oak Falls/Bus 120

The dotted line on this map shows the route of Bus 120.

Here are some of the transfer points along the route of Bus 120. That's where you can catch other buses.

See any symbols on the map? They're explained in the key.

MAP KEY

Bus 120 to Oak Falls Apartments

Connecting Buses at **T** Transfer Points

- - - Bus 120 Route

○ Bus Stop

T Transfer Point

T1 12
T2 88
T3 105
T4 91

" The map key says this bus is going to Oak Falls Apartments. But that's just the last stop. The bus makes lots of stops along the way. "

Map It Out!

Review the bus map and the tips that go with it. Then use them to answer the following questions. Write your answers on your own paper.

1. How many stops does Bus 120 make from the bus terminal to the Oak Falls Apartments?
   a. 9 (not including the bus terminal or last stop)
   b. 7 (not including the bus terminal or last stop)
   c. 5 (not including the bus terminal or last stop)

2. You're at the Oak Falls Apartments and would like to get to the Downtown Movie Complex. On which street would you catch Bus 120?
   a. Kennedy Avenue
   b. Broadway
   c. King Boulevard

3. You're on Bus 120. You're headed for the Downtown Movie Complex. At which transfer point should you get off Bus 120 and catch a bus that will go to the Downtown Movie Complex?
   a. T1
   b. T2
   c. T3

4. Which bus will drop you off right in front of the Downtown Movie Complex?

5. You want to take the bus from the Oak Falls Apartments to the Oak Falls Middle School. Write a description of how you'd get there.

Tour the Town

You're at the bus terminal. You want to take the bus to pick up a friend who lives on Park Avenue, then a friend who lives on School House Road. You three will then go to Garrison Park. Write a description of what buses you'll take and where you'll transfer.

Plan Your Route

Plan a bus route from your school to a place close by. What is the most direct route? Where would the bus stop?

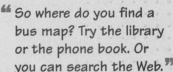

" So where do you find a bus map? Try the library or the phone book. Or you can search the Web. "

Shorter Poems

By Angela Johnson

Picture your own neighborhood. Now, imagine how it might feel to see it for the last time.

Angela Johnson gets a letter from her grandmother. It contains some sad news: "They're pullin' Shorter down." Shorter is the small town in Alabama where Angela grew up. So she takes a trip back for one last visit. These poems describe what she saw and how she felt.

Welcome to Shorter, Alabama.

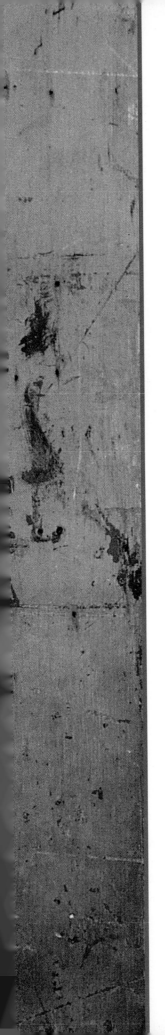

Pullin' Shorter Down

Got the letter yesterday.
"They're pullin' Shorter down," Grandmama writes.
Some big company wanting to make a dog track.
In a few weeks we're on the road and can't get
there fast enough.
Town's coming down in a few months.
"Everybody sold out and mostly gone already," Grandmama
says in the letter and, "Come see your past before it's all dust, baby."
I loved and hated the place.
Not enough room in the world
to tell my feelings about Shorter.
And now they're pullin' it all down.

Shorter

Got to Shorter and saw it all
from the car window.
House music blasting from the
cassette player.
Mama in a **daze** and not saying much
except, "Look at that," at the fields
and the boarded-up houses that just
last year I used to run in and out of.
"Can't count on much anymore."
And I think, No
you can't. . . .

Hiding Place

Yesterday found the old shack by Line Creek
that hid me for a whole afternoon when I was seven.
Ran away when my dog died.
Uncle Jack having to shoot it after it got hit.
No vets in Shorter then.
No doctors, dentists, or drugstores either.
The shack might be the only thing that
stays standing in Shorter, but I can't hide
there anymore.
Looked at it for a while, then passed it up
to face the **reality** of Shorter.

ASK Yourself

- Where does the narrator hide
  when she is seven?

Go over the details in the poem
"Hiding Place."

crazy

You'd have to be
crazy
to want to live
your life in
a place like Shorter, Alabama.
The heat,
the red ants, and
twenty miles to
any mall.
You'd have to be crazy
to want to live
in a place where
every other person is
related to you
and thinks they know
everything about your
life.
You'd have to be crazy
to want to wake
up every morning to sweet
magnolia and **moist** red
dirt.
You'd have to be
crazy.

War II

My daddy had Vietnam dreams.
Nightmares that used
to rip him out of bed screaming
and running into the living room.
Helicopters machine-gunned
down on him, and he
used to yell that he couldn't
get the blood off.
And near the end I didn't even
wake up anymore.
I didn't hear Mama saying,
"Baby, baby, baby."
And I couldn't hear him crying.
So at the end I was almost
deaf,
and the silence wrapped
me up warm.
And I didn't know it,
but that war in the jungle
had followed my daddy all the way
to Shorter.

Words, WORDS, Words

daze: the state of being stunned and unable to think clearly
reality: the facts of life that must be faced
related: part of the same family
moist: slightly wet

Where You Been

Grandmama says
when the last of Shorter is gone,
everybody's gonna talk what's left of it
all to the
ground.
And they're gonna say
it's not where we've been
but where we're going,
and that would be a lie.
We've been away
and come back.
We lived in back of the woods
and moved to town.
We've died in wars
and sometimes waited for
the wars to come home to kill us.
She looks at me,
and wipes her face
with a lace handkerchief,
and I know the world is a
whole lot different when you're
fourteen and leaving,
finally leaving,
the red, red dirt of Alabama. ●

ASK Yourself

- How do you think the narrator feels about leaving Shorter in this poem?

Retell what you think the poem is about in your own words.

Luck

by Elena Castedo

For some people, the grass is always greener someplace else.
For others, home is sweet no matter where it is.
Which attitude is most like your own?

Cast of Characters

GROUP 1	GROUP 2
Person 1	Person 6
Person 2	Person 7
Person 3	Person 8
Person 4	Person 9
Person 5	Person 10

ACT 1

As the story begins, people in Group 1 are living in the valley.

Person 1: We are in shadows here already. Look, the mountain back there still has sunshine. *(The person points to the people living on the mountain.)*

Person 2: That's why I hate living down here in the valley; it's dark in the morning and dark in the evening.

Person 3: We don't get any views down here.

Person 4: Up there on the mountain, they get all the summer breezes.

Person 5: Why should they get all the luck? It's not fair.

Person 1: There must be something we can do.

Person 2: Why don't we move to the mountain?

Person 3: Because there are only five houses up there, and they took them all. *(The person motions to the people living on the mountain.)*

Person 4: Maybe we can **exchange** our houses for theirs.

Person 5: What a great idea!

Person 3: They probably won't want to do that.

Person 4: Maybe we should pay them some extra money.

Person 2: How much money do we have?

(They take out bills from their pockets, count, and share.)

Person 1: We'll make them an offer they can't refuse.

People 1 to 5: Yes, yes, what a great idea. Let's go. Let's go ask them!

ACT 2

Person 1: Hello, we are the people from the valley. We are interested in exchanging houses; our houses are very nice.

(People in Group 2 look at one another with surprise.)

Person 6: Hi, thank you for your offer, but we don't want to exchange houses.

Person 7: We like it up here on the mountain. We get a lot of sunshine.

Person 8: And breezes in the summer.

Person 9: And we like the beautiful view of the valley.

Person 10: The air is very clean up here.

Person 7: We are so lucky to be here on the mountain.

Person 6: We are sorry you got the idea we wanted to exchange houses.

Person 2: Our houses are in better shape than yours; it would be a very good deal for you.

Person 1: And we are prepared to pay you extra. *(Person 1 hands a wad of bills to Person 6.)*

Person 6: Okay. We'll exchange houses.

*(People in Group 1 shake hands to **congratulate** one another and smile as they move to the mountain.)*

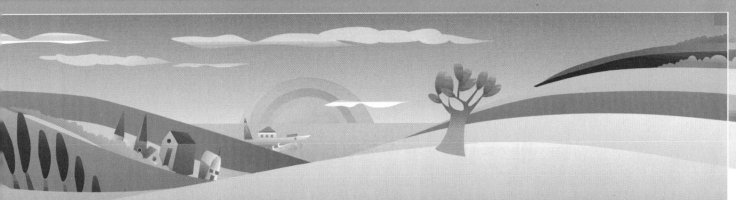

ACT 3

*(People in Group 1 make **gestures** of being cold and tired. People in Group 2 are talking in the area that represents the valley.)*

Person 6: I had no idea life was so pleasant down here in the valley.

(People in Group 1, now living on the mountain, stop and listen to the other group. First, they put a finger to their lips, then put a hand behind an ear or lean forward to show they are listening.)

Person 7: Me, too. These wells are full of delicious water.

Person 8: It doesn't cost much to keep houses warm in the valley.

Person 9: It's lovely not to have so much wind.

Person 10: Have you noticed how easy it is to plant a garden?

Person 6: The view of the mountains is beautiful.

Person 8: Everything is so much easier than going up and down slopes.

Person 7: We are so lucky to be in the valley.

(People in Group 1 are unhappy. They whisper to one another, nod in agreement, and search their pockets.)

Person 1: We would like to get our houses back.

Person 6: These are our houses now, and we like them.

Person 2: You said before that you liked living on the mountain.

Person 3: We are prepared to pay you extra.

Person 1: We think you'll find this very attractive. *(Person 1 hands the bills to Person 6.)*

Person 6: Okay. We'll exchange houses.

*(People in Group 2 return to the mountains. People in Group 1 shake hands to congratulate one another but without as much **enthusiasm** as before.)*

Person 6: How nice, we still have sunshine; look, down in the valley it's all in shadows already. *(Person 6 points to the people in the valley.)*

Person 9: The air is so fresh here.

Person 10: What a beautiful view!

Person 8: And we have lots of money that the people from the valley gave us.

Person 7: The main thing is, we are so lucky to be here on the mountain. ●

exchange: to switch one thing for another
congratulate: to express happiness about something
gestures: actions that express a feeling
enthusiasm: excitement

TALK ABOUT IT

Now that you've read *Shorter Poems* and *Luck,* what do you have to say about these questions?

▶ What do you think you might remember most about your hometown? Explain.

▶ Do you agree that people make their own luck? Explain why or why not.

COMPREHENSION CHECK

Write your answers to the questions below. Use information from the poems and the play to support your answers.

1. Why does the poet take the trip back to Shorter?

2. Do you think the poet cares that Shorter is being torn down? Why or why not?

3. Do you think most people have strong feelings about where they grow up? Explain.

4. Why do people in Group 1 want to leave the valley at the beginning of the play?

5. Do you think the poet feels lucky that she lived in Shorter?

VOCABULARY CHECK

Answer each question below with a complete sentence. Before you answer, think about the meaning of the vocabulary word in bold.

1. Why might you **exchange** a shirt you got as a present?

2. How would you describe someone who is in a **daze**?

3. How might you **congratulate** a friend who did well on a test?

4. What **gestures** could you make to stop someone from talking too loudly?

5. How would you like having more people that you are **related** to go to your school?

WRITE ABOUT IT

Choose one of the writing prompts below.

▶ Write a poem about a special memory or place from your childhood. Use a lot of interesting details.

▶ Write a short newspaper article about Shorter being torn down. Include information you learned from the poems. Think about how this will change people's lives.

▶ How important is luck? Write a paragraph stating your opinion. In it, give reasons that explain your point of view.

About the AUTHOR

Angela Johnson often writes about her childhood, but she doesn't just write poems.

Check out these other books by Angela Johnson:

Heaven

At 14 Marley knows two things. She has her Momma's hands. And she shares her Pop's love for ice cream. But Marley soon discovers that she doesn't know the most important thing about her family—the truth.

Songs of Faith

It is 1975 and 13-year-old Doreen is dealing with the usual struggles of being a kid. She lives in a small town in Ohio, and her parents are getting divorced. She tells her own story in this moving novel.

Following Instructions

You've just gotten hired to baby-sit. You really want to do a good job. How will you make sure you do? You'll have to follow instructions.

Take a look at this list Tim's parents left for his baby-sitter. Could you follow these instructions?

Baby-sitting Instructions

Pay careful attention to the times at which you are supposed to follow each instruction.

Some of these instructions *must* be followed. Others are optional. Be sure you know the difference.

Important Phone Numbers

The Newmans (neighbors)   555-5678
Poison Control   555-9012
                          (or 911, in an emergency)
Police Department   555-3456 (or 911)
Fire Department   555-7890 (or 911)

Reminders

- Tim may not have sweets after 6 p.m.
- Let out the dog around 7 p.m.
- Make sure the doors are locked if you and Tim go outside.
- If you get locked out, the spare key is hidden under the planter near the front door.
- Tim may watch one-half hour of TV before bedtime.
- Make sure Tim brushes his teeth before bed.
- Bedtime is 8 p.m.
- Tim may read for a few minutes at bedtime, or you may read him a story.
- We'll be home by 10 p.m.
- Help yourself to food and drinks in the refrigerator.
- In case of an emergency, call us at the Halls, 555-4992.

Make sure you know what to do in an emergency.

"Read through the instructions while your employer is still there. That way, you can ask him or her about anything that's unclear."

Follow Along

Are you ready to get to work? Reread the instructions on the left and the tips that go with them. Then use them to answer these questions. Write your answers on your own paper.

1. Where are Tim's parents? What is the phone number where they can be reached?

2. At what time should you let out the dog? What should you do if you leave the house?

3. It's 7:30 P.M. Tim wants a snack. Which two snacks could you give him?
   a. a chocolate bar
   b. a slice of cheese
   c. a dish of ice cream
   d. some carrot sticks

4. You and Tim go for a walk. You lock the door behind you—but forget to take the key! What should you do?
   a. Go to the Newmans' house.
   b. Call the police.
   c. Get the spare key from its hiding place.
   d. Call Tim's parents.

5. What must Tim do before he goes to bed?
   a. Walk the dog.
   b. Brush his teeth.
   c. Watch TV.
   d. Eat some sugar.

Report on It

Write a note to Tim's parents, telling them how the evening went. Make sure you tell what Tim ate, what he did, and when he went to bed.

Write Instructions

You've got a pet (real or imaginary). Your friend is going to take care of it while you are away on vacation. Write a set of instructions for your friend.

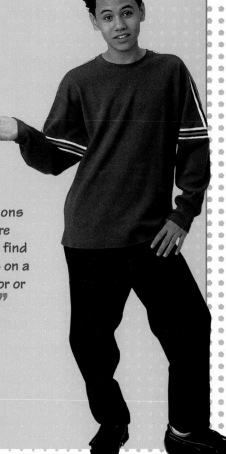

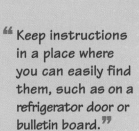
" Keep instructions in a place where you can easily find them, such as on a refrigerator door or bulletin board. "

instructions: a set of rules or directions for doing a task
optional: okay, but not necessary
spare: extra

Narrative of the Life of

FREDERICK DOUGLASS

**A GRAPHIC CLASSIC BY
TERRY M. WEST**

**BASED ON THE AUTOBIOGRAPHY BY
FREDERICK DOUGLASS**

Frederick Douglass grew up in slavery. For 20 years, he worked on other people's farms. He chopped other people's wood. He took care of other people's children. For all his hard work, he received no money. He was given no bed and not enough food. And he was beaten.

In 1838, he escaped. Later, he wrote a book about his life. He wanted people to know the horrors of slavery. He wanted them to know that it was wrong. His book became one of the most famous autobiographies in American history.

"You have seen how a man was made a slave," Frederick Douglass wrote. "You shall see how a slave was made a man."

In 1865, an amendment to the Constitution ended slavery in this country forever. Frederick Douglass lived to see this happen—and lived 30 years more.

I WAS BORN IN MARYLAND. I BARELY KNEW MY MOTHER. HER OWNER TOOK ME FROM HER WHEN I WAS A BABY. I'M NOT EVEN SURE HOW OLD I AM.

MY MOTHER'S NAME WAS HARRIET BAILEY. I SAW HER ONLY FOUR OR FIVE TIMES WHEN I WAS A CHILD. SHE LIVED ABOUT 12 MILES AWAY.

SHE WORKED ALL DAY. THEN SHE WALKED TO SEE ME AT NIGHT. SHE SANG ME TO SLEEP. WHEN I WOKE UP, SHE WAS GONE.

I WAS TOO YOUNG TO WORK IN THE FIELDS. MY JOB WAS TO KEEP THE CHICKENS OUT OF THE GARDEN.

Be good! Or you'll feel my whip!

I WASN'T WHIPPED VERY OFTEN, BUT I WAS HUNGRY AND COLD A LOT.

AT NIGHT I HAD NO BED. I STOLE A LARGE CANVAS BAG. I WOULD CRAWL INTO IT ON THE COLD, DAMP FLOOR. THERE I WOULD SLEEP.

AT DINNER, THEY FED US BOILED CORNMEAL. IT WAS PLACED IN A LARGE WOODEN TRAY AND SET ON THE GROUND. THEN THEY CALLED THE CHILDREN TO EAT. THERE WAS NEVER ENOUGH.

ASK YOURSELF

- What were some of Frederick's problems growing up?

Make a list on a separate piece of paper.

WHEN I WAS SEVEN OR EIGHT, MY MASTER SENT ME AWAY.

You'll leave in a few days, Frederick.

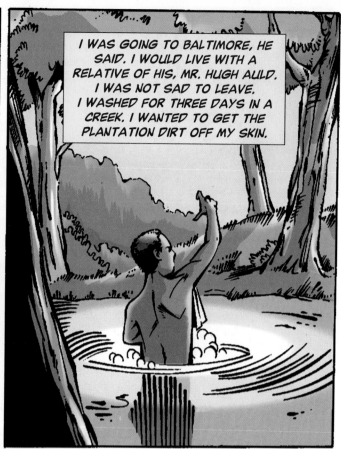

I WAS GOING TO BALTIMORE, HE SAID. I WOULD LIVE WITH A RELATIVE OF HIS, MR. HUGH AULD. I WAS NOT SAD TO LEAVE. I WASHED FOR THREE DAYS IN A CREEK. I WANTED TO GET THE PLANTATION DIRT OFF MY SKIN.

I GOT ON A BOAT HEADED FOR BALTIMORE.

AND I DID NOT LOOK BACK.

ASK YOURSELF

- Why do you think Frederick was glad to go to Baltimore?

Think about what life was like on the plantation.

MR. AND MRS. AULD MET ME AT THE DOOR. THEIR LITTLE SON, THOMAS, WAS WITH THEM. MY JOB WAS TO LOOK AFTER HIM.

Welcome to our home, Frederick.

SOPHIA AULD DECIDED TO TEACH ME TO READ.

Soon you two will be reading to me!

SHE HAD NEVER HAD A SLAVE BEFORE. I WAS SHOCKED BY HER KINDNESS.

ONE DAY, MR. AULD FOUND OUT WHAT WAS GOING ON. HE TOLD HIS WIFE TO STOP TEACHING ME.

You cannot teach a slave to read! It's dangerous and against the law!

If you teach Frederick how to read, he will feel like he's equal to us.

He will be unhappy. He will think he shouldn't be a slave.

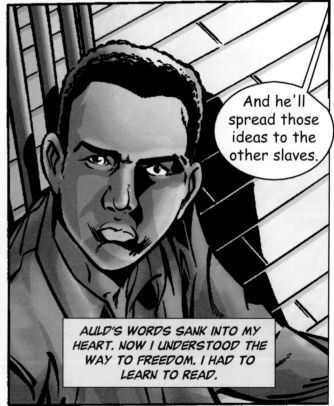

And he'll spread those ideas to the other slaves.

AULD'S WORDS SANK INTO MY HEART. NOW I UNDERSTOOD THE WAY TO FREEDOM. I HAD TO LEARN TO READ.

OWNING A SLAVE CHANGED MRS. AULD. HER HEART BECAME STONE. IF SHE SAW ME READING A NEWSPAPER, SHE WOULD SNATCH IT FROM MY HANDS.

How often must I tell you?

You must not read!

BUT I DID NOT GIVE UP. I MADE FRIENDS WITH POOR WHITE BOYS ON THE STREET. I BROUGHT THEM BREAD. AND THEY HELPED ME LEARN.

Watch me, Frederick. This is how you spell "house."

HOUSE

ON MONDAYS I WAS LEFT ALONE IN THE HOUSE. I SPENT THE TIME WRITING. I FILLED IN THE SPACES IN THOMAS'S NOTEBOOK.

I COPIED WHAT HE WROTE. SLOWLY, MY HANDWRITING BEGAN TO LOOK LIKE HIS.

I WAS ABOUT 14 WHEN I WAS SENT BACK TO THE PLANTATION.

MY NEW MASTER WAS VERY CRUEL. HE KEPT US SLAVES HUNGRY.

You've gone soft from the city life! Now go get my horse!

HE WAS NEVER HAPPY WITH ME. I WAS ALWAYS LETTING HIS HORSE RUN OFF.

THIS WAS NOT AN ACCIDENT. IT WOULD RUN FIVE MILES TO ANOTHER FARM. I WOULD GO AFTER IT. WHEN I GOT THERE, I ALWAYS GOT SOMETHING GOOD TO EAT.

Don't worry. I'll teach this boy to obey!

MY MASTER COULDN'T STAND IT. HE SENT ME TO LIVE WITH A MAN NAMED EDWARD COVEY. COVEY WAS KNOWN FOR BREAKING THE SPIRITS OF SLAVES.

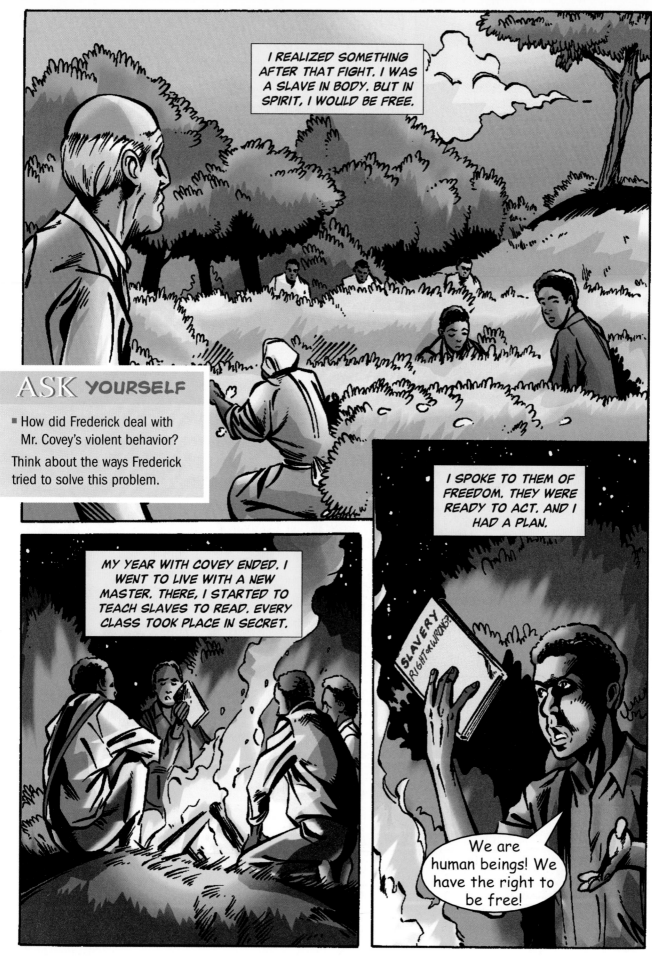

IN THE NORTH, SLAVERY WAS ILLEGAL. WE HAD TO GET THERE.

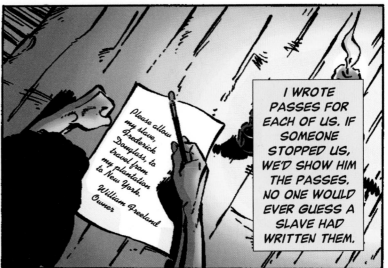

Please allow my slave, Frederick Douglass, to travel from my plantation to New York.

William Freeland Owner

I WROTE PASSES FOR EACH OF US. IF SOMEONE STOPPED US, WE'D SHOW HIM THE PASSES. NO ONE WOULD EVER GUESS A SLAVE HAD WRITTEN THEM.

I'm afraid.

THE DAY OF OUR ESCAPE FINALLY CAME. WHEN I WOKE UP, I HAD A BAD FEELING. SOMETHING SEEMED WRONG.

I WAS RIGHT. SOMEONE HAD TOLD ON US. WE WERE ALL ARRESTED. WE WERE LUCKY THEY DID NOT HANG US.

I WAS RETURNED TO MY OLD MASTER. HE SENT ME BACK TO HUGH AND SOPHIA AULD IN BALTIMORE.

AULD GOT ME A JOB. AND HE KEPT MOST OF THE PAY.

Here's 12 dollars. It's what I earned this week.

Keep six cents for yourself.

STILL, I ALWAYS WORKED HARD. I WANTED MY MASTER TO THINK THAT I WAS HAPPY. I DIDN'T WANT HIM TO GUESS THAT I WAS PLANNING MY ESCAPE. THEN, ONE DAY, I WAS GONE....

BEFORE LONG, I MARRIED A WOMAN NAMED ANNA MURRAY. WE MOVED TO MASSACHUSETTS. THERE I TOOK ANY WORK I COULD FIND. I SAWED AND CARRIED WOOD. I SHOVELED COAL. I SWEPT CHIMNEYS.

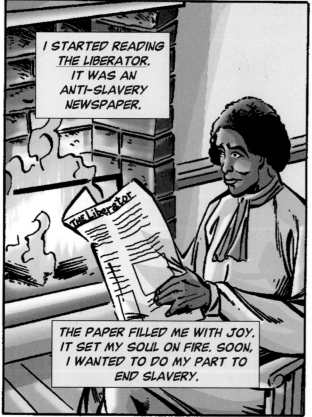

I STARTED READING THE LIBERATOR. IT WAS AN ANTI-SLAVERY NEWSPAPER.

THE PAPER FILLED ME WITH JOY. IT SET MY SOUL ON FIRE. SOON, I WANTED TO DO MY PART TO END SLAVERY.

I WAS NERVOUS AT FIRST. BUT I KNEW I HAD TO TELL MY STORY. SO I BEGAN TO SPEAK AT ANTI-SLAVERY MEETINGS.

TALK ABOUT IT

Now that you've read *Narrative of the Life of Frederick Douglass,* what do you have to say about these questions?

▶ Why is reading so important? What power does it give you?

▶ Do you think Frederick Douglass's autobiography might have helped to end slavery? Why or why not?

COMPREHENSION CHECK

Write your answers to the questions below. Use information from the graphic classic to support your answers.

1. How does Frederick's life change after he moves from the plantation to Baltimore?

2. Why was Frederick Douglass no longer willing to take beatings from Mr. Covey?

3. Why do you think that learning to read would make someone even more unhappy about being a slave?

4. Who do you think might have told on the slaves who were trying to run away?

5. How did reading about Frederick Douglass's life make you feel about him? about slavery?

WRITE ABOUT IT

Choose one of the writing prompts below.

▶ Frederick Douglass never says what his escape plan was. He wanted other slaves to be able to use it. Make up an escape plan Douglass might have used to get to the North. Describe what he might have done.

▶ Imagine that you are a slave and want to learn to read. Write a list of three reasons why you feel this is an important thing to do. Explain each reason.

▶ Frederick Douglass gave many anti-slavery speeches. Write a short speech that he might have given when slavery was ended in the United States.

More to READ

Escape From Slavery: The Boyhood of Frederick Douglass In His Own Words
by Frederick Douglass and Michael McCurdy (editor)

For more of the Frederick Douglass story, read this shortened version of his autobiography. With the power of his words, Douglass brought to life the horrors of slavery and his own struggle for freedom.

Harriet Tubman: Conductor on the Underground Railroad
by Ann Petry

From the time she was a small child, Harriet Tubman was forced to work as a slave in the fields. She was treated badly by her owner. Finally, leaving her family behind, she ran away to the North. There she became a "conductor" on the Underground Railroad. This is the story of the courageous woman who guided over 300 slaves to freedom.

Reading a Train Schedule

You're planning a visit to your grandmother's house. You're going to take the train to her town. But how will you know when to head for the train station? You need to check a schedule.

Take a look at the train schedule below. Read all about it. Will you be able to make your train?

Tree Line Train Schedule

Pinesville to Forestown
Express and Local Trains
Weekend Schedule, valid April – September

Tree Line Trains

STATION	A.M.	A.M.	A.M.	A.M.
Pinesville	8:02	8:25	8:48	9:10
Birchton	8:15	-----	9:01	----
Oakdale	8:32	8:44	9:18	9:29
Dogwood	8:41	----	9:27	----
Beechgrove	8:52	----	9:38	----
Forestown	9:05	9:15	9:51	10:00

> Make sure you look for A.M. or P.M. The trains on this schedule all run in the morning.

> No time is listed here because this train does not stop at this station. Trains that skip stations are called "express" trains.

> Each column represents a different train. The times show when the train stops at each station.

> " Notice that this train schedule is for weekend mornings from April to September. Train lines often have different schedules for weekdays and weekends. "

All Aboard

Ready to ride the rails? Review the schedule and the tips that go with it. Then use them to answer the questions below. Write your answers on your own paper.

1. How many stations are on the Tree Line train line?
   a. 4
   b. 5
   c. 6

2. You're traveling from Birchton to Forestown. You need to be in Forestown by 9:20 A.M. Which train should you take?
   a. the 8:15 A.M. train from Birchton
   b. the 9:01 A.M. train from Birchton
   c. the 9:10 A.M. train from Pinesville

3. You're taking the 8:48 A.M. train from Pinesville to Dogwood. What time will you get to Dogwood? Your friend in Oakdale wants to take the same train. What time should he catch it?

4. Which trains are express trains? At which stations do the express trains stop?

5. How long is the trip from Pinesville to Forestown on the express train? On the local train?
   a. 63 minutes express; 50 minutes local
   b. 45 minutes express; 40 minutes local
   c. 50 minutes express; 63 minutes local
   d. 1 hour express; 2 hours local

Plan It

Tell which train each of these people should catch. Cori lives in Birchton. She's meeting her cousin at the Dogwood station at 8:45 A.M. Kyle lives in Oakdale and works in Beechgrove. Her job begins at 10 A.M. on Saturdays.

Schedule It

Add an afternoon train that leaves Forestown at 1 P.M. and goes to Pinesville. It will make all express stops. Where will it stop? What time will it arrive at each stop?

" Need a train schedule? Try looking on the Web. Just type the name of the train service into a search engine. "

Real-World Words

express: a train that skips stops in order to reach other stops more quickly
local: a train that stops at every station
valid: okay to use

Secrets of the

Mumm

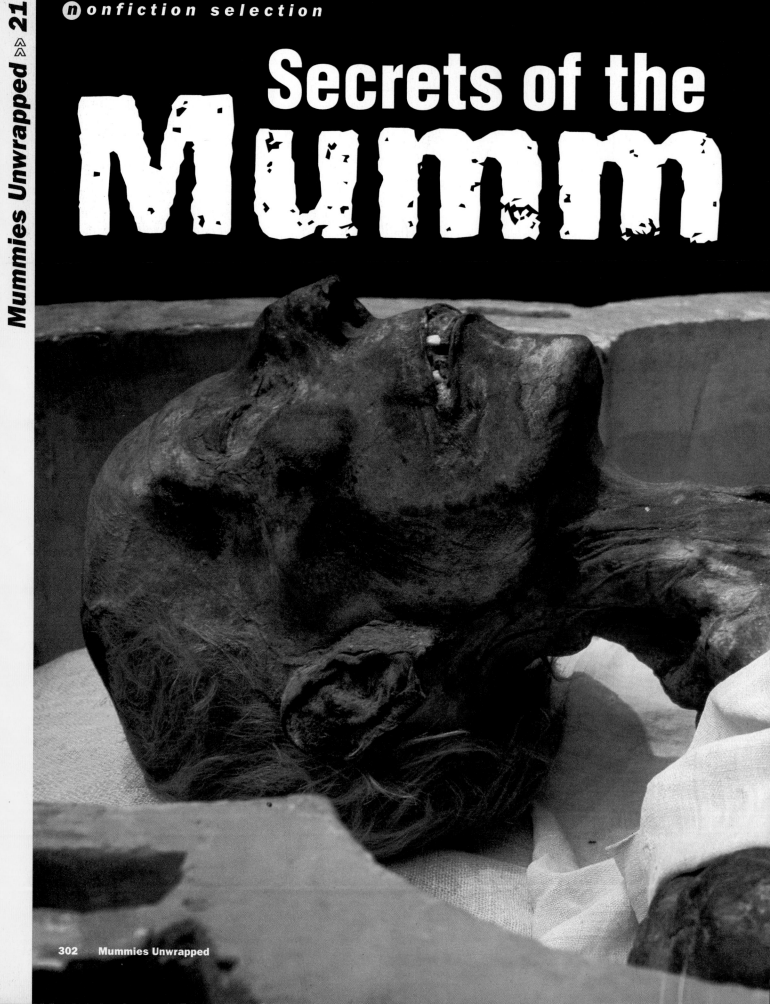

ies

from the book by
Shelley Tanaka

If mummies could talk, what would they tell us?

Throughout history, in many different parts of the world, people have wanted to preserve their dead. Once a living being dies, its body begins to decay. Slowly the soft parts rot away and are eaten by insects until only the bones and teeth are left. Over time, even these will crumble away to nothing. If this process, called decomposition (DEE-comp-uh-ZIH-shun), can be stopped, you end up with a preserved corpse—a mummy.

There are many different kinds of mummies that have survived thousands of years.

Most mummies we know about, however, come from Egypt. They were made three to four thousand years ago, and many have been discovered during the past 200 years. For the Egyptians, mummy making was a serious art. It was an important part of their beliefs. And it said a great deal about how they viewed their world and their lives.

Old Beliefs

The Egyptians believed that a person's spirit lived on after death. During the day, the spirit would leave the body and fly freely around the next world. But at night, it had to return to its tomb in the present world. Unless the body was kept looking lifelike, the spirit would not recognize it. (Many mummies were given masks, and coffins had faces painted on them to help the spirit recognize its earthly home.)

To remain whole, a body had to be protected from things that would cause it to decompose: air, moisture, and insects. First, embalmers (em-BAHL-mers) removed the brain, lungs, stomach, liver, and intestines. Then they

The mummy of Ramses II, a famous Egyptian king, was found in 1881.

packed and covered the body with a kind of salt, which would dry it out. Finally, they covered the mummy with resin, a gummy liquid from plants. Then, they wrapped it in bandages, usually placing jewelry and charms between the layers of cloth to protect the body in the afterlife. The wrapped mummy would be placed in a coffin and buried in a tomb deep in the earth. And there it was supposed to rest, undisturbed, forever.

Mummy Hunters

In fact, the Egyptian mummies did not rest peacefully for long. Robbers broke into the tombs to steal from the graves and tear apart the mummies for jewelry and charms.

In the nineteenth century, European tourists traveling to Egypt would bring mummies home—as souvenirs! They would invite their friends over to come and view the unwrapping. Once the body had been uncovered and everyone had had a good look, the mummy was usually tossed into the garbage. Many were sold as antiques, to be collected by the rich. Others were ground up to make brown wrapping paper. Some were even used as fuel for trains.

The Face of a King

Most of the major Egyptian burial sites were discovered and robbed thousands of years ago. But a few carefully hidden graves remained. In 1881, as many as 40 royal mummies were found in an unmarked chamber that was in an area known as the Valley of the Kings. Among them was the mummy of a famous Egyptian king, or pharaoh (FAIR-oh), named Ramses II. During his long reign, he built more temples and monuments and had more children than any other pharaoh in history. As pharaoh, Ramses had the most **elaborate** funeral preparations available at the time.

Scientists wondered: What condition would the body be in? What would it reveal about how the Egyptians mummified their dead?

They quickly cut through the bandages from head to foot. And suddenly they were staring into the face of a king.

It was clear that the ancient embalmers had done their work well. His skin was close to its natural color. The embalmers had even dyed his hair red to make him look more youthful.

A King Decays

Back in the 1880s, the technology available wasn't advanced. Scientists weren't able to learn much from the mummy of Ramses. So, once the body had been unwrapped, poked, and prodded, it was replaced in its coffin and put on display in a museum in Cairo, the capital of Egypt. The mummy of Ramses had remained perfectly preserved for more than three thousand years. Now, stripped of its cocoon of bandages, it slowly began to **deteriorate**. In 1974, museum officials noticed that Ramses was being eaten by beetles. Insects help bodies decompose. Unless the beetles were stopped, the great king's body would soon turn to dust.

The officials sent the body to Paris, where it was **sterilized** and studied. Using X-rays and small surgical microscopes,

elaborate: complicated and detailed
deteriorate: to get worse
sterilized: cleaned so as to be free from germs and dirt
ailments: illnesses that usually aren't serious

The tomb of a young pharaoh named Tutankhamen (King Tut) was discovered in 1922. It contained thousands of treasures, including his gold coffin.

scientists discovered that the pharaoh had had **ailments** that many people have today. He'd had arthritis and bad teeth. He'd also had heart disease.

As people realized that the supply of mummies was dwindling, they began to take more care with the ones that were left. Museums around the world discussed how to treat the mummies that remained in their collections. Was it a good idea to unwrap them and open them up? Should they be put on display?

Some argued that mummies should be examined only by X-ray, which allows scientists to study the bones and location of organs in a body without cutting it open.

Ask Yourself

- What is this selection mainly about?

Think about why people are interested in mummies.

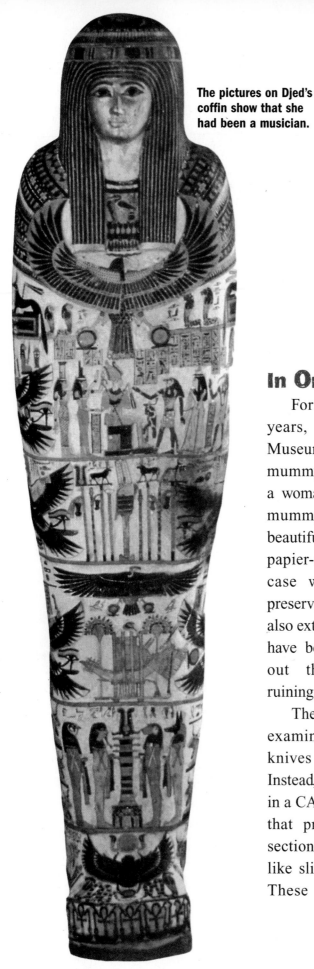

The pictures on Djed's coffin show that she had been a musician.

1 A CAT scan image shows the outlines of Djed's coffin and her skeleton inside.

2 A computer image of Djed's skull offers a clue about what Djed may have looked like.

3 and **4** An artist imagines Djed's face.

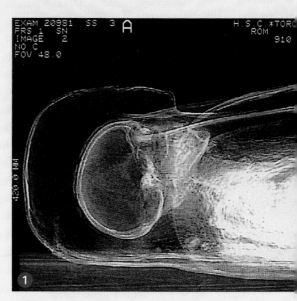

In One Piece

For almost one hundred years, the Royal Ontario Museum in Canada had a mummy in its collection— a woman named Djed. Djed's mummy was housed in a beautiful casket made of linen, papier-mâché, and glue. Its case was one of the best preserved of its period. It was also extremely **fragile**. It would have been impossible to take out the mummy without ruining the priceless case.

The mummy was finally examined in 1994, but no knives or saws were used. Instead, scientists put the case in a CAT scanner — a machine that provides several cross-section X-rays of the body, like slices in a loaf of bread. These X-rays can then be reconstructed to form a 3-D computer image. The CAT scan revealed what lay inside Djed's case: linen wrappings, skin and bones, her internal organs, and jewelry. Scientists also got a picture of what Djed's life must have been like before she died.

Call the Dentist!

Djed had terrible teeth. In her upper left jaw was a cavity the size of a quarter. It would have contained a large **abscess** that may have burst, spreading infection to her blood, brain, and heart and eventually poisoning her to death. The infection had actually eaten away at the bone, creating several holes.

This abscess would have been horribly painful. Her cheek would have been red and swollen. Pus would have drained

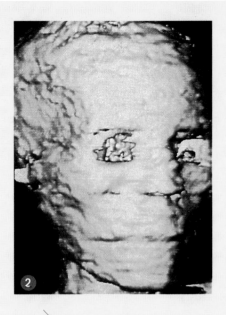

into her cheek, and may have eaten into the top of her mouth. There were also many smaller abscesses, and 24 of her teeth had been exposed right down to the roots. Eating, even breathing, would have really hurt.

Today, when people cringe from one small cavity, it is hard to imagine how Djed lived with her pain. Yet poor teeth were extremely common in ancient Egypt. The desert sand blew everywhere. It was in the air people breathed. It was in the food they ate. Sand was also in their bread. It was used to help grind flour. Over the years, eating gritty bread would wear down the teeth, leaving the sensitive roots painfully exposed.

The CAT scan gave scientists unique insight into Djed's life and death. More important, this examination left the mummy intact. Today, the case is as beautiful as ever, and Djed's body lies undisturbed inside it.

More to Learn

The Egyptian mummies are amazing discoveries. And we are as drawn to them today as mummy hunters were years ago. When we look at mummies, it is sometimes easy to forget that these were once real people. After they died, they were **painstakingly** prepared for a long afterlife. They expected their bodies to remain in their tombs forever. Mummies were never meant to be unwrapped and viewed by the world.

But mummies are a **precious** source of information about ancient peoples. They can help us understand ourselves. We know now that if we treat them with care and respect, they may have even more secrets to tell us.

Ask Yourself

- How are scientists able to study mummies without cutting them open?

Explain how scientists learned about the mummy Djed.

How to Make

Just how did the ancient Egyptians make a mummy?

Egyptians weren't the first or only people to make mummies, but they are the most famous for it. Making mummies became popular 4,000 years ago. Egyptian pharaohs wanted their bodies to last forever. They believed that they would need their bodies in the afterlife.

Mummy making became an important art. And the Egyptians did it very well. Their process was very scientific. First they removed the organs from the body. That's because the organs are the first thing to decay. They took out everything but the heart. They believed that the heart was the organ people used to feel and think.

Next they dried out the body. That's because water causes things to rot. (Ever notice that dried fruit lasts longer than fresh fruit?) Flesh and skin are full of water. So, bodies were covered in hundreds of pounds of salt.

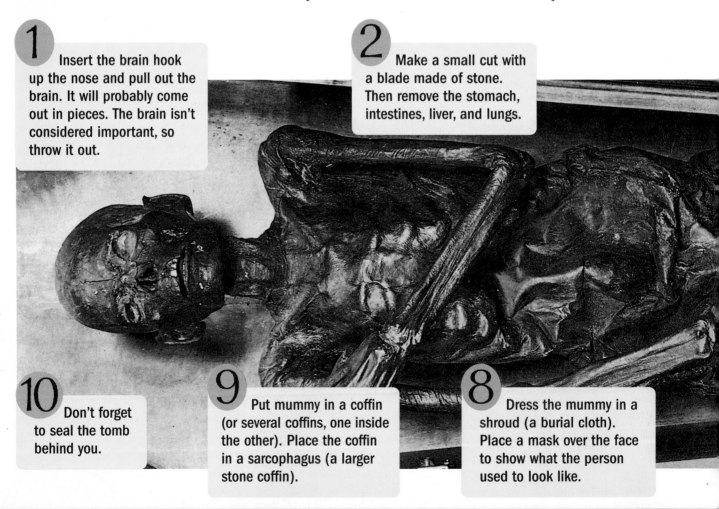

1 Insert the brain hook up the nose and pull out the brain. It will probably come out in pieces. The brain isn't considered important, so throw it out.

2 Make a small cut with a blade made of stone. Then remove the stomach, intestines, liver, and lungs.

10 Don't forget to seal the tomb behind you.

9 Put mummy in a coffin (or several coffins, one inside the other). Place the coffin in a sarcophagus (a larger stone coffin).

8 Dress the mummy in a shroud (a burial cloth). Place a mask over the face to show what the person used to look like.

a Mummy

Follow these ten easy steps.

The salt soaked up the water like a super sponge. They also washed the flesh to kill germs that cause decay. Finally, skin was covered with resin, or tree sap. This creates a hard, tough coating that works better than plastic wrap.

After a while you didn't even have to be royalty to be mummified. Of course, mummies of regular people weren't buried in fancy tombs. Also, the ancient Egyptians didn't just stick to human mummies. They also mummified animals that were important to them, such as cats, crocodiles, and bulls. One Egyptian princess was buried with her pet baboon!

So, if you want to learn exactly how it was done, look at the diagram below. There you can see the ten easy steps to making a mummy—just like the Egyptians did.

3 Preserve the organs with salt and wrap them in linen cloth. Place the organs in small jars with animal-headed stoppers.

4 Drain off body liquids and pack body in salt. Leave for 40 to 50 days till all that's left is the hair, skin, and bones.

5 Wash the body and rub it with perfume. Protect the skin with tree sap.

7 Tightly wrap the body with strips of linen. Add jewels and good luck charms between layers. Place a scarab beetle (a charm, not a real one) over the heart.

6 Fill the body and face (now hollow) with linen cloth, mud, or sawdust. Carefully fill in eye sockets and nostrils. Shape body and face to look lifelike.

Talk About It

Now that you've read *Secrets of the Mummies* and "How to Make a Mummy," what do you have to say about these questions?

▶ Do you think it is a good idea to display mummies in museums? Why or why not?

▶ If you had been a member of Egyptian royalty, which personal possessions would you have wanted buried with you?

Comprehension Check

Write your answers to the questions below. Use information from the selection and the how-to guide to support your answers.

1. Why did the Egyptians mummify their dead?

2. How do you know that Ramses II was an important king?

3. A tomb was discovered in Egypt that may have up to 1,000 mummies inside it. If you were in charge, what would you do?

4. What happens to most of the organs of a person being made into a mummy?

5. Why is salt used to mummify a body?

Vocabulary Check

elaborate   painstakingly   deteriorate
abscess   ailments

Complete each sentence with the correct vocabulary word.

1. You're lucky if you don't suffer from many _____ during your life.

2. Eating junk food can cause your health to _____.

3. Cavities are pretty common, but an _____ is unusual.

4. I worked _____ on the model car I was building.

5. It was an _____ idea that took a long time to explain.

Write About It

Choose one of the writing prompts below.

▶ How do you think a mummy might feel about being dug up? Disgraced? Honored? Curious? Write a message from the mummy's point of view.

▶ Write a diary entry describing a day in the life of someone who made mummies 4,000 years ago.

▶ Write a short newspaper article describing the discovery of an Egyptian tomb. What treasures were found? What was done with them?

THE MUMMY'S CURSE

Some people believe there is a curse on the tombs of pharaohs. They believe whoever enters such a tomb will die.

In 1922, Howard Carter discovered the tomb of the boy King Tutankhamen (commonly known as King Tut). Lord Carnavon had supplied the money for the work. Carter and Carnavon entered the tomb together.

Here's what happened:

▶ Lord Carnavon was bitten on the cheek by a mosquito. The bite became infected. Lord Carnavon died.

▶ People say that at the exact instant of Lord Carnavon's death, all the lights in Cairo, Egypt, went out. No one could ever explain why.

▶ Some say that back in England, Lord Carnavon's dog howled and dropped dead.

On the other hand, Carter lived to a ripe old age. Was it all a coincidence? Or was it the curse? What do you think?

Reading a Manual

You can't wait to try out your new answering machine. But first you have to figure out how to use it! That's where the manual comes in handy.

Look over this page from an instruction manual. Can you follow the steps?

Instructions for Using an Answering Machine

Most manuals include a diagram of the machine that labels the different parts.

TO START

1. Plug telephone-line cord into phone jack.
2. Plug AC adapter (power cord) into electric outlet.

TO RECORD A GREETING

Instructions in a manual are usually numbered. Do the steps in order, or else the machine might not work.

1. Press the Record button (■▶), and then release it.
2. Speak clearly and loudly. Make sure you are about 8 inches from the microphone. Do not pause for more than 5 seconds.
3. Press the Stop button (■) when finished.
4. To check your greeting, press the Check button (▼).
5. To change the volume, press the Volume Down button (▼) to make it lower. Press the Volume Up button (▲) to make it louder.

TO OPERATE

1. Press the Answer On button. A red light light above the button will light up. The machine is ready to play the greeting and record messages.

Some instructions can be confusing. Look at the pictures for extra help.

"When reading instructions in a manual, it helps to have the machine in front of you. That way, you can match the pictures in the diagram with the actual parts on the machine."

Please Leave a Message

Let's see if you're ready to set up an answering machine. Reread the manual and the tips that go with it. Use them to answer the questions below. Write your answers on your own paper.

1. What types of cords are needed to run the answering machine?
   a. a telephone-line cord and an AC adapter cord
   b. an AC adapter cord and an extension cord
   c. a telephone-line cord and an extension cord

2. What must you do right after you finish saying your greeting?
   a. press the STOP button
   b. move 8 inches from the microphone
   c. pause for 5 seconds

3. If you press the ▲ button, what will happen to the volume?
   a. It will get louder.
   b. It will get softer.
   c. It will stay the same.

4. How do you know that the answering machine is working and is ready to receive and record messages?

Write About It
Think of a machine you use regularly, such as a CD player or a toaster. What are the steps you take to use the machine? Write step-by-step instructions that tell others how to use it.

Talk About It
Exchange your step-by-step instructions with a partner. Ask your partner if the steps are clear and easy to follow. Revise your instructions based on your partner's feedback.

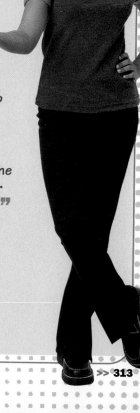

" If you need extra help to get your machine working, look for a Web site address in the manual. Or call the special "help" number for extra assistance."

Real-World Words

adapter: an item used to connect one machine to another so that they can work together
jack: an opening into which you plug a cable or wire
outlet: an electrical socket on a wall, used to plug in appliances

short story

THE ESCAPE

By J.B. Stamper

1

Boris looked down the long, dark hall of the prison. It looked endless.

He was being taken to a place that few people had seen. But everyone feared it. Solitary. The other prisoners said the word with a shudder.

Behind him, the guard laughed. "Well, this will teach you a lesson," he said. "Once you've been in solitary, there will be no more bad behavior from you."

Boris forced his feet down the hall. He knew there was no hope for him.

Seven years ago, he had committed a crime. It was a crime so terrible that even he could not believe that he had done it.

Now he was in prison for the rest of his life. He was trapped like an animal in a cage. He could not face it any longer!

That's why he had tried to escape.

It had been just after sunset. He was all alone in the yard. The guard who was supposed to be there had made a mistake. He had left Boris alone.

Boris had run for the wall like an animal. He had climbed up and was almost over. Then he had heard the words "Freeze, prisoner!"

And he had frozen.

That was just yesterday. Now he was headed to an even worse cage.

"You don't have to put me in solitary," Boris said to the guard in a scared voice. "I'll never try that again. I promise."

The guard just laughed. "You'll learn your lesson," he said again. "Maybe they'll let you out after a few months. But you're a tough one. I know what you did to get inside. You don't deserve anyone's pity."

Boris felt hopeless. It was no good trying. He would just have to deal with it, somehow.

They were coming to the end of the hall. Boris saw the door at the end. He saw the bars across the small window in the door.

He knew that this was it. The others had told him what it would be like inside.

They were right. The guard unlocked three locks. Then he swung open the door. He pushed Boris inside.

The room was like a pen. It was long and narrow, with one bed. High up there was a small window with bars across it.

The walls were of old, rough stone. To Boris, it felt as if they were closing in on him.

His breath started to come in short gasps. His heart pounded. Boris turned to the guard.

"No," he begged. "I can't take it in here. Let me go back to where I was. I'll never do anything wrong again."

"You should have thought of that before," the guard said. Then he slammed the door in Boris's face.

Boris reached for the door. He grabbed the bars in his hands and tried to shake them.

"You'll be sorry!" he yelled after the guard.

The guard just looked back and laughed.

Boris sat down on the bed. He shut his eyes. He didn't want to look around the cell. He was afraid that he would lose his mind.

Thunder woke Boris from a terrible nightmare. In the nightmare, rats were running at him, screeching.

He opened his eyes. He was afraid that the rats were really there. He hated rats more than anything. It was his biggest worry . . . that there might be rats in solitary.

Boris looked around the cell. It was almost dark. Then a flash of lightning lit up the room. Boris jumped in fear.

There was a loud clap of thunder. Then another streak of lightning lit up the cell. The light fell on the wall at the head of his bed.

In those few seconds of light, Boris saw something that made his heart leap. One of the stones in the wall looked different. There was a thin crack in the cement around it.

Boris tried to fight off a new feeling of hope. But he couldn't stop himself.

Maybe another prisoner had dug around the rock. No one could see the **crevice** unless he was lying on the bed. He had only seen it because of the lightning.

His hands were shaking. He reached down and grabbed the large stone. He moved it back and forth.

Then, suddenly, it came loose! Boris pulled, and the rock fell forward into his hands.

As Boris stared into the hole left by the rock, a flash of lightning lit it up. A tunnel stretched before him . . . with a rat hurrying down into it.

Boris jumped back in horror when he saw the rat. He thought about putting the large stone back in place.

Then another flash of lightning cut through the darkness of the cell. The tunnel lit up in front of him. It seemed to welcome him to freedom.

Boris measured the size of the tunnel with his eyes. It was narrow at the beginning. But then it became wider. It looked wide enough for him to crawl through.

Another flash of lightning lit up the tunnel. He searched for any sign of the rat.

"Maybe I didn't see it at all," Boris said to himself. "Maybe it was just a shadow of my nightmare."

Boris looked into the tunnel. He saw no sign of the rat. But his eyes fell on something else. There was a scrap of paper lying on the tunnel floor.

He reached in and pulled it out. He felt its dry surface. The paper was wrinkled with age.

He waited for the lightning to light up the cell again. When it did, he quickly read the message on the paper.

"To the next prisoner who finds this paper," Boris read. "I escaped the horror of this cell by this tunnel. May you share my good luck."

The light faded away before Boris could finish reading the message. He sat in the darkness, shaking with fear and hope.

The message seemed to be written in dark red liquid. He **assumed** that it was the blood of the person who had written it.

At last, the lightning came again. He read on, "This is the only way out!" The message was signed with two initials, "T.K."

Just then, Boris heard the guard's footsteps outside his cell. He threw himself over the stone and hole. He pressed his body against the wall.

He waited as the footsteps came to a stop outside his cell.

Then the footsteps moved away. They slowly went down the hallway. Finally, the noise faded into the night.

Suddenly, Boris knew he could not

ASK YOURSELF

■ Why does Boris hide the hole until he hears the footsteps fade away?
Think about who might be making those footsteps.

WORDS, Words, WORDS

crevice: a crack
assumed: guessed

Boris stood up on his trembling legs. He tried to see into the darkness ahead. He put his hand out in front of him and walked slowly through the black tunnel.

The rocky walls were sharp and tore at his hands. He wiped the sweat from his forehead with one hand and felt warm blood **oozing** from it.

Boris felt sick. His legs became weak with fear. He dropped to his knees and fell forward onto his hands. Then he felt tiny, clawed feet run over his fingers.

Boris heard his own scream echo and echo through the tunnel.

Once again, the tiny claws of a rat dug into his hands. Boris jumped to his feet, hitting his head on the low ceiling of the tunnel.

Then he felt them all around him. The rats were running over his shoes. They were clawing at his legs.

Boris opened his mouth to scream. But he knew he had to be quiet. He dug a fist into his mouth. He made himself move forward into the tunnel.

He hoped that the rats would not climb up his leg. If they did, he knew he would lose his mind.

Suddenly, the tunnel **sloped** down at a sharp angle. Boris's feet slipped forward. He landed on his back. He slid deeper and deeper into the tunnel. He no longer felt the rats

wait any longer. He stuck his head into the tunnel and pushed the rest of his body through.

He tried to look back, but the tunnel was too narrow. There was no turning back now.

Boris **squirmed** deeper and deeper into the tunnel. Crawling on his stomach, he felt like a snake slithering into its hole. He felt the tunnel grow damper and colder.

Just as the tunnel began to grow slimy, it opened up and became wider.

WORDS,
Words,
WORDS

squirmed: wriggled about uncomfortably
oozing: flowing out slowly
sloped: was at an angle
relief: freedom from worry

around him. He no longer heard their claws scratching the rock.

Boris came to a stop where the floor of the tunnel suddenly became flat. His breath was coming in short gasps that tore at his lungs.

He picked himself up. He reached for the slimy walls of the tunnel that he had just fallen down.

Then the truth hit him like a blow. He could never go back. The walls of the tunnel behind him were too steep and slippery.

He had only one chance. He had to push on. He had to push on . . . and hope that there was an end to the tunnel.

Boris moved forward. He clawed at the walls with his hands, trying to hurry.

The tunnel was beginning to feel more and more narrow. His breath was coming in shorter and shorter gasps.

Then the tunnel made a sharp turn to the left. Suddenly, Boris saw something that made him cry out with **relief.** Through an opening in the distance, he could see the pale rays of the moon.

He was almost there. He could smell the night air. Boris struggled toward the patch of moonlight ahead of him.

The tunnel was turning upward. Boris had to grab both sides of the wall and dig his feet into cracks in the wall. Slowly, he pulled himself up.

His hands were becoming more and more torn by the sharp rocks. Boris felt the blood from his cuts run down into his sleeves.

But the pain didn't matter. All that mattered was the patch of light ahead. Boris felt the night air against his face. He was close now. Close to freedom.

Then a sound behind him scared him. It was the sound of those clawed feet. They were following him.

Boris scrambled up to the top of the tunnel even faster. The moonlight was so bright now that he could see his hands in front of him. He felt a rat brush against his leg. But he had only a few yards to go.

With his last bit of strength, Boris pushed himself toward the light. He felt his head crash into something hard and cold. For a moment he was stunned.

Then he opened his eyes. In front of him, the moon shone through the bars of a heavy gate. Still pressed up against it were the cold, white bones . . . of a skeleton.

There was no escape. There was no going back. This was it. Just Boris . . . and the rats. ●

ASK YOURSELF

■ When do you think the first prisoner wrote the note—before or after entering the tunnel?

Think about where Boris found the note.

Teen Court: The Cheater

Jason asked Bob to cheat on a test. Bob said no, and told the teacher. Jason got a zero, so he's mad at Bob. See how Teen Court solves this conflict.

CHARACTERS

Amelia: Teen Mediator
Bob: The Accuser
Jason: The Accused

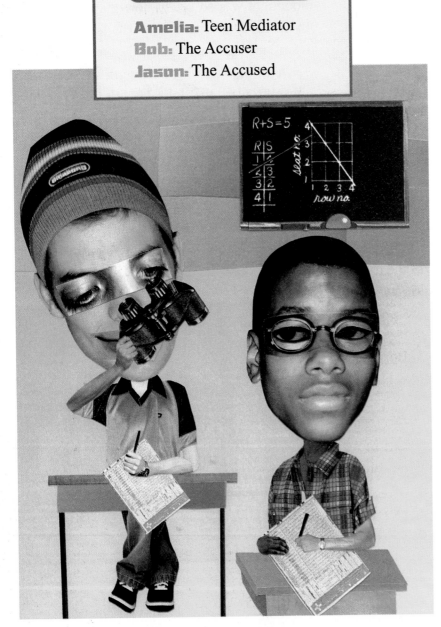

Amelia: Teen Court is now in session. I'm your mediator. My name is Amelia. Our goal is to figure out what the problem is between you two, and to come to some kind of solution. Now, tell me what happened.

Bob: Jason came up to me after math class. He got in my face and started yelling at me.

Jason: Well, you ratted me out. I was given a zero—a zero! Coach is going to cut me from the team. Yeah, I was in your face. What do you expect?

Bob: It's not my fault that you're a cheater.

Jason: You're a rat!

Amelia: Stop it! You know the rules of mediation—no name-calling. Bob, you go first. What happened?

Bob: Yesterday we had a big test in math. Jason wanted me to leave my paper uncovered so that he could cheat.

Jason: Oh, man!

Amelia: Go on, Bob.

Bob: I told him no, and he made this face, like he was going to do what he wanted to anyway, so . . .

Jason: He told the teacher!

Amelia: No interrupting! Is there anything else, Bob?

Bob: Yeah. The thing is, unlike Jason, I work really hard in school. Jason has no right to have a free ride. He thinks he's all that because he was named one of the basketball team's starting five. Meanwhile, Coach has me warming the bench. But I'm just as good a player.

Amelia: It sounds like it upsets you that Jason has a starting position on the basketball team.

Bob: Maybe, a little.

Amelia: Okay. Jason, what's your side of the story?

Jason: First of all, Bob is my friend. At least, I thought he was. And he's a teammate. I'm doing really badly in math. Plus I didn't study for the test. I can't afford to fail

that class. If I do, I can't play ball. Coach is strict. I asked Bob to help me out. I asked. He said no. I wasn't going to cheat after that. There was no reason for him to go to the teacher.

Amelia: Bob, was there a reason you went to the teacher rather than just keeping your test covered?

Bob: I just want to be a starter on the team.

Amelia: I see. Jason, what are you thinking right now?

Jason: I just didn't want to fail that test.

Amelia: Do you think that it is right to cheat?

Jason: No, I know it's not right.

Amelia: Is it right to ask your friend to cheat?

Jason: No, no.

Amelia: I think we've come a long way here.

Bob: Really?

Amelia: Well, it seems that the real reason you're upset, Bob, is because you're not happy with your position on the basketball team. Maybe you even saw this whole thing as an opportunity. If Jason

was cut, maybe you'd get his position, right?

Bob: Maybe.

Amelia: And Jason, you don't want a bad grade, because you want to stay on the team, right?

Jason: Yeah, sure. That's all I want.

Amelia: How can we find a win-win solution to this conflict?

Jason: What's a win-win solution?

Amelia: A win-win solution is a solution that will make you both happy. How can you both be players in the classroom and on the court?

Jason: I've already gotten a zero.

Amelia: If you work hard, Jason, is there a chance you could still pass math class?

Jason: I don't know. It's possible, I guess.

Amelia: And Bob, what could you do to have the coach notice you?

Bob: I have to improve my jump shots.

Amelia: This seems perfect. You guys could work together. You were good friends before this. It looks like you two could help each other. ●

Talk About It

Now that you've read "The Escape" and "Teen Court," what do you have to say about these questions?

▶ Did you expect the story to end the way it did? Why or why not?

▶ Do you think it's better for teens to help each other work out their own problems, or do you think adults should get involved?

Comprehension Check

Write your answers to the questions below. Use information from the story and court case to support your answers.

1. When Boris meets the rats in the tunnel, why doesn't he go back to the cell?

2. Why does Boris try to escape prison instead of accepting the punishment for his crime?

3. Do you think justice was served in the story? in "Teen Court"? Explain.

4. Why does Jason ask Bob to let him cheat on a test?

5. Are some crimes too serious to be handled by mediation (the way it was handled in "Teen Court")? Why or why not?

Vocabulary Check

Complete each sentence starter below. Before you answer, think about the meaning of the vocabulary word in bold.

1. The shelf was **sloped,** so . . .

2. When I felt something **oozing** from my lunch bag, I guessed it was . . .

3. I **assumed** you were late because . . .

4. The kitten **squirmed** in my arms because . . .

5. It was a big **relief** when I found out . . .

Write About It

Choose one of the writing prompts below.

▶ Create a different ending to "The Escape." What if there had been no gate at the end of the tunnel?

▶ Write a note that Boris might have written when he got to the end of the tunnel and found the gate.

▶ Write up a contract for Jason and Bob. In the contract, explain what Jason can do to help Bob and what Bob can do to help Jason.

Fact FILE

Teen courts really do exist in many schools across the country. Their procedure is called peer mediation. What kinds of problems are usually handled by mediation? Name-calling, bumping into students in the hallways, spreading rumors, and bullying are typical. Peer mediation has proven to be very successful. Want to know more about how it works? Read on.

First, the participants must agree to:

▶ tell the truth.
▶ listen without interrupting.
▶ be respectful.
▶ keep the situation confidential.

Then, the mediator and participants:

▶ listen to both sides of the story.
▶ discuss the stories.
▶ generate solutions.
▶ discuss solutions.
▶ select a solution.
▶ sign a contract.

Are you interested in becoming involved in peer mediation? If so, discuss the idea with your teacher or the school guidance counselor.

Understanding Nutrition

You hear it all the time. It's important to eat right. But how do you know whether your diet is good for you?

Check out the food pyramid below. It shows what kinds of foods—and how much of each kind—make up a healthy daily diet.

The Food Pyramid

Fats, oils, and sweets (use sparingly)

You need lots of the foods from the bottom of the pyramid. You should eat less of the foods from the top.

Milk, yogurt, and cheese (2–3 servings)

Meat, fish, poultry, dry beans, eggs, and nuts (2–3 servings)

Vegetables (3–5 servings)

Fruits (2–4 servings)

Bread, cereal, rice, and pasta (6–11 servings)

" All food packages include nutrition labels. The labels list food ingredients and other information about the foods. "

These numbers tell you how many servings of each type of food you should eat in one day. The size of a serving is different for each type of food.

Food for Thought

Are you ready to eat right? Review the food pyramid and the tips that go with it. Then use them to answer the following questions. Write your answers on your own paper.

1. From which section of the food pyramid should you eat the most foods each day? From which section should you eat the fewest foods each day?

2. For each of these food types, list the numbers of servings you should eat per day:
   a. vegetables
   b. milk, cheese, and yogurt
   c. fruits

3. From which **two sections** of the pyramid do oranges and oatmeal come?
   a. fruits; vegetables
   b. vegetables; milk, yogurt, and cheese
   c. fruits; bread, cereal, rice and pasta

4. For lunch, you had an apple, a glass of milk, and a turkey sandwich on whole-wheat bread with lettuce and tomatoes. How many sections of the food pyramid were included in your lunch?
   a. 2
   b. 5
   c. 4

Favorite Foods

What are your favorite foods? List your top three favorite things to eat. In which section of the food pyramid does each belong?

Menu Planning

Use the food pyramid as a guide. Plan one day of good eating. Write menus for three meals. Include two snacks in your plan, as well.

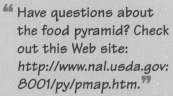

" Have questions about the food pyramid? Check out this Web site: http://www.nal.usda.gov: 8001/py/pmap.htm. "

Real-World Words

healthy: wholesome; good for your health
sparingly: in small amounts

play
BRIDGE

TO COURAGE

ADAPTED FROM THE NOVEL BY ANN GABHART

Luke couldn't pass the Truelanders' test of courage.
Now he must build his own bridge to courage.

CAST OF CHARACTERS

Narrator 1*

Narrator 2*

Luke, a boy who lives in Oak Ridge*

Jacob, Luke's best friend

Eric, leader of the Truelanders

Dad, Luke's dad

Willie, a Truelander

Mike, a Truelander

Jeremy, a Truelander

Shea, a girl who lives in Oak Ridge*

Ray, Shea's brother

Skeets, a boy who is known as a bully*

*Starred characters are major roles.

SCENE 1

Narrator 1: Luke's father builds bridges. For years Luke and his family moved around the country, living wherever a bridge needed to be built. But for the past two years, Luke's family has lived in Oak Ridge, while Luke's dad takes trips to different bridge sites.

Narrator 2: Luke likes Oak Ridge, his school, and his best friend, Jacob. His life feels settled for the first time. But all that is about to change. Luke and Jacob have been asked to join the Truelanders. All the boys in Oak Ridge want to become Truelanders.

Of course, Luke and Jacob must first pass the tests of bravery. Luke's dad thinks joining the Truelanders is a great idea.

Dad: Are you ready for the Truelanders' camping trip, son?

Luke: Yeah, Dad.

Dad: Do you know what the tests of courage will be?

Luke: Not really. We camp out in the woods all night. They have us do different things. Jacob really wants to join.

Dad: I'm sure you do, too. A group of boys who camp and have adventures is just what you need. Remember to be brave, son.

Luke: I will, Dad.

Narrator 1: But an uneasy feeling settles in the pit of Luke's stomach. Why is it so important to Jacob to join this group? Why is it so important to his dad that he be brave? Luke shakes these thoughts from his head and listens to the leader of the Truelanders talk.

Eric: Okay, men—the first test should be easy. We take you into the woods blindfolded. We spin you around and leave. You have to find your way through the woods and back to the

campsite. We'll be watching to make sure you don't cheat.

Luke: No problem.

Narrator 1: Left alone, Luke and Jacob begin to make their way through the woods. Jacob begins to panic; he doesn't know where they are. But Luke has always had a great sense of direction. They make it back to the campsite with ease.

Eric: Next, you run the gauntlet.

Narrator 2: Luke and Jacob run past a line of Truelanders. They are hit with tree branches as they go by. Luke and Jacob are bruised but not hurt badly.

Eric: Now for the final test— walk across the railroad bridge. Then you'll be Truelanders.

Narrator 2: Luke looks at the bridge. It has no railings. It is narrow and goes over a canyon. Luke feels the sweat dripping down his back. He feels as if he can't breathe.

Luke: What if a train comes?

Eric: Only a coward would worry about that. A Truelander wouldn't be **intimidated**.

Luke feels the sweat dripping down his back. He feels as if he can't breathe.

Narrator 1: Luke looks at the bridge, and a vision of himself falling off the bridge overtakes his mind and body. He is so scared he can barely move.

Luke: You go ahead, Jacob. I'm going home.

Jacob: You can't quit now. We're almost in. Come on.

Narrator 1: Luke pushes his way up a small rocky cliff to where the Truelanders stand in a curving half circle.

Eric: Where are you going, you little chicken?

Luke: I'm going home.

Willie: Coward!

Mike: Chicken!

Jeremy: Why don't you scat, fraidy-cat!

Narrator 2: Luke ignores them and heads home.

Eric: You're a chicken. We won't forget this. Ever.

ASK Yourself

- What happens before Luke fails the Truelanders' test? Retell what happens in your own words.

SCENE 2

Narrator 1: Luke is too ashamed to tell his Dad what happened. So he doesn't go home. He camps out in a field. When he wakes and opens his eyes, he is staring into the eyes of a large black dog. The dog growls at him.

Luke: Easy, boy.

Narrator 2: The dog growls again. Suddenly, a girl calls the dog.

Shea: Shandy! Where are you?

Narrator 1: Shea, a girl in Luke's class, comes over.

Luke: Would you call off your dog, please?

Shea (*teasing*): Why should I? You're **trespassing**.

Luke (*joking*): Then tell him to attack. Let's get this over with.

Shea (*laughing*): Come on, Shandy. We'll let him live.

Narrator 2: Luke gets up and starts toward home.

Shea: Wait a minute, Luke. Why were you sleeping here? Weren't you supposed to be with the Truelanders last night?

Luke: You know about them?

Shea: That's all my twin brother, Ray, talks about. He's **desperate** to join.

Luke: Maybe he still can. I know about a spot that just became open.

Shea: You mean you're not going to join? That's unheard of in this town.

Luke: I decided it's not for me. They wanted me to do something I didn't want to do.

Shea: Was Eric Harden there?

Luke: Of course he was. He's their leader.

Shea: He and I used to go out. But then he joined the Truelanders and got sort of mean. We're not even friends now.

Luke: His loss.

SCENE 3

Narrator 1: Later that day, Jacob comes to Luke's house.

Luke: Did things go okay after I left? They didn't take it out on you or anything?

Jacob: No.

Luke: No train came?

Jacob: No train came.

Luke: So now you're in?

Jacob: Yeah.

Luke: That's great. I know how much you wanted to be a Truelander.

Jacob: Why did you leave? Crossing the bridge was the very last test. Nothing to it.

Luke: I just couldn't do it, Jacob. Like they said, I chickened out.

Jacob: But I would have helped you, like you helped me when we had to find our way back to camp.

Luke: I couldn't have done it Jacob. If I walked out on that bridge, you would have had to carry me off.

Jacob: It won't be as much fun without you.

Luke: Maybe it will. And you won't be with them all the time.

Jacob: No. But they won't let me talk to you.

Luke (*hurt*): What? How could they stop you?

Jacob (*staring at the ground*): I'm sorry, Luke. I don't want to stop being friends. But my father and my brother were Truelanders. I've wanted to be one all my life. And Eric says

Words, WORDS, Words

intimidated: made to feel afraid or worried
trespassing: entering someone's private property without permission
desperate: willing to do anything to change a situation

it's the Truelanders or you. I have to choose.

Luke: Oh. Okay.

Jacob: One more thing, Luke. They'd kick me out if I told you this. But I have to warn you. Eric's going to get Skeets on you. I don't know how, if he's going to pay him or what, but he said he'd take care of it.

Narrator 2: Skeets is the local bully, a large boy whom everyone is scared of. There's a rumor that he once pushed a guy's head into a toilet at school. No one knew for sure if this was true, but no one wanted to find out, either.

SCENE 4

Narrator 1: At school, Luke becomes an **outcast**. Word has spread that he failed the Truelander test of courage. No one will talk to him except Shea.

Narrator 2: A few days later, Skeets knocks the books out of Luke's hands. He steps on Luke's algebra homework.

Skeets: Hey, kid. Don't you want your paper?

Luke: No. That's okay. Help yourself.

Narrator 1: Luke walks quickly to class.

"Eric says it's the Truelanders or you. I have to choose."

Narrator 2: Later, Luke opens his locker. Inside is a note from Skeets and a dead snake.

Skeets *(from a distance)*: What are you doing with that snake?

Luke: You should know.

Skeets: Not me, kid.

Narrator 1: Luke holds the snake out toward Skeets.

Luke: Why don't you take it back?

Skeets *(backing up)*: I didn't have anything to do with it.

Narrator 2: Luke is surprised to see that Skeets is afraid. He clearly didn't put the snake in the locker. And only one person knew Luke's locker combination. Luke goes to **confront** Jacob.

Luke *(angrily)*: You gave them my combination. Tell your new friend Eric that I'm not afraid of snakes.

Jacob: I didn't know about the snake. They only said they'd leave a note. They said I had to prove my loyalty. You understand, don't you?

Luke: No, Jacob. I don't understand.

ASK Yourself

- Do you think Jacob is being a good friend to Luke?

Think about how you would feel if Jacob were your best friend.

SCENE 5

Narrator 1: Luke is walking with Shea. He likes her a lot. He doesn't know if she likes him.

Shea: You said the Truelanders wanted you to do something you didn't want to do. What was it?

Luke: I had to walk across the railroad bridge.

Shea: Nobody in his right mind would do a stunt like that. It's much too dangerous.

Luke: Jacob did. I couldn't. I'm afraid of bridges.

Shea: Sounds to me like you're the brave one. You stood up to them. You have **integrity**.

Luke: I don't feel very brave. I feel like a failure. And now the Truelanders have Skeets breathing down my neck. I really don't feel brave around that guy.

Shea: You should get to know Skeets. He helps out on my dad's farm. He's really not so bad. In fact, we're friends. My brother gets along with him too.

Luke: He seems to be afraid of snakes, you know.

Shea: Yeah, I know. Everybody's afraid of something.

Luke: Not like I am, Shea. And I don't even know why. I mean, why bridges?

Shea: There has to be some reason for it, Luke. Maybe something happened to you a long time ago.

Luke: I don't know. I've always been afraid of bridges. I've had nightmares about falling off of them for just about as long as I can remember.

Shea: You should make yourself go on one. Face your fears, maybe that would help.

Narrator 2: Luke shudders at Shea's words. He has heard

them before. His father used to say, "To grow up to be a strong man, you have to face your fears." His father still says that sometimes.

Luke: I've tried, Shea. I really and truly have.

Shea: Maybe you should try a little harder.

Narrator 1: Luke doesn't want to hear this. So he decides to change the subject.

Luke: How is your brother? I hear the Truelanders have

finally asked him to join.

Shea: Yeah. But I'm **suspicious**. I'm afraid something bad might happen. Eric may use him to get back at me. He was so angry when we broke up.

Luke: Ray will be okay.

Narrator 2: Luke walks Shea home. On his way back to his house, he runs into Skeets.

Skeets *(threatening Luke)*: I saw you with Shea. Stay away from her. She doesn't need a coward hanging around her.

Words, WORDS, Words

outcast: someone who is not accepted by other people
confront: to challenge
integrity: honesty; sticking up for what you believe
suspicious: thinking that something might be wrong or bad

SCENE 6

Narrator 1: The next week is horrible for Luke. On Monday Skeets reminds Luke that he'd better stay away from Shea—or else. On Tuesday he trips Luke. But Luke doesn't stay away from Shea. So Skeets pushes Luke's face against a wall and threatens him again.

Narrator 2: On Friday night there's a knock on Luke's door. And Luke is not surprised to find Skeets standing there.

Luke: What now?

Skeets: You can relax. I'm not going to beat you up tonight.

Luke: Then why are you here?

Skeets: Shea says you can find the Truelanders. She says you don't get lost in the woods.

Luke: Yeah, so?

Skeets: Ray went out with the Truelanders tonight. Shea thinks something bad has happened to Ray. She wants us to find him.

Luke: I don't understand you, Skeets. You act like you don't care about anyone. So why are you so concerned about Ray now?

Skeets: Shea is my friend. If she says Ray's in trouble, we have to find him.

Narrator 1: Skeets and Luke meet Shea. Then they start through the woods. They find the place where the Truelanders hold their meetings.

Shea (*looking at the ground*): That's Ray's sleeping bag.

Luke: His is the only sleeping bag here. I wonder where the others are.

Narrator 2: Just then, they hear a movement in the bushes. It's Jacob. Luke runs over.

Luke: Jacob! Where's Ray? What did you guys do to him?

Jacob: Eric blindfolded Ray and told him to find his way back to the campsite.

Luke: But where's Eric and the rest of the Truelanders?

Jacob: They all left. It was a big joke. Ray wasn't going to be invited to join the Truelanders. Eric just did this because he wanted to get back at Shea.

Luke: Why are you still here?

Jacob: I went looking for Ray. I thought the trick was mean. You were right about the True-landers, Luke. I'm quitting.

ASK Yourself

- What happens after Luke and Skeets get to the woods?

Think about why Shea is worried about her brother, Ray.

"You were right about the Truelanders, Luke. I'm quitting."

SCENE 7

Narrator 1: Luke leads Jacob back to Shea and Skeets. Jacob explains what happened.

Skeets: Shea, you and Jacob better go back and get help. Luke and I will look for Ray.

Narrator 2: Shea and Jacob leave. Skeets and Luke split up.

Luke: Whistle once if you get lost. Twice if you find Ray. Three times if you need help.

Skeets: Yeah, okay.

Narrator 1: As Luke reaches the river, he hears three whistles. He races to find Skeets on the bridge. Skeets has caught his foot on the railroad track.

Skeets: Don't just stand there. Help me! I'm stuck. I think I broke my ankle.

Narrator 2: Luke stands there frozen. He is terrified.

Skeets (*panicking*): You've got to help me. I can feel a train coming.

Luke (*sweating*): I can't come out there. I can't do it.

Skeets: Please! You have to!

Narrator 1: Luke can't believe it: Skeets is actually begging and saying "Please." He closes his eyes. He inches his way onto the bridge. He can hear a train whistle coming closer and closer. He freezes for a moment.

Skeets: Hurry! Hurry!

Narrator 2: Luke reaches Skeets and struggles to loosen his foot. The train whistle is getting louder, and Luke can feel the rumbling of the train on the track. He pulls and pulls. Finally, with a yank, he pulls Skeets's foot out of his boot. The boot goes plunging toward the water below.

Skeets: Let's get out of here.

Narrator 1: But Luke can't move. He's frozen in fear, staring at the boot as it plummets toward the water. Except it doesn't look like Skeets's boot, it looks like a shoe—a little boy's shoe. It is Luke's shoe and he is a little boy again. His father is holding him in the air on a bridge and saying "See, I told you there was nothing to be afraid of.

"They think I'm a coward like you!"

I won't let anything happen to you, and my bridges won't either."

Skeets: LUKE! THE TRAIN! MOVE IT!

Narrator 2: Luckily, they are not far from the other side. As the train races toward them, Skeets grabs Luke. He's in pain, but he drags them both off the bridge. Seconds later the train whizzes past. They both fall to the ground.

Narrator 1: It takes a minute before Luke is himself again.

Skeets: Hey—what happened back there?

Luke: I'm scared of bridges.

Skeets: But doesn't your dad work on bridges? It seems kind of weird to me that you'd be afraid of them.

Luke: I had a really scary experience on one when I was younger. Ever since then, I've had a problem with heights.

Skeets: Well, if you ask me, you picked a really good time to face that fear. Thanks.

SCENE 8

Narrator 2: Luke goes off to find Ray. After a little while, he finds him. He is staggering.

Luke: Ray, are you okay?

Ray: My head hurts. I must have fallen and hit it on something. I don't remember much.

Narrator 1: Luke knows Ray must have a head injury. He leads Ray back to where Skeets is.

Ray: Where are the Truelanders?

Narrator 1: Luke doesn't want to tell him, but Skeets blurts it out.

Skeets: They played a trick on you, Ray. They all split and left you out here alone.

Narrator 2: Ray gets upset. He is out of control.

Ray (to Luke): They think I'm a coward like you! I'll show them I'm not afraid. I'm going to cross the bridge. Then they'll let me be a Truelander.

Narrator 1: Ray runs onto the bridge. In the middle of it, he stops and sways unsteadily.

Luke (to Skeets): What are we going to do? It's too dangerous out there. His balance is off.

Skeets: You have to go after him. I think my ankle is broken. You can do it. Step by step. Come on, Luke!

Narrator 2: Luke again edges out onto the bridge. He keeps his eyes on Ray. He doesn't look down. Ray is stumbling on in front of Luke. Finally, Luke gets hold of Ray and pulls him to safety.

Narrator 1: Meanwhile, Shea and Jacob arrive with help.

Shea: Is Ray okay?

Luke: He hurt his head. He'd better get it checked out.

Shea: How about you? Are you all right? I saw you out there on the bridge.

Luke (smiling): Bridge? What bridge?

Shea: That was very brave of you. Thank you, Luke!

Narrator 2: Luke feels a new sense of confidence as they all walk off. Luke knows he has more bridges to cross. Maybe he will even talk to his dad tonight. ●

Where Do You Fit In?

Peer pressure can be a big problem or a big help.

Read the situations and think about what you'd do. Record your answers on a separate sheet of paper.

How far are you willing to go to be part of the in crowd?

1 You and a group of your friends go to the movies on Saturday afternoon. One of your friends starts tossing popcorn at the people in front of you. You think this is so embarrassing. But the rest of your friends are laughing.

What should you do?

a Ignore them and say nothing. What they do is their business. What you do is your own.

b Laugh, but don't throw any popcorn. You don't want them to think that you're no fun.

c Get up and move away. You don't want anyone to think that you're with these people.

d Tell your friends to stop. Ask them how they'd feel if someone were doing that to them.

e Another solution I would choose would be _____.

2 Some of your friends are planning to play a trick on a new kid in school. You've been the new kid before and know how it feels. Plus, you think that what your classmates are planning is mean.

What should you do?

a Go along with the prank so that your friends don't think you are a chicken.

b Tell the teacher what the kids are planning, but don't say which kids will be involved.

c Tell your friends that the trick is mean and you don't think they should do it.

d Don't go to school the day the kids are planning the trick.

e Another solution I would choose would be _____.

Can you count on your friends to support good decisions?

3 Your last report card wasn't all it could be. Now you have a strict rule about homework. You promised yourself that you would do it first, before you make any other plans. There's a big game after school, and all your friends are going.

What should you do?

a Rush home and do your homework as quickly as you can. Maybe you can catch the second half.

b Tell your friends that you'd like to go, but you have other plans. Your study habits are none of their business.

c Go home in a bad mood. You'll do your homework, but you won't be happy about it.

d Go to the game. If you have time to do your homework later, great. If not, oh well.

e Another solution I would choose would be _____ .

4 Your friends are planning to go bike-riding after school. They've all got helmets. You've always thought that helmets looked really stupid. Besides, you're not a baby anymore. They tell you they'll wait for you if you want to go home and get yours.

What should you do?

a Tell your friends that they're a bunch of babies. Then ride off without them.

b Tell your friends you don't normally wear a helmet and nothing's ever happened before.

c Think it over and decide maybe your friends have a point. Better safe than sorry.

d Tell your friends that you're going home for your helmet, but that they shouldn't bother to wait. Then watch TV instead. You'd rather not go than look like a dork.

e Another solution I would choose would be _____ .

Talk About It

Now that you've read *Bridge to Courage* and "Where Do You Fit In?" what do you have to say about these questions?

▶ How important is it to be part of a group?

▶ What is your definition of a brave person? Are there different kinds of bravery?

Comprehension Check

Write your answers to the questions below. Use information from the play and the quiz to support your answers.

1. What makes Luke finally overcome his fear of bridges?

2. Why doesn't Luke stay away from Shea after Skeets threatens him?

3. Would you want to join a group that asks that you pass a test of courage? Why or why not?

4. Is peer pressure always a bad thing? Explain your answer.

5. How does Luke respond to peer pressure?

Vocabulary Check

Answer each question below with a complete sentence. Before you answer, think about the meaning of the vocabulary word in bold.

1. Why is **trespassing** against the law?

2. How do you think it feels to be an **outcast**?

3. Why is it difficult to have **integrity**?

4. Why might you be **suspicious** if your backpack were suddenly a lot lighter?

5. What could you say to someone who **intimidated** you?

Write About It

Choose one of the writing prompts below.

▶ Write a conversation between Luke and his father. Have Luke tell his father how it felt to be dangled off the bridge.

▶ Write a short newspaper article about how Luke saved Ray.

▶ Write a letter from Skeets to Luke. In the letter, explain how you used to feel about Luke. Then explain how your feelings changed.

More to READ

If you enjoyed *Bridge to Courage*, you might also like reading these tales of bravery:

Call It Courage
by Armstrong Sperry

Mafatu's name means "Stout Heart," but his people call him a coward. Ever since the sea took his mother's life and spared his own, he has lived with deep fear. And even though his father is the Great Chief of Hikueru—an island whose seafaring people worship courage—he is terrified, and therefore shunned by his people.

By the time he is 12 years old, Mafatu can bear it no longer. He must conquer his fear alone . . . even if it means certain death.

Hatchet
by Gary Paulsen

Thirteen-year-old Brian Robeson is on his way to visit his father. But after his plane crashes, Brian finds himself alone in the Canadian wilderness. He has nothing but the clothes on his back and a hatchet—a present from his mother. Now it will take all of Brian's skill and courage to survive.

Reading Airline Monitors

Your grandparents are flying in from South America. Your mother drops you off at the airport and tells you that she'll meet you at their gate. What's your first stop? The flight monitor. That's the screen that tells you when and where all the flights are coming in.

Check out this flight monitor. Then get ready to look for your grandparents.

Flight Monitor

> Every flight has a number. The letters before each number stand for different airlines. The "From" column tells you the city the flight is coming from.

> If you're meeting someone who is arriving, look for the "Arrivals" screens. If you're leaving on a flight, look for the "Departures" screens.

ARRIVALS

Flight	From	Scheduled	Status	Gate
SAA618	Bogotá	1:52 P.M.	Delayed 3:05	C10
CA687	Bogotá	8:20 P.M.	On time	C22
AM237	Buenos Aires	3:35 P.M.	On time	D11
SAA1098	Buenos Aires	6:20 P.M.	On time	C12
SAA329	Buenos Aires	10:40 P.M.	On time	C4
MEX1220	Mexico City	3:18 P.M.	On time	D20
CA182	Mexico City	5:25 P.M.	Delayed 6:10	D8
MEX1301	Mexico City	8:20 P.M.	Canceled	
SAA802	Rio de Janeiro	2:30 P.M.	Delayed 3:45	E3
TC890	Rio de Janeiro	9:45 P.M.	On time	E18

" Passengers arriving on international flights must go through "customs," where their passports and bags are checked. "

> So how do you know where each flight is arriving? Check this column. Planes park in areas called gates.

Find a Flight

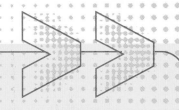

Are you ready to fly around the airport? Take another look at the flight monitor. Review the tips that go with it. Then answer the questions below. Write your answers on a separate sheet of paper.

1. Your grandparents are arriving from Buenos Aires on South American Airlines (SAA) flight 1098. When is their plane going to land?
   a. 3:35 P.M.   b. 6:20 P.M.
   c. 7:15 P.M.   d. 10:40 P.M.

2. At what gate will your grandparents arrive?
   a. Gate C12   b. Gate C4
   c. Gate D11   d. Gate C10

3. How many flights could your grandparents have chosen from on this particular day?

4. Since your grandparents are arriving on an international flight, they must pass through customs. If it takes an hour to get through customs, around what time will you be able to meet them?
   a. 7:20 P.M.   b. 5:00 P.M.
   c. 8:15 P.M.   d. 11:40 P.M.

5. Suppose your grandparents' luggage didn't make it onto their flight. South American Airlines says it will be on the next flight out of Buenos Aires. What time should that flight arrive?

" Want to know if a flight is on time before you leave for the airport? Call the airline or check their Web site. "

Real-World Words

monitor: video screen used to display information
customs: a checkpoint in an airport where officials make sure you're not carrying anything illegal

Think Fast

Suppose the monitor tells you your grandparents' flight has been delayed. Write a few sentences explaining what you would do.

Time It

Suppose it's a 45-minute drive to the airport. It takes international passengers about an hour to get through customs. What time would you leave home to meet friends on the following flights: SAA1098, CA182, TC890?

White

Bread Competition

by Jo Ann Yolanda Hernández

The competition begins with a spelling contest. Where will it end?

My sister's big smile would be very heavy to carry home if she didn't win today.

The auditorium at South San High School was jammed full with people waiting for the spelling bee to start. Luz, my sister, was older than me by two years, and in the ninth grade. She didn't look at anyone else on stage; she just sat there with a big smile on her face.

My three best friends, Sofia Cuellar, Diana Ortíz, Sally Jane Mendoza, and I stood up and shouted, "Viva Luz!" several times. Sofia stuck a fist in the air. Diana jiggled in her seat with excitement.

Across the aisle from us, Kathy, Virginia, and two of their girlfriends, all from the fancy Alamo Heights area, were laughing at us as the school monitor walked away. Each held a sign with one word that, all together, read, "All the way Debbie." Debbie, Kathy's older sister, was sitting on the stage next to Luz.

I knew how important this was for Luz. She had a straight-A report card and each correct answer got her closer to the scholarship she wanted for college.

I gripped Sally Jane's hand, my knuckles turning white. Luz had sworn me to secrecy. Our parents didn't know she was in the finals. It would be too hard to have to tell them if she lost.

Now it was only Debbie and Luz standing alone on each end of the stage. I held my breath when Luz had to spell *Mississippi*. Luz could do it. I just knew she could.

As my big sister, she had always done everything first and better. I was proud of her. When she spelled the next word right, I stuck my fist into the air. She was a winner, no matter what happened next, and she was my sister!

Then Debbie missed.

Luz was silent for what felt like a thousand years. Then she smiled a face-cracking smile and spelled "C-H-R-Y-S-A-N-T-H-E-M-U-M." We were on our feet. Everyone, brown, black, red, and yellow, was yelling and cheering. Luz had won!

"You're in America now. Why don't you eat American food?"

Glossary

taquitos: little tacos

mis amigas: my friends

hijo: child

frijoles: beans

hola: hello

mijita: my little girl

qué?: what?

el sol: the sun

Usually I ate lunch outside with the other girls who had bean *taquitos* just like mine. But this time my friends wanted to be included with the older students.

Mis amigas and I were on one side of the lunchroom table. Sofia, tiny, five feet, flushed with excitement, her dark skin crimson, sat next to me. She brushed her long black hair off one shoulder. Taller by three inches and several pounds heavier, Diana, whose brown hair was held back by pink butterfly barrettes, sat next to her.

Sally Jane sat at the end. She had light brown hair and light skin and a *mamá* who made sure that everyone knew her grandparents had come from Spain. We didn't care, except when Sally Jane would forget she was the same brown as we were. The three of us would ignore her for a little while, and soon the white girls would remind Sally Jane that they never forgot she was mostly *Mexicana*.

My sister, her best friend, Arturo, and two other Chicanas from her class sat opposite us. I took bites from my tortilla, hidden underneath the waxed paper.

Debbie and her girlfriends stopped at our table. Even her little sister Kathy trailed behind them.

"Congratulations, Luz," said Debbie. "But don't think you're going to represent San Antonio at the National. This was only the first round. Don't get too comfortable."

Arturo took a big bite from his sandwich and said, "Yeah—you should know, runner-up!"

Everyone laughed, including me. Kathy nudged Debbie and pointed at me. They sniffed.

"You're eating peanut butter on a tortilla! How gross!" Debbie cried for everyone to hear.

I looked into Kathy's blue eyes as she said, "You're in America now. Why don't you eat American food?"

Arturo jumped to his feet. Several boys who were sitting across the aisle sprang to their feet.

The cafeteria monitor bounced out of his chair and headed in our direction.

Words, Words, Words

avoided: stayed away from purposely
snubbing: ignoring

Debbie took Kathy by the arm.

"C'mon, Kathy. You know, you can take them out of the field, but you can't take the field out of them." The four girls, my two classmates, and all the students eating lunch laughed. Everyone except us at our table.

I hung my head.

My sister hissed at me from across the table. "Keep your head up high, Justina."

I did as she told me. "I'm sorry to ruin your happy day," I said.

"Eat your taco with pride."

I stared at her, trying to see if some monster from outer space had taken over her body. My bossy sister was telling me to eat this tortilla with pride? Just yesterday she made me walk with her down the hallway to throw away the plastic wrapper with "Tortillas made in San Antonio" written across the front. Now she was telling me to eat my food with pride just because some white girls made fun of me.

I was about to say something back to her when another burst of loud laughter came from the table across the aisle. I swallowed my anger at my sister, crumpled the paper with the taco inside it, and tossed the heap onto the pile of trash on the cafeteria tray.

On the way home from school, mis amigas were talking about what they were going to wear when they went to see Luz win. They had no doubts. She would be the first Chicana to win, and they wanted to look fine.

I walked, watching my feet drag alongside the others. Sweat stung my eyes, but I didn't wipe it away because I didn't want anyone to think I was crying. I had disappointed my sister. I had taken my sister's great moment and messed it up. She had **avoided** me after school and I didn't blame her. I wished I could avoid me, too.

"Justina, where are you?" whined Sally Jane.

"Let's go." I walked past them and they followed, complaining. I walked through the double glass doors of the H.E.B.

Diana shuddered and wrapped her arms around herself. "*Hijo*, this grocery store is freezing."

"Let's go," I said, and headed down the aisle.

"What for?" asked Sofia, pulling Diana by the arm to stay even with Sally Jane and me.

I stopped in front of the bread rack. The others crashed behind me.

I felt as if I had opened the book to the math quiz and all the problems with all the angles were there in front of me. "So many kinds."

ASK YOURSELF

- Why does Justina want to buy white bread?

Think about her experience in the cafeteria and what Kathy said.

Sally Jane said in a voice that sounded a lot like our teacher, "Oh yeah. We've tried this kind and this one, too. They were too cheap." With her chin, she pointed at the row of white bread above our heads. "That's the kind we eat. It's way too expensive for you."

"This is the one I'm gonna buy," I said, and picked the one Sally Jane had pointed to. **Snubbing** her as I walked by, I headed for the checkout with Diana and Sofia on my heels and Sally Jane trailing behind.

The next morning, we woke late. Mamá hurried us out the door, but I **stalled** to check my lunch bag. At the bottom of the bag sat the white bread sandwich, wrapped in waxed paper. I gave my mother a squeeze around her waist and ran to join mis amigas.

At our lockers, I announced to my girlfriends that I was eating lunch in the cafeteria.

"I know why she wants to eat in the cafeteria." Sally Jane's ponytail danced.

Sofia and Diana watched; Sofia bit her lip, and Diana twirled her finger around her hair.

Sally Jane pointed at my lunch bag with her elbow. "She brought a sandwich in her lunch."

"Really?" Sofia and Diana responded, their eyes growing as big as pesos.

"You do what you want. I'm eating in the cafeteria." I spun away. I knew they would follow me. I knew they would stick by me, as we had always done for each other. At least, I was hoping really hard that they would, so I wouldn't be alone.

A few minutes later, Sofia and Diana sat across from me. Sally Jane sat next to me. We smiled at each other.

Debbie, her girlfriends, and her sister Kathy cornered the last table and walked down the aisle. I popped open my lunch bag and pulled out my sandwich. I flattened the brown paper bag with one hand and set my prize on top. I carefully unfolded the waxed paper, spreading each piece flat against the table.

Debbie and the others were setting their trays down next to the boys from eighth grade, when Kathy glanced over at our table and spotted my sandwich. She nudged Debbie.

I wrapped both hands around the sandwich. Loud laughing and hollering filled the room. Everyone at the table where my sister sat was poking each other and acting funny. My sister sat in the middle of all that noise, quiet and small.

The bean broth had soaked the bottom slice of bread and turned it brown. The pressure from my hands ripped the soggy bread. The *frijoles* were dropping out from the side of the bread and landing on top of the waxed paper like brown freckles. My hands dripped with juice and sliding *frijoles*. It was a bean sandwich.

When I arrived home, I opened the door and ran to my bedroom. My mother cried out, *"Hola!"* from the living room, but I didn't answer, and I shut my bedroom door very quietly. I didn't want my mother coming in to ask me a bunch of questions that I didn't have answers for.

I lay on my bed and watched the skies turn a bruised blue through the window. I didn't change my clothes; I didn't cry.

I wondered why I was so different. Why couldn't I want what everyone else in my family wanted, to be happy with the things that were here? Why did it matter what anyone else thought?

A long arm of light cut across my bed when my mother opened the door. "Justina, are you feeling well?"

I nodded, afraid for her to hear the pain in my voice.

"*Mijita.*"

She sat on the edge of the bed and stroked my arm. "I've talked to your sister."

I jumped into my mother's waiting arms and cried. She rubbed my back and rocked the pain from my body.

"I just wanted to be something nice like them." I sobbed between the words.

"*Mijita*, you have to be strong. You can't let them get you down. We think you're very special."

"You're my mother. You're supposed to say that."

My mother pushed me back from her, smiling. "*Mijita*, I can tell you what I believe. It's up to you to decide how beautiful you are."

"But, but . . ."

"*¿Qué?*"

"You just don't understand, Mom. It's a lot different from when you were little. Lots different."

ASK YOURSELF

- Why is Justina so upset? Reread what happens at lunch and what Justina thinks about when she gets home.

Two days later, during third period, the teacher announced, "Today we have a guest speaker. She has volunteered to speak to us about something very important. It is about the food we eat. Say hello to Mrs. Rosaura Ríos."

I slipped down in my seat, trying hard to become invisible. Sally Jane and Sofia looked at me. I shrugged. I hadn't known she was coming. Diana waved at my mother with a big smile on her face.

The whole class rang out, "Hello, Mrs. Ríos." Several boys, who sat in a bunch in the back, snorted. One called out, "Beaner."

Mrs. Letts stepped to the front of the room and clapped her hands. "Silence. Mrs. Ríos was **gracious** enough to come in to make this presentation. We owe her the **courtesy** of giving her our complete attention and our most respectful behavior." She waited a moment, the weight of her **gaze** silencing each student.

"Good. Mrs. Ríos, the class is yours." The blonde teacher stretched her hand out, palm up, offering my mother the room.

I was thankful that she had on a red-and-yellow-flowered dress instead of the janitor's

Words, Words, Words

stalled: delayed doing something on purpose
gracious: kind; considerate
courtesy: respect
gaze: a steady look; a stare

white uniform; it made her look pretty and her skin richer, darker like cinnamon. I felt a mixture of pride and total embarrassment.

"Today I want to tell you a story that began before there were any people from Europe living in this country. Thousands of years ago, there was a tribe of people called the Aztecs that lived in a place we now call Mexico."

I saw Kathy, Debbie's little sister, look at Virginia and roll her eyes.

"There was much hunger. People and their children didn't have enough to eat. There was much suffering in all the villages.

"One day, a woman was walking through the woods searching for something to feed her family. She discovered a trail of ants, coming out of their home and traveling up into the mountain.

"She hid to watch these ants because she knew they were very hard workers." My mother crunched her shoulders forward as if she were hiding, and I covered my eyes with my hand.

"Soon she discovered that they were coming back carrying blue corn. She asked the ants to show her where the blue corn was hidden because her family was very hungry. But the ants would not tell her their secret. She went home very, very tired." She leaned against the teacher's desk and wiped her brow. I wanted the floor to open and swallow me whole.

ASK YOURSELF

- Why do you think Justina's mother is telling this story to the class?

Read on and think about what her mother might be trying to do.

My mother perked up and raised a finger into the air. "Her youngest children were twin boys who became very sad when they saw their mother crying.

"Morning came and the twins asked the sun if he would help their mother. *El Sol* made angry clouds at the ants for being so selfish. There was a great storm with giant bolts of lightning. The sun sent one huge bolt of lightning, which split the mountain in two. All the blue corn inside spilled out, and the village people rushed to fill their baskets."

Once again my mother slouched into her disappointed position. A couple of boys in the back of the room snickered. The teacher, standing behind my mother, shook her head at them.

"The sun was very disappointed in the ants and sent another bolt of lightning, which turned the ants red. They were so hot to touch; no one wanted anything to do with them. There was such a cry from all the ants. The lightning was the hottest the sun had ever made, so hot that it turned all the corn yellow. And that is how we know the corn today."

Her hands moved in circles in front of her like propellers. "Everyone was very happy for a long time. Then some men from across the ocean came upon our land. They were pale and weak from their trip. When they saw the fields of yellow corn growing, they thought they had found the land of gold." She arched her hands over her head.

"They had a little of the white bread they had brought from their home, but it was green with mold and was making everyone sick.

They were all about to die, when the king of the tribe invited them to eat with him."

At this point, my mother stood taller, more proud. "At the king's table, he had a kind of bread the men from across the ocean had never seen. It was flat, but stronger than their white bread. It could hold more food to keep them from hunger as they traveled. They asked the king what was this food. He told them it was a tortilla."

Here my mother lowered her voice with **doom.** "These men took our homes, broke up our villages, and even killed many of us, but they never could take away our language and our food.

"To this day, the food we eat is the same food that kept those men from across the ocean alive. It is the same food that the priest would offer up to the gods in the heavens, the same food that was served to the Aztec kings of many years ago."

My mother stood up straight, her hands slowly coming to rest, one cupped in the other, at her waist. "The food of the Chicanos is not just everyday food. It's food that has come down many **generations.** Our food is our history."

No one made a sound when my mother finished. The Chicano students sat taller in their seats.

My stomach flipped as if I were on a roller coaster when Kathy raised her hand. She smiled as she stood. "Isn't it true that that kind of food is really only for poor people?"

My mother smiled and I thought, oh, oh. I knew that smile well. "Do you and your parents ever eat out?"

Kathy threw a look at Virginia, then answered, "Of course."

The smile never changed and I knew the machete was coming fast. "Where was the last place you ate out?"

Without **hesitation,** Kathy answered, *"La Hacienda."*

The smile disappeared. She stood with her head arched out. "People pay lots of money to eat our poor, simple food that kings ate." She winked to Diana who smiled brightly in return.

doom: a sense that something bad will happen
generations: families born to a shared ancestor
hesitation: a pause or delay

The teacher ended the question period. She shook my mother's hand and had the whole class say "thank you" aloud.

I felt so much relief that my mother didn't talk to me in the classroom before she left.

After class at our lockers, Sofia and Diana were taking their lunches out of their lockers. Sally Jane looked around me. I heard Kathy's group coming up behind me.

"That story was so **quaint,**" said Kathy. "It actually brought tears to my eyes." The rest of the girls in her group giggled.

Another girl cut into the laughter. "Didn't she talk funny? Her accent was so cute!" She pushed her thick glasses up her nose with her middle finger.

I balled my hands into fists with a look filled with threat and **menace.** Sally Jane edged beside me, fists in the air. Diana **hoisted** me back by the arm, **halting** our forward motion as a teacher strolled by, smiling at us all.

As the teacher rounded the corner, Kathy shoved Sally Jane as she walked by.

Sally Jane bounced off the locker and the three of us stepped in front of Sally Jane to keep her from tackling Kathy.

Virginia stepped out of the gang of girls as the group moved on.

"I thought the story was, you know, really great." She hugged her books to her chest.

Diana sneered. "Who cares?"

Kathy reeled Virginia back into the group with a smile that had sharp teeth in it. "What did you say to them? Something really good?"

"Yeah. Of course." Virginia looked back and blinked both eyes.

Sally Jane muttered curses.

Sofia shook her head. "Now you're gonna have to go to confession."

Diana nodded. "For having bad thoughts."

Sally Jane smiled. "Nah. These are really good thoughts."

We all laughed.

"Let's go eat in there." I moved ahead of them toward the cafeteria.

Diana looked at me as if I had *frijoles* stuck in my hair. "Justina, are you bonkers?" She and Sofia got on either side of me.

Sally Jane said, "You looking for trouble? Because I'm ready."

Sofia and Diana nodded at Sally Jane's invitation.

"Nah. No trouble."

"Then what?" persisted Sally Jane as she followed me toward the cafeteria.

"My mom. It took a lot of guts today. If she can do that, I can go in there."

Sally Jane grinned. "Let's do it."

Sofia nodded. "We have as much right to be in there as they do."

Diana didn't say anything; she just opened the door for us. ●

quaint: charming in an old-fashioned way	
menace: danger	
hoisted: lifted	
halting: stopping	

Vocabulary Check

...nplete each sentence starter below. Before you
...wer, think about the meaning of the vocabulary
...rd in bold.

I started to answer, but **stalled** when . . .

...s I looked around, my **gaze** fell upon . . .

...**avoided** my friend because . . .

If you act without **hesistation**, you . . .

...Vhen I looked at the clock, I had a feeling of **doom** ...because . . .

Write About It

Choose one of the writing prompts below.

▶ Write a letter from Justina to her mother. In the letter, explain how proud you feel and why.

▶ Write another ending for the story. What do you think might happen after Justina and her friends go back into the cafeteria?

▶ Is there anything else you'd like to know about the author? Make a list of five questions you'd like to ask her.

More to READ

Justina bravely faces people who make fun of her culture and background. If you enjoyed reading this story, you might like to read about other people who have done the same.

Bat 6
by **Virginia Euwer Wolff**

Sixth-grader Aki Mikami joins a softball team and finds out that hatred dies a slow death. It's three years after World War II. Shazam, a player on a rival team, still blames all Japanese (even Japanese Americans) for her father's death during the war. The story unfolds as each member of both teams tells the shocking story.

The Watsons Go to Birmingham—1963
by **Christopher Paul Curtis**

Kenny Watson is going on a family vacation to Birmingham, Alabama. His mother grew up there. But after the Watsons head south from their home in Flint, Michigan, they notice that more than the weather has changed. Then a bomb goes off and Kenny's little sister is nowhere to be found. Suddenly, it's no longer just a normal family vacation.

Interpreting Surveys

You probably believe in wearing a seat belt—right? But you wonder if others feel the same way. One way to find out is by looking at survey results.

Check out the graph below. It shows the results of a survey about seat-belt use.

Seat-Belt Use in the U.S.

Seat-Belt Use on the Rise
The percentage of passengers and drivers wearing seat belts

68.9%

61.3%

58%

1994

1996

1998

Source: National Occupant Protection Use Survey by the National Highway Traffic Safety Administration.

The graph shows the percentage of drivers and passengers who used seat belts each year. In 1994, the figure was 58%. That means that 58 out of every 100 people used seat belts that year.

" The 'source' information next to the graph tells who took the survey. The National Highway Traffic Safety Administration took this one. "

Survey Sense

Do many Americans wear their seat belts? Review the survey results and the tips that go with them. Then use them to answer the following questions. Write your answers on your own paper.

1. In which years was the seat-belt survey taken? From 1994–1998, which years were **skipped** by this survey?

2. What percentage of people used seat belts in 1996? In 1998?

3. From 1994–1998, what happened to the percentage of people using seat belts?
   a. It went down.　　**c.** It went up.
   b. It stayed the same.　　**d.** It's impossible to tell.

4. How many people were included in this survey?
   a. 100
   b. 1000
   c. all U.S. passengers and drivers
   d. The graph doesn't tell.

" You can find lots of survey results on the Internet. Just search for the topic you're interested in, plus the word survey. "

Take a Survey
Do your own survey. Ask 10 classmates a yes-or-no question. Make a graph showing what percentage of kids said yes and what percentage said no.

Write About It
You work for a traffic safety group. You are glad that seat-belt use is on the rise. But your mission is to get *everyone* to wear them. List two or more reasons that people should wear seat belts.

Real-World Words

percentage: a fraction or proportion, expressed as a number out of a hundred

results: answers; findings

survey: a report, study, or poll on people's opinions or activities

Glossary

You will find all your vocabulary words in alphabetical order in the Glossary. Look at the sample entry below to see how to use it.

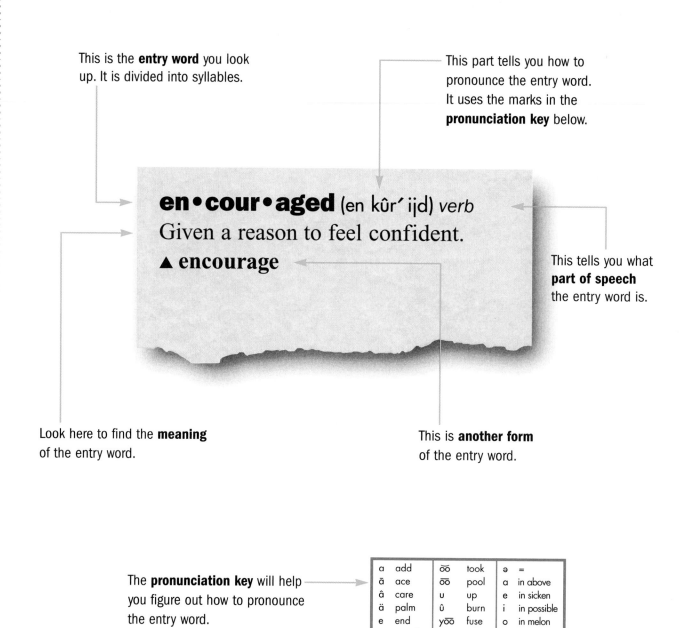

This is the **entry word** you look up. It is divided into syllables.

This part tells you how to pronounce the entry word. It uses the marks in the **pronunciation key** below.

en•cour•aged (en kûr′ ijd) *verb*
Given a reason to feel confident.
▲ encourage

This tells you what **part of speech** the entry word is.

Look here to find the **meaning** of the entry word.

This is **another form** of the entry word.

The **pronunciation key** will help you figure out how to pronounce the entry word.

a	add	ōō	took	ə	=
ā	ace	ōō	pool	a	in above
â	care	u	up	e	in sicken
ä	palm	û	burn	i	in possible
e	end	yōō	fuse	o	in melon
ē	equal	oi	oil	u	in circus
i	it	ou	pout		
ī	ice	ng	ring		
o	odd	th	thin		
ō	open	th	this	′	stressed
ô	order	zh	vision		syllable

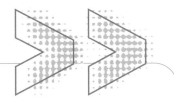

a•ban•doned
(ə ban′dənd) *verb*
Left alone.
▲ **abandon**

ab•scess
(ab′ses) *noun*
A painful swelling caused by
an infection.

ac•com•plished
(ə kom′plisht) *verb*
Did something important.
▲ **accomplish**

ad•mired
(ad mīrd′) *verb*
Liked and respected someone.
▲ **admire**

af•fec•tion
(ə fek′shən) *noun*
A great liking for someone or
something.

ail•ments
(āl′mənts) *noun*
Illnesses that usually aren't
serious.
▲ **ailment**

a•las
(ə las′) *interjection*
Sadly.

al•leg•ed•ly
(ə lej′ id lē) *adverb*
Supposedly.
▲ **allege**

anx•ious•ly
(angk′shəs lē) *adverb*
In a worried way.
▲ **anxious**

ap•pre•ci•ates
(ə prē′shē āts′) *verb*
Values someone or something.
▲ **appreciate**

ap•proach•ing
(ə prōch′ ing) *verb*
Moving nearer.
▲ **approach**

as•sumed
(ə sōōmd′) *verb*
Guessed.
▲ **assume**

a•void•ed
(ə void′ id) *verb*
Stayed away from.
▲ **avoid**

baf•fling
(baf′fling) *verb*
Confusing.
▲ **baffle**

be•trayed
(bi trād′) *verb*
Failed to help in a time of need.
▲ **betray**

bi•lin•gual
(bī ling′gwəl) *adjective*
Able to speak two languages.

bor•ing
(bôr′ing) *verb*
Drilling or digging.
▲ **bore**

Word Usage

The words **boring** and **boring** are **homonyms**. Homonyms are words that sound the same and have the same spelling, but have different meanings. **Boring** means "drilling or digging." It also means "dull and not interesting."

---

boy•cott
(boi′cott) *verb*
To protest by refusing to buy or
support something.

a	add	o͞o	took	ə	=
ā	ace	o͞o	pool	a	in above
â	care	u	up	e	in sicken
ä	palm	û	burn	i	in possible
e	end	yo͞o	fuse	o	in melon
ē	equal	oi	oil	u	in circus
i	it	ou	pout		
ī	ice	ng	ring		
o	odd	th	thin		
ō	open	ŧh	this	′	stressed
ô	order	zh	vision		syllable

Glossary

cap•tured
(kap´chərd) verb
Won; took possession of.
▲ capture

cas•ing
(kā´sing) noun
An outer cover.

cat•e•go•ry
(kat´ə gôr´ē) noun
A class or group of things that have something in common.

col•lapsed
(kə lapst´) verb
Fell or caved in.
▲ collapse

com•bat
(kom´bat) noun
A serious fight or struggle.

com•ic
(kom´ik) adjective
Funny.

com•mu•ni•cate
(kə myoo´ni kāt´) verb
To give or share information, ideas, and feelings.

com•pli•cat•ed
(kom´pli kā´tid) adjective
Difficult; complex.
▲ complicate

con•cerned
(kən sûrnd´) verb
Worried about.
▲ concern

con•dens•es
(kən dens´iz) verb
Turns from a gas, or vapor, to a liquid, usually as a result of cooling.
▲ condense

con•fessed
(kən fest´) verb
Admitted.
▲ confess

con•front
(kən frunt´) verb
To challenge.

Thesaurus

confront

resist

oppose

challenge

con•grat•u•late
(kən grach´ə lāt´) verb
To express happiness about something.

con•science
(kon´shəns) noun
A person's knowledge of right or wrong.

con•sist
(kən sist´) verb
To be made up of.

cour•te•sy
(kûr´tə sē) noun
Respect.

crev•ice
(krev´is) noun
A crack.

cring•ing
(krin´ jing) verb
Shrinking back in fear or panic.
▲ cringe

cri•sis
(krī´sis) noun
A time of difficulty.

crit•i•cal
(krit´i kəl) adjective
Very important.

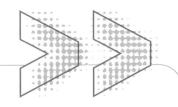

crit•i•cize
(krit′ə sīz′) *verb*
To point out what another person has done wrong.

crouched
(kroucht) *verb*
Bent over.
▲ **crouch**

cul•tures
(kul′chərz) *noun*
Groups of people that share the same way of life.
▲ **culture**

daze
(dāz) *noun*
The state of being stunned and unable to think clearly.

de•feat•ist
(di fē′tist) *adjective*
Expecting to lose or accepting loss very easily.
▲ **defeat**

de•fect
(di fekt′) *verb*
To escape to another country, especially one that's hostile to your own.

de•fi•ance
(di fī′əns) *noun*
A challenge or dare given to an opponent.

de•pend•ed
(di pend′id) *verb*
Counted on.
▲ **depend**

de•prive
(di prīv′) *verb*
To deny or take away.

de•signed
(di zīnd′) *verb*
Came up with an idea for something.
▲ **design**

des•per•ate
(des′pər it) *adjective*
Willing to do anything to change a situation.

des•tin•y
(des′tə nē) *noun*
Fate, or future events to come.

de•te•ri•o•rate
(di tēr′ē ə rāt′) *verb*
To get worse.

de•ter•mined
(di tûr′mind) *verb*
Settled on an idea.
▲ **determine**

di•gest
(dī jest′) *verb*
To take in and break down inside your body.

dis•guised
(dis gīzd′) *verb*
Changed one's appearance to hide something.
▲ **disguise**

Word Usage

The prefix **dis-** adds meaning to a word. It means either "not," "the opposite," or "lack of."

dis•own
(dis ōn′) *verb*
To no longer recognize as your own.

a	add	o͞o	took	ə	=
ā	ace	o͞o	pool	a	in above
â	care	u	up	e	in sicken
ä	palm	û	burn	i	in possible
e	end	yo͞o	fuse	o	in melon
ē	equal	oi	oil	u	in circus
i	it	ou	pout		
ī	ice	ng	ring		
o	odd	th	thin		
ō	open	th	this	′	stressed
ô	order	zh	vision		syllable

Glossary

dis•solves
(di zolvz´) *verb*
Breaks up into small pieces.
▲ dissolve

dis•tin•guish
(di sting´gwish) *verb*
To be able to tell one thing
from another.

dis•tress
(di stres´) *noun*
Sadness; worry.

dom•i•nat•ed
(dom´ə nāt´ id) *verb*
Controlled or ruled.
▲ dominate

doom
(do͞om) *noun*
A sense that something bad will
happen.

dread•ed
(dred´id) *verb*
Was afraid of or unwilling to do
something.
▲ dread

e•lab•o•rate
(i lab´ər it) *adjective*
Complicated and detailed.

Word Origin

The word **elaborate** comes
from the Latin root **lab**,
which means "work."

en•cour•aged
(en kûr´ijd) *verb*
Given a reason to feel
confident.
▲ encourage

en•dorse•ments
(en dôrs´mənts) *noun*
Acts of supporting or approving
a product on the radio or
television.
▲ endorsement

en•thu•si•asm
(en tho͞o´zē az´ əm) *noun*
Excitement.

en•vi•ron•men•tal•ists
(en vīrən men´t'l ists) *noun*
People who protect the earth
and its living things.
▲ environmentalist

ep•i•der•mis
(ep´i dûr´mis) *noun*
The top layer of your skin.

ex•change
(iks chānj´) *verb*
To switch one thing for another.

ex•haust•ed
(ig zôst´id) *adjective*
Really, really tired.

ex•po•sure
(ik spō´ zhər) *noun*
Media attention.

ex•ter•mi•na•tor
(ik stûr´mə nā´tər) *noun*
A person who gets rid of insect
pests.

fare•well
(fâr´wel´) *adjective*
Good-bye.

fear•some
(fēr´səm) *adjective*
Frightening.

feast
(fēst) *verb*
To eat with great pleasure.

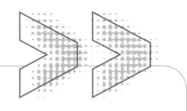

fibs
(fibz) *noun*
Small lies.
▲ **fib**

fiend•ish
(fēn´dish) *adjective*
Evil or wicked.
▲ **fiend**

fierce•ly
(fērs´ lē) *adverb*
In a strong and powerful way.
▲ **fierce**

flail•ing
(flāl´ ing) *verb*
Moving or swinging wildly.
▲ **flail**

flam•ma•ble
(flam´ə bəl) *adjective*
Easy to burn.

for•eign
(fôr´in) *adjective*
From another country.

foun•da•tion
(foun dā´shən) *noun*
An organization that gives money to worthy causes.

found•ers
(foun´dərs) *noun*
People who begin an organization, club, company, etc.
▲ **founder**

frag•ile
(fraj´əl) *adjective*
Delicate, or easily broken.

fu•ri•ous
(fyoor´ē əs) *adjective*
Very angry.

gape
(gāp) *verb*
To open widely.

gath•ered
(gath´ərd) *verb*
Stood together in a group.
▲ **gather**

gaze
(gāz) *noun*
A steady look; a stare.

Thesaurus

gaze

look

gape

stare

gen•er•a•tions
(jen´ə rā´shənz) *noun*
Families born to a shared ancestor.
▲ **generation**

ges•tures
(jes´chərz) *noun*
Actions that express a feeling.
▲ **gesture**

glimpse
(glimps) *noun*
A brief look.

a	add	o͝o	took	ə	=
ā	ace	o͞o	pool	a	in above
â	care	u	up	e	in sicken
ä	palm	û	burn	i	in possible
e	end	yo͞o	fuse	o	in melon
ē	equal	oi	oil	u	in circus
i	it	ou	pout		
ī	ice	ng	ring		
o	odd	th	thin		
ō	open	th	this		
ô	order	zh	vision	´	stressed syllable

Glossary

gra•cious
(grā´shəs) *adjective*
Kind; considerate.

halt•ing
(hôlt´ing) *verb*
Stopping.
▲ **halt**

hes•i•tant•ly
(hez´i tənt lē) *adverb*
In an uncertain way.
▲ **hesitant**

hes•i•ta•tion
(hez´i tā´shən) *noun*
A pause or delay.

hoist•ed
(hoist´id) *verb*
Lifted.
▲ **hoist**

hyp•no•tized
(hip´nə tīzd) *verb*
Unable to stop staring at
something.
▲ **hypnotize**

ig•nored
(ig nôrd´) *verb*
Did not pay attention to
something.
▲ **ignore**

im•ag•i•na•tion
(i maj´ə nā´shən) *noun*
The ability to form pictures
in your mind of things that are
not real.

im•pressed
(im prest´) *verb*
Thought highly of something.
▲ **impress**

Word Usage

Impress is a **homonym**. A
homonym is a word that has
more than one meaning.
Impress means "to think
highly of something." It also
means "to make a mark by
pressure."

in•di•cat•ed
(in´di kāt´id) *verb*
Showed.
▲ **indicate**

in•di•vid•u•al•i•ty
(in´də vij´ o̅o̅ al´i tē) *noun*
The things that make a person
different from others.

in•her•it
(in her´it) *verb*
To be given something after
someone has died.

in•jured
(in´jərd) *verb*
Hurt.
▲ **injure**

in•spired
(in spīrd´) *verb*
Influenced or encouraged
someone.
▲ **inspire**

in•teg•ri•ty
(in teg´ri tē) *noun*
Honesty; sticking up for what
you believe.

in•tim•i•dat•ed
(in tim´i dāt´ id) *verb*
Made to feel afraid or worried.
▲ **intimidate**

in•trude
(in tro̅o̅d´) *verb*
To come in uninvited.

keen
(kēn) *adjective*
Sharp.

launched
(lônchd) *verb*
Started.
▲ **launch**

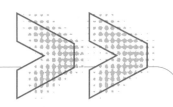

leg•a•cy
(leg′ə sē) *noun*
Something to be remembered
by in the future.

lux•u•ries
(luk′shə rēz) *noun*
Things that aren't needed but
bring comfort or pleasure.
▲ **luxury**

man•da•to•ry
(man′də tôr′ē) *adjective*
Necessary; important.

ma•te•ri•al•is•tic
(mə tēr′ē ə lis′ tic) *adjective*
Concerned with money or the
objects it can buy.
▲ **materialism**

men•ace
(men′is) *noun*
Danger.

merged
(mûrjd) *verb*
Joined together.
▲ **merge**

moist
(moist) *adjective*
Slightly wet.

Thesaurus

moist

damp

dank

wet

neg•a•tive
(neg′ə tiv) *adjective*
Bad; depressing.

nom•i•nat•ed
(nom′ə nāt′ id) *verb*
Recommended, usually for an
award.
▲ **nominate**

nu•tri•ents
(noō′trē ənts) *noun*
Things in food that your body
needs to be healthy.
▲ **nutrient**

o•dor
(ō′dər) *noun*
A smell or scent.

ooz•ing
(ōōz′ ing) *verb*
Flowing out slowly.
▲ **ooze**

op•por•tu•ni•ties
(op′ər tōō′ni tēz) *noun*
Chances to do something.
▲ **opportunity**

out•cast
(out′kast′) *noun*
Someone who is not accepted
by other people.

o•ver•whelmed
(ō′vər hwelmd′) *verb*
Having too many feelings; not
able to take action.
▲ **overwhelm**

Word Usage

The prefix **over-** adds
meaning to a word. It
means "too much."

a	add	ōō	took	ə	=
ā	ace	ōō	pool	a	in above
â	care	u	up	e	in sicken
ä	palm	û	burn	i	in possible
e	end	yōō	fuse	o	in melon
ē	equal	oi	oil	u	in circus
i	it	ou	pout		
ī	ice	ng	ring		
o	odd	th	thin		
ō	open	th	this		
ô	order	zh	vision	′	stressed syllable

Glossary

pace
(pās) *noun*
Rate of speed.

pains•tak•ing•ly
(pānz´tā´king lē) *adverb*
Done carefully or thoroughly.
▲ **painstaking**

pan•icked
(pan´ikt) *verb*
Terrified or fearful about something.
▲ **panic**

pe•ri•od•ic
(pēr´ē od´ik) *adjective*
Happening from time to time.

po•di•um
(pō´dē əm) *noun*
An elevated platform or stage.

Word Origin

The word **podium** comes from the Greek root **pod**, which means "foot."

pos•ses•sive
(pə zes´iv) *adjective*
Jealous and protective.

pout
(pout) *noun*
The act of pushing out your lips to show anger or disappointment.

pre•cious
(presh´es) *adjective*
Rare and valuable.

prej•u•dice
(prej´ə dis) *noun*
An unfair opinion based on race, religion, or culture.

pub•lic•i•ty
(pə blis´i tē) *noun*
Information that is given out to the public through the media.

quaint
(kwānt) *adjective*
Charming in an old-fashioned way.

rag•es
(rāj´iz) *verb*
Continues violently.
▲ **rage**

re•al•i•ty
(rē al´i tē) *noun*
The facts of life that must be faced.

re•flec•tion
(ri flek´shən) *noun*
An image thrown back by a surface.

re•gret
(ri gret´) *verb*
To be sorry for something.

re•im•burse
(rē´im bûrs´) *verb*
To pay someone back.

re•lat•ed
(ri lā´tid) *adjective*
Part of the same family.

re•leased
(ri lēst´) *verb*
Made available to the public for the first time.
▲ **release**

re•lief
(ri lēf´) *noun*
Freedom from worry.

re•mark•a•ble
(ri mär´kə bəl) *adjective*
Worth noticing.

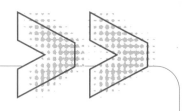

re•quire•ments
(ri kwī′ ər mənts) *noun*
Things that are needed; terms of a deal.
▲ requirement

re•vealed
(ri vēld′) *verb*
Seen or shown.
▲ reveal

rhythm
(ri<u>th</u>′əm) *noun*
A regular beat.

ri•val•ries
(rī′ vəl rēz) *noun*
Competitions between two opponents.
▲ rivalry

romped
(rompt) *verb*
Played in a carefree and lively way.
▲ romp

rough•housed
(ruf′houzd′) *verb*
Played at fighting.
▲ roughhouse

sat•is•fac•tion
(sat′is fak′shən) *noun*
A good feeling that comes from getting something done.

scat•ter
(skat′ər) *verb*
To spread.

scent
(sent) *noun*
A nice smell.

Word Usage

The words **scent** and **sent** are **homophones**. Homophones are words that sound the same but are spelled differently and have different meanings. **Scent** means "a nice smell," and **sent** means "to have made something go somewhere."

screeched
(skrēcht) *verb*
Made a high, unpleasant sound.
▲ screech

scuf•fling
(skuf′fling) *verb*
Scratching or scraping.
▲ scuffle

sealed
(sēld) *adjective*
Closed up.

se•cu•ri•ty
(si kyŏŏr′i tē) *noun*
Protection or safety from crime.

slew
(slōō) *verb*
Killed.
▲ slay

sloped
(slōpt) *adjective*
Was at an angle.
▲ slope

sly
(slī) *adjective*
Crafty and secretive.

Thesaurus

sly

tricky

deceptive

shifty

a	add	ŏŏ	took	ə	=
ā	ace	ōō	pool	a	in above
â	care	u	up	e	in sicken
ä	palm	û	burn	i	in possible
e	end	yōō	fuse	o	in melon
ē	equal	oi	oil	u	in circus
i	it	ou	pout		
ī	ice	ng	ring		
o	odd	th	thin		
ō	open	<u>th</u>	this		
ô	order	zh	vision	′	stressed syllable

Glossary

snub•bing
(snub´ing) *verb*
Ignoring.
▲ **snub**

soared
(sōrd) *verb*
Rose or increased very quickly.
▲ **soar**

so•nar
(sō´när) *noun*
A means of determining how far away something is by sending out sound waves.

source
(sōrs) *noun*
The place, person, or thing from which something comes.

squint•y
(skwint´ē) *adjective*
With eyes nearly closed.
▲ **squint**

squirmed
(skwûrmd) *verb*
Wriggled about uncomfortably.
▲ **squirm**

stalled
(stäld) *verb*
Delayed doing something on purpose.
▲ **stall**

ster•i•lized
(ster´ə līzd´) *adjective*
Cleaned so as to be free from germs and dirt.
▲ **sterilize**

stride
(strīd) *noun*
A person's step.

stunned
(stund) *verb*
Shocked.
▲ **stun**

sup•port•ive
(sə pôrt´iv) *adjective*
Helpful.

Word Origin

The word **supportive** comes from the Latin root **port**, which means "carry."

sur•ren•der
(sə ren´dər) *verb*
To give up.

sur•round•ings
(sə roun´dingz) *noun*
The setting that a person or thing is in.

sur•vive
(sər vīv´) *verb*
To stay alive through or after some dangerous event.

sus•pi•cious
(sə spish´əs) *adjective*
Thinking that something might be wrong or bad.

taunt•ed
(tônt´id) *verb*
Teased in order to make someone angry.
▲ **taunt**

ter•ror
(ter´ər) *noun*
Very great fear.

threat•ened
(thret´´nd) *verb*
Put in danger.
▲ **threaten**

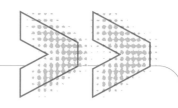

thrust
(thrust) *noun*
The forward-moving force produced by a rocket engine.

trac•es
(trās´iz) *noun*
Small amounts.
▲ trace

trained
(trānd) *verb*
Taught a person or animal how to do something.
▲ train

trea•son
(trē´zən) *noun*
Betrayal of your country.

trem•bling
(trem´bling) *verb*
Shaking.
▲ tremble

tres•pass•ing
(tres´pas ing) *verb*
Entering someone's private property without permission.
▲ trespass

twitched
(twicht) *verb*
Made a small, jerky movement.
▲ twitch

typ•i•cal
(tip´i kəl) *adjective*
Just like any other.

un•dis•put•ed
(un´di spyo͞ot´id) *adjective*
Agreed upon without argument.
▲ dispute

u•nique
(yo͞o nēk´) *adjective*
One of a kind; unlike any other.

up•lift•ed
(up lift´id) *verb*
Inspired.
▲ uplift

Thesaurus

uplifted
raised
elevated
lifted

ves•sels
(ves´əlz) *noun*
Tubes in the body that fluids pass through.
▲ vessel

vowed
(voud) *verb*
Promised.
▲ vow

whirled
(wûrld) *verb*
Spun around.
▲ whirl

winc•es
(wins´iz) *verb*
Shrinks back, as if in pain or expecting it.
▲ wince

wolf
(wo͝olf) *verb*
To eat or gobble food quickly.

a	add	o͞o	took	ə	=
ā	ace	o͞o	pool	a	in above
â	care	u	up	e	in sicken
ä	palm	û	burn	i	in possible
e	end	yo͞o	fuse	o	in melon
ē	equal	oi	oil	u	in circus
i	it	ou	pout		
ī	ice	ng	ring		
o	odd	th	thin		
ō	open	th	this		
ô	order	zh	vision	´	stressed syllable

Literary & Reading Terms

author A person who writes a short story, play, poem, novel, article, essay, or book.

autobiography An account of a person's life written by that person. An autobiography is an example of nonfiction.

base word A word from which other words can be made. By adding a prefix to the beginning of a base word or a suffix to the end, you can change a word's meaning (such as *view/preview/viewing*).

biography An account of a person's life written by another person. A biography is a form of nonfiction.

cause and effect The cause is something that makes another thing happen. What happens is called the effect. The reader figures out why an event happened or how one event caused another to occur.

characterization The way the author presents the personality of a character. The reader learns about a character through descriptions, actions, speech, and thoughts. Character traits are the qualities that a character possesses.

characters People in a story, play, novel, and so on. There are major and minor characters in a story, major characters being more important than minor ones. The main character is the most important character.

compare and contrast To compare is to figure out how events, characters, or ideas are similar. To contrast is to find out how they are different.

compound word A word that is made up of two or more smaller words, such as *homework.*

conflict A struggle between characters, between a character and a force of nature, or between opposing views held by different characters. An internal conflict takes place in the mind of a character who must resolve something.

connotation The implied meaning of a word or phrase as opposed to its exact dictionary meaning or denotation. The connotations of a word are the ideas and feelings associated with it.

contraction A word formed by leaving out and combining parts of other words. For example, the word *can't* is made from the words *can* and *not.* The n and the o in *not* are dropped and are replaced by the apostrophe.

debate A discussion between parties with different opinions or points of view.

denotation The exact dictionary meaning of a word as opposed to its implied meaning, or connotation.

dialogue The conversation in a story or play. The exact words spoken by the characters. In a story, quotation marks point out the dialogue.

diphthong Two vowels that spell a sound that is formed by a gliding action in the mouth (such as *oy, oi, ou, ow*).

draw conclusions To make decisions about a story and its characters. To draw conclusions, a reader thinks about events and details in a story and comes to a new understanding.

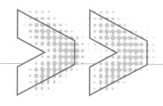

editorial An article or a statement that reflects the opinions of a newspaper, magazine, or other information source.

encyclopedia entry An informative article found in an encyclopedia (a set of books with alphabetized entries about many different subjects).

essay A short, nonfiction piece of writing on a subject or theme that expresses a specific point of view.

exaggeration The overstatement of an idea beyond the limits of truth.

fiction An invented story. Although fiction may be based on actual personal experience, it involves invented characters, actions, and settings.

figurative language Words used in a special way to give added meaning. In figurative expressions such as "I'm up to my ears in homework," the words are not intended to be interpreted in a word-for-word, or literal, sense. Stories, and especially poems, use figurative language to create images, or mental pictures. (See also **metaphor, personification, simile.**)

flashback A technique that interrupts the present action in a story, play, or novel to tell about something that happened in the past.

foreshadowing A storytelling device that an author uses to give the reader advance warning of events to come.

graphic classic A well-known story told through pictures in a comic-book format.

historical fiction A story or novel whose setting is in some period in the past. Often real people from the past or important historical events are used in works of historical fiction.

homophone A word that sounds like another word but has a different meaning and spelling (such as *hear* and *here*).

humor The quality of being comical or funny.

imagery Words that create mental pictures, or images, that appeal to one or more of the reader's five senses. For example, "The moon floated above the clouds like a ship lost on the stormy seas" appeals to the reader's sense of sight.

irony The contrast, or difference, between what is said and what is meant. For example, if we say in conversation that something feels good when it really feels bad, we are using irony.

lyrics The words of a song. Lyrics often express personal thoughts or feelings. Originally, lyric poems were sung and accompanied by a musical instrument called a lyre.

main idea The most important idea in a paragraph or selection. The reader may find the main idea in a topic sentence or heading and will find details that support the main idea in the rest of the paragraph or selection.

make inferences A reader makes an inference when he or she combines text information with his or her own prior knowledge to figure out something that is not directly stated in a story.

media literacy An understanding of the ways in which mass communication is used in society.

Literary & Reading Terms

metaphor A figure of speech in which there is an indirect or implied comparison between two things. "Her eyes were stars in the midnight sky" is a metaphor.

mood The general atmosphere or feeling in a work of literature. Mood is created largely through description and setting.

motivation The reason a character in a work of literature acts in a particular way. The character's motivation may be stated directly or hinted at by what he or she does, thinks, or says.

myth A story told by people in ancient times to explain life and nature. Many myths, including Greek myths, are about gods and goddesses.

narrative poem A poem that tells a story or relates a sequence of events.

narrator The teller of a story.

nonfiction Writing about real people and factual events. Journal accounts, diaries, essays, interviews, articles, textbooks, biographies, auto-biographies, and letters are examples of nonfiction.

novel A book-length piece of fiction that usually has a plot and deals with human experience.

personal narrative A true story about a person's life told in the first person.

personification A figure of speech that describes an object, idea, or animal as if it had human characteristics. For example: "The light spring rain danced upon our heads."

photo essay A collection of photos and words that tells a story or presents information.

play A work written to be performed before an audience. A play may be written in parts called acts and scenes. Stage directions tell the director or actors how the stage is to look and how the characters are to move and speak. The dialogue, or lines, are the words the characters speak.

plot The sequence of events in a short story, novel, play, or poem. The major element in a plot is the conflict, or struggle, between opposing forces. Rising action is the part of the plot in which the action builds and a problem, or conflict, develops. The turning point is the part of the plot in which the struggle between the forces comes to a head in some incident—the crisis, or climax. The resolution is the part of the plot in which the problem is solved.

plot twist A turn of events in the structure of a story, novel, or play that is unexpected, yet logical based on the reader's knowledge of the plot and character.

poetry Literature that uses language chosen for its sound and for its ability to express and evoke emotion. Many poems use images, or mental pictures, that appeal to the senses. Most poetry is written in lines that have a particular rhythm, or pattern of stressed syllables. Poetry can either be rhymed or unrhymed.

point of view The vantage point from which the narrator tells the story. In the first-person point of view, the narrator is usually a character in the story. This narrator tells the story by using the pronouns *I* or *we*. In the third-person point of view—the most

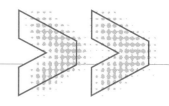

common form of telling a story—the narrator may or may not be a character in the story. This narrator uses the pronouns *he*, *she*, or *they*. When the narrator in the third-person point of view seems to know what every character is thinking and feeling, this narrator is called omniscient, or all-knowing.

possessive The form of a noun or pronoun that shows possession or ownership.

prefix A word part added to the beginning of a word to change its meaning (such as *view/preview*).

problem and solution A problem is a difficult situation that a character in a story has to solve. The solution is how the problem is solved.

profile A brief account of someone's life or accomplishments.

read for detail A detail is a small piece of information. Details help the reader to better understand the who, what, when, how, where, or why of a part of a story or piece of nonfiction.

root A word or word part from Latin or another language that is the basis of an English word. One example of a root is *port,* which means "to carry" (such as *import/portable*).

science fiction A fantasy story that is often set in the future, on other planets, or in other dimensions in time. Scientific impossibilities may be used in the plot.

sequence of events The order in which events occur. The reader can look for time-order words, such as *first, then,* or *next,* and other clues to determine the sequence of events.

setting The time, place, and general environment of a story. The setting tells when and where the story takes place. The reader determines the setting by noticing descriptions and events.

short story A brief piece of fiction, usually of 500 to 5,000 words in length.

simile A figure of speech in which two things are compared directly, using *like, as,* or *than*. "Her eyes sparkled like diamonds" is an example of a simile.

stanza A group of two or more lines in a poem that are printed as a unit and held together by length, rhyme scheme, and meter.

style The individual, creative way an author expresses ideas and presents characters, setting, and action.

suffix A word part added to the end of a word to change its meaning (such as *slow/slowly*).

summarize To identify, organize, and combine the most important parts of a story so they can be retold in a brief statement.

suspense The tension readers feel because they are uncertain how events are going to turn out.

symbol Something that has meaning in itself and yet stands for something else. For example, in a story, a heart may represent love.

theme An important truth about life expressed by the author of a work of literature. It may be the author's thoughts about a certain topic, or the author's view of human nature. The theme is conveyed by the whole story—by the title, the plot, the characters, the setting, and the mood.

Author & Title Index

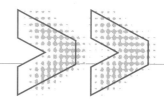

Acknowledgments

Cover: Boy on bike photograph from THE AIR DOWN HERE by Gil C. Alicea with Carmine DeSena. Photograph copyright © 1995 by Gil C. Alicea. Reprinted by permission of Barbara J. Zitwer Agency.

"S.O.R. Losers" from S.O.R. LOSERS by Avi. Copyright © 1984 by Avi Wortis. Reprinted with the permission of Atheneum Books for Young Readers, an imprint of Simon & Schuster Children's Publishing Division.

Four "Eat Your Bugs" photographs and "Grasshopper Tacos" recipe from MAN EATING BUGS: THE ART AND SCIENCE OF EATING INSECTS by Peter Menzel and Faith D'Aluisio. Images copyright © 1998 by Peter Menzel. Published by Material World Books, distributed by Ten Speed Press, Berkeley, CA. Reprinted by permission.

"Cockroach Cafeteria" by Lynda Jones from Science World magazine, October 21, 1994. Copyright © 1994 by Scholastic Inc. All rights reserved.

"Dreaming of You: The Life and Music of Selena" from SELENA! by Sandhya Seshan with Elvira Ortiz. Copyright © 1999 by Scholastic Inc. All rights reserved.

"No Quiero Saber" by A.B. Quintanilla III and Pete Astudillo from Siempre Selena. Lyrics reprinted by permission of Hal Leonard Corporation. All rights reserved.

"Selena on the Web" from "Web Holds Almost Everything About Selena" by Glaston Ford from Corpus Christi Caller-Times (Caller.com), March 31, 1997. Copyright © 1998 by Corpus Christi Caller Times. All rights reserved. Corpus Christi Caller Times and Caller.com are registered trademarks of the Company.

"Dreaming of You" by Franne Gold and Tom Snow from Dreaming of You. Lyrics reprinted by permission of Chesca Tunes and Warner Brother Publications. All rights reserved.

"The Hostage" play adaptation by Scott Brodeur and Debra Hess adapted from THE HOSTAGE by Theodore Taylor. Copyright © 1987 by Theodore Taylor. Play adaptation originally published in Scholastic Action magazine, April 21, 1995. Play adaptation copyright © 1995 by Scholastic Inc. Reprinted by permission of Theodore Taylor and the Watkins/Loomis Agency.

"Can It Rain Cats and Dogs?" from SCHOLASTIC QUESTION AND ANSWER SERIES: CAN IT RAIN CATS AND DOGS? QUESTIONS AND ANSWERS ABOUT WEATHER by Melvin and Gilda Berger. Text copyright © 1999 by Melvin and Gilda Berger. Published by Scholastic Inc. All rights reserved.

"Why Don't Haircuts Hurt?" from SCHOLASTIC QUESTION AND ANSWER SERIES: WHY DON'T HAIRCUTS HURT? QUESTIONS AND ANSWERS ABOUT THE HUMAN BODY by Melvin and Gilda Berger. Text copyright © 1998 by Melvin and Gilda Berger. Published by Scholastic Inc. All rights reserved.

"Can You Hear a Shout in Space?" from SCHOLASTIC QUESTION AND ANSWER SERIES: CAN YOU HEAR A SHOUT IN SPACE? QUESTIONS AND ANSWERS ABOUT SPACE EXPLORATION by Melvin and Gilda Berger. Text copyright © 2000 by Melvin and Gilda Berger. Published by Scholastic Inc. All rights reserved.

"Code Red" by Paul E. Stawski from VALYRA AND THE DRAGONS AND OTHER FANCIFUL ADVENTURE STORIES. Copyright © 1984 by Highlights for Children, Inc. Reprinted by permission of Highlights for Children, Inc., Columbus, OH. All rights reserved.

"Victory a Milestone for Female Athletes" from "Glory for U.S. Women—and Girls: Victory a Milestone for Female Athletes" by Allen Salkin from The New York Post Online Edition: Sports, July 11, 1999. Copyright © 1999 by NYP Holdings. Reprinted by permission of NYP Holdings.

"King Arthur" from KING ARTHUR, a graphic classic by Terry M. West based on the story "The Sword in the Stone." Copyright © 1999 by Scholastic Inc. All rights reserved.

"Miles" from SPACE STATION SEVENTH GRADE by Jerry Spinelli. Copyright © 1982 by Jerry Spinelli. Reprinted by permission of Little, Brown and Company Inc.

Cover from MANIAC MAGEE by Jerry Spinelli. Copyright © 1990 by Jerry Spinelli. Reprinted by permission of Little, Brown and Company.

Cover from THERE'S A GIRL IN MY HAMMERLOCK by Jerry Spinelli. Copyright © 1991 by Jerry Spinelli. Reprinted with the permission of Simon & Schuster Books for Young Readers, an imprint of Simon & Schuster Children's Publishing Division.

Photographs from THE SNAKE SCIENTIST by Sy Montgomery, photographs by Nic Bishop. Photographs copyright © 1999 by Nic Bishop. Reprinted by permission of Houghton Mifflin Co.

"Smiffy Blue and the Case of the Missing Ruby" and "Smiffy Blue and the Case of the Stolen Formula" play adaptations by Debra Hess adapted from SMIFFY BLUE: ACE CRIME DETECTIVE by Walter Dean Myers, illustrated by David J.A. Sims. Copyright © 1996 by Walter Dean Myers. Illustrations copyright © 1996 by Scholastic Inc. Published by Scholastic Inc. All rights reserved.

"Every Living Thing" from EVERY LIVING THING by Cynthia Rylant. Copyright © 1985 by Cynthia Rylant. Reprinted with the permission of Simon & Schuster Books for Young Readers, an imprint of Simon & Schuster Children's Publishing Division.

"Tarzan" from TARZAN retold by Robert D. San Souci, illustrated by Michael McCurdy. Copyright © 1999 by Edgar Rice Burroughs, Inc. Trademark TARZAN® owned by Edgar Rice Burroughs, Inc. and used by permission. Reprinted by permission of Hyperion Books for Children.